Radiation-Induced

Chromosome

Aberrations

Report of A CONFERENCE ON BIOCHEMICAL AND BIOPHYSICAL MECHANISMS IN THE PRODUCTION OF RADIATION-INDUCED CHROMOSOME ABERRATIONS *held in* SAN JUAN, PUERTO RICO, NOVEMBER 16–18, 1961, *sponsored by* THE NATIONAL ACADEMY OF SCIENCES AND THE NATIONAL RESEARCH COUNCIL

Radiation-Induced Chromosome Aberrations

Edited by Sheldon Wolff

K. C. ATWOOD, C. AUERBACH, A. D. CONGER, E. H. Y. CHU,

H. J. EVANS, B. KIHLMAN, J. S. KIRBY-SMITH, D. L. LINDSLEY,

S. H. REVELL, C. P. SWANSON, J. H. TAYLOR, G. YERGANIAN

COLUMBIA UNIVERSITY PRESS

NEW YORK AND LONDON 1963

Preface

This book is a report of the ninth in a series of conferences on basic mechanisms in radiobiology that have been organized by the Subcommittee on Radiobiology, of the Committee on Nuclear Science, National Academy of Sciences-National Research Council. The funds for the support of the conference were provided by the National Institutes of Health and the Atomic Energy Commission.

The purpose of these conferences has been to bring together scientists from different disciplines so that they might consider various aspects of basic radiobiology. An attempt has always been made to make the conferences conducive to frank and detailed informal discussions. With this end in view the participants were urged to interrupt the speakers at any point. A transcript of the meetings was obtained by a stenotypist. Each participant then edited his remarks. The editing was kept to a minimum, however, to preserve both the flavor and the spontaneity of the meeting.

The conference was divided into five sessions of which Drs. Gray, Neary, Totter, Giles, and Sparrow were the chairmen. No rigid schedule was maintained, however, and on occasion a chairman found himself presiding over a paper that should have been in the previous session.

The conference committee which consisted of Sheldon Wolff, Chairman, H. Quastler, and E. C. Pollard wishes to express its profound thanks to Dr. J. Bugher, the director of the Puerto Rico Nuclear Center, and his staff who acted as local hosts during this conference. Their efforts contributed immeasurably to the success of the meeting. In particular the following members of Dr. Bugher's staff should be mentioned: Mrs. Marie Barton, Dr. H. J. Teas, and Dr. C. Garcia-Benitez.

Summer, 1962   SHELDON WOLFF
Oak Ridge, Tennessee

Committee on Nuclear Science

Invited Participants

Atwood, K. C., Department of Microbiology, University of Illinois, Urbana, Illinois

Auerbach, Charlotte, Institute of Animal Genetics, West Mains Road, Edinburgh 9, Scotland

Bugher, John C., Office of the Director, Puerto Rico Nuclear Center, Rio Piedras, Puerto Rico

Caldecott, Richard, Division of Biology and Medicine, U.S. Atomic Energy Commission, Washington 25, D.C.

Chu, E. H. Y., Biology Division, Oak Ridge National Laboratory, Oak Ridge, Tennessee

Conger, A. D., Botany Department, University of Florida, Gainesville, Florida

Evans, H. J., MRC Radiobiological Research Unit, Atomic Energy Research Establishment, Harwell, Didcot, Berkshire, England

Garcia-Benitez, Carlos, Radiobiology Division, Puerto Rico Nuclear Center, Rio Piedras, Puerto Rico

Giles, N. H., Jr., Botany Department, Yale University, New Haven, Connecticut

Gray, L. H., BECC Research Unit in Radiobiology, Mount Vernon Hospital, Northwood, Middlesex, England

Hart, Edwin J., Argonne National Laboratory, 9700 South Cass Avenue, Argonne, Illinois

Hollaender, Alexander, Biology Division, Oak Ridge National Laboratory, Oak Ridge, Tennessee

Kihlman, Bengt, Institute of Physiological Botany, University of Uppsala, Uppsala, Sweden

Kirby-Smith, J. S., Biology Division, Oak Ridge National Laboratory, Oak Ridge, Tennessee

Klein, W. H., Smithsonian Institute, Washington, D.C.

Lindsley, D. L., Biology Division, Oak Ridge National Laboratory, Oak Ridge, Tennessee

Moses, Montrose J., Department of Anatomy, Duke University School of Medicine, Durham, North Carolina

Neary, G. J., MRC Radiobiological Research Unit, Atomic Energy Research Establishment, Harwell, Didcot, Berkshire, England

Nebel, B. R., Division of Biological and Medical Research, Argonne National Laboratory, 9700 South Cass Avenue, Argonne, Illinois

Nickson, James J., Memorial Hospital, 444 East 68 Street, New York 21, New York

Parker, D. R., National Science Foundation, Washington, D.C.

Pavan, C., Departamento de Biologia Geral, Universidade de São Paulo, Caixa Postal 8105, São Paulo, Brazil

Pollard, E. C., Pennsylvania State University, University Park, Pennsylvania

Revell, S. H., The Chester Beatty Research Institute, Institute for Cancer Research, Royal Cancer Hospital, Fulham Road, London, S. W. 3, England

Ris, Hans, University of Wisconsin, Madison, Wisconsin

Sparrow, A. H., Biology Department, Brookhaven National Laboratory, Upton, Long Island, New York

Steffensen, Dale, Botany Department, University of Illinois, Urbana, Illinois

Swanson, C. P., Biology Department, The Johns Hopkins University, Baltimore, Maryland

Taylor, J. H., Botany Department, Columbia University, New York, New York

Teas, Howard J., Agricultural Bio-Sciences Division, Puerto Rico Nuclear Center, Rio Piedras, Puerto Rico

Totter, John, University of Georgia, Athens, Georgia

Valencia, Juan, University of Buenos Aires

Yerganian, George, The Jimmy Foundation Building, Children's Hospital, Boston, Massachusetts

Wolff, Sheldon, Biology Division, Oak Ridge National Laboratory, Oak Ridge, Tennessee

Contents

Part 1
General Survey and Interpretation
of Effects

Introduction

Dr. Wolff: I would like to welcome you to this conference, which is sponsored by the National Academy of Sciences-National Research Council's Subcommittee on Radiobiology, and introduce to you the Chairman of the Subcommittee on Radiobiology, Dr. James Nickson, who would like to explain the general purpose of the Subcommittee in having conferences and the specific purpose of this conference.

Dr. J. J. Nickson: Thank you, Dr. Wolff. I would like to welcome you to the meeting on behalf of the NAS-NRC. In Dr. Bugher's absence, he has asked that I welcome you also on behalf of the Puerto Rico Nuclear Center.

This conference is one of a series which may be said to have begun with the Oberlin Conference in 1950. The Subcommittee on Radiobiology, which had been formed some time prior to that and which had a strong hand in the design and execution of the Oberlin Conference, primarily through Dr. Hymer Freidel, felt that the possibility of having symposia at fairly frequent intervals, once a year or so, in areas of radiation biology where two kinds of people who do not normally get together could be thrown together for the interchange of ideas, would be fruitful in the future.

We admit prejudice but we like to think that these series of symposia which the Subcommittee and others have sponsored and which some people have come to call the "Highland Park" Conferences, after the name of a hotel in that suburb of Chicago, which we used for the first of the series of conferences, have been worth-while.

This conference was proposed by Dr. Wolff at one of the Subcommittee meetings. He felt that it would be a good idea to consider this very rapidly expanding field with particular reference to the human aspects, to put the two kinds of people together so that they could exchange their ideas in the hope that some of the translocations would be viable.

Dr. L. H. Gray: The Radiobiological Subcommittee of the National Research Council has given us a splendid opportunity to step out of the grooves in which we normally run and stand back and take a look at the subject as a whole, and I think I probably speak for all of you when I say that we feel this is a very great privilege enjoyed by the small group which is here; we express our sincere thanks to Dr. Nickson, Chairman of that Subcommittee, Dr. Wolff, and all those who have helped to make this meeting possible.

As Dr. Nickson said, we are not really expecting to solve a lot of problems in three days. These problems get solved in the laboratory or in the study or in the bath or any other solitary place rather than in conferences. What we can do is to help one another become aware of what the real problems are so that we may concentrate on these, and I suggest that we make this our objective. We want to see where the difficulties lie, and to see what the challenging points are. If we achieve this, the discoveries will come, after we get back to our laboratories.

Time is short and I have asked our participants to make their remarks challenging, to point to the weaknesses in the existing order, and to evaluate the experimental evidence for these weaknesses rather than to give us a tidy picture of the field as a whole. We all want to think imaginatively during these three days.

Dr. Wolff has made a good, judicious choice in selecting the specialities represented among all of the people who are here, but there are a few who could not be present. I happened to have one or two snapshots of missing colleagues, so I thought we might start by showing two or three slides.

The first is of Karl Sax who is still turning out some very interesting papers. The next is Douglas Lea who probably many of you have met. The last one is a snap I happened to take of John Read when I was out in New Zealand a couple of years ago. I think these are all people who have made such big contributions that they are bound to affect our thinking throughout this conference.

Lea's book, which was written 15 years ago, gave a very clear and logical analysis of the relation between the initial physical events and the aberrations which we actually see. What we are trying to do is to fill in that big gap which falls between the physical events and the changes we observe in terms of biophysical and biochemical events. In attempting this I think we are at a very serious disadvantage inasmuch as we really don't know what a chromosome looks like. Is it, in fact, one or two threads coiled and recoiled, or is it 32 or 64 strands lying side by side? There are those present who, I hope, will be able to inform us on this important point, and I would urge them to speak up early in the proceedings, lest we discuss the mechanism of radiation damage in terms of a model which is utterly different from the structure of a chromosome as it exists within a living cell.

We start this morning with papers that are concerned with dose-response relations and with their formal analysis. My job is only to regulate your discussions, but I thought that there were, perhaps, two or three points which ought to be made at the beginning.

The first concerns dose relations; what we can hope to infer from a dose relation is something about the number of particles which participate in the initiation of the aberration, and not, of course, the number of targets. Thus, although two chromatids may be involved in the production of an aberration, we may infer from a linear dose relation that only one particle is involved in the initiation; or, conversely, there may be aberrations which look as if they involve only one chromatid, but for which the aberration frequency varies more rapidly than as the first power of the dose, and in such cases we must infer that more than one particle is involved in the production of this type of aberration.

When we compare the effectiveness of different radiations (e.g., gamma and alpha radiation) we must, I think, always keep in mind that, unfortunately, the change in the type of radiation changes two things simultaneously: It changes the radiation chemistry which follows after the initiating event, and it also changes the number of particles required to deliver a given amount of energy to the cell; and, hence, on geometrical grounds, the chance that a single particle having deposited energy in one critical site could go on to deliver energy in a neighboring site, relative to the chance that the same result will be produced by two particles. These two factors—the chemical and the geometrical—have somehow to be disentangled.

The third point I wish to make here is that unfortunately most of the experiments that we shall be talking about concern the induction of chromosome aberrations in cells which form part of an organized tissue. This is the situation which exists in the *Tradescantia* anther, the *Vicia* root tip, and the *Drosophila* testis. We now know that in all these situations we are liable to be dealing with a population of cells whose sensitivities are being influenced to varying degrees by the fact that the oxygen tension is not uniform throughout the irradiated structure. This is very beautifully illustrated in some recent observations made by Dr. Alvin Beatty and Dr. Jeanne Beatty on the frequency with which chromosome aberrations are induced at different sites within the *Tradescantia* anther.

I am greatly indebted to Dr. Beatty for sending me the data from which it is possible to compute the yield of aberrations per 100 cells in three different zones in each of the two locules of the anther. The aberrations were scored separately in three concentric zones in each locule—an inner, an intermediate, and an outer zone. When the anther is situated in oxygen, the aberration frequency is approximately the same in all three zones. When the anther is irradiated in helium, and therefore completely devoid of oxygen, the aberration frequencies are again the same in all three zones. If, however, the anther is irradiated in a gas phase which contains 5 percent oxygen, the aberration frequencies are very different in the three zones, being greatest in the outer zone and least in the inner zone. Even when the gas surrounding the anther is air, very marked differences in aberration frequency are observed in the three zones. We may infer, therefore, that when an anther is situated in air, or in gas less rich in oxygen than air, the population of cells which is being irradiated is heterogeneous with respect to oxygen tension. Since the gradients in oxygen tension which are demonstrated by these observations arise on account of cellular respiration, we have also to reckon with the fact that a change in any factor, such as temperature, which changes the magnitude of cellular respiration will change this oxygen gradient, and likewise the heterogeneity of the radiosensitivity of the cell population. Furthermore, we have also to remember that the Q_{O_2} of cells almost certainly varies throughout the mitotic cycle, and when synchrony exists, as it does within the anther, the oxygen gradient will also undergo cyclic variation. Thus, the heterogeneity of the microspores in early interphase, when chromosome aberrations are induced, might be different from that at later interphase, when chromatid aberrations are induced. Miss Gillian Douglas and I have measured the total oxygen consumed by anthers at different degrees of development as a function of the oxygen tension in the gas phase surrounding the anther. The relation is temperature-dependent, and markedly different for early-interphase and late-anaphase anthers.

We will now proceed to the papers. I think speakers will have different preferences as to the manner in which you raise your questions. I think Dr. Evans will be very happy to have you interject your questions at any time in the course of his talk.

Chromosome Aberrations and

Target Theory

Dr. H. J. Evans: If I understand my assignment correctly, I have to try to give some sort of general background on chromosome aberrations and target theory in 10 minutes or a quarter of an hour and, at the same time, try to get you to stand up and argue with me or, preferably, argue with others around the table. I think the best thing for me to do is to very briefly describe some of the findings made in experiments using *Tradescantia,* because the target hypothesis and its application is perhaps more widely or better understood in terms of chromosome aberrations in plant microspores than in *Drosophila;* but this does not mean we are not to discuss *Drosophila.* At the same time I want to raise a number of questions relating to the scoring of the aberrations, the nature of the target, and, finally, if time permits, to discuss the importance of the modifying effects of certain physiological factors as exemplified by some recent fractionation experiments such as those carried out by Elkind and Sutton (1960) and Davies and Wall (1961).

I should start by saying that the first critical cytological evaluation of radiation-induced chromosome aberrations was made by Sax (1938, 1939, 1940, 1941) using *Tradescantia* microspores, and I would like to begin by enumerating some of the basic findings which resulted from Sax's experiments.

First, it was shown that simple terminal deletions and isochromatid aberrations increased *approximately* linearly with increasing dose. I would stress the word approximately, for later data indicate that this statement is not quite true.

The yield of these aberrations was apparently unaffected by altering the dose rate or by splitting the radiation treatment into two equal doses separated by varying time intervals (fractionation).

The yield of aberration which involved an exchange of parts between chromosomes or chromosome arms, i.e., those which may appear as dicentrics and rings, was very much dependent upon the dose rate. If doses were given over the same relatively short period of time, these aberrations increased in proportion to the square of the dose.

From these findings and the appearance and frequencies of the various aberration types it was concluded, on the lines of Stadler's (1931) hypothesis, that radiation produced breaks in the chromatin threads which were independent of one another, their frequency being directly proportional to the radiation dose. That a considerable proportion of the initial primary breaks must restitute was indicated by the fact that the yield of exchanges produced by a given dose of x rays diminished with increasing duration of exposure, so that at low intensities many of the breaks restitute before other breaks with which they could interact are produced. These dose-response results were discussed in terms of a hit theory, the aberrations which increased linearly with dose being interpreted as one-hit effects and the dose-rate-dependent aberrations as being a consequence of the interaction between the results of two separate hits.

The general conclusion was, therefore, that a small proportion of the initial or primary breaks were believed to remain unjoined and to appear as simple deletions, but in the majority of cases rejoining occurred to give rise either to the original configuration (restitution) or to the formation of exchange aberrations (illegitimate fusion). Furthermore, on the basis of fractionation experiments where the time interval between dose fractions was varied, it was shown that breaks in *Tradescantia* microspore chromosomes could remain open —or available for rejoining—for 26 to 60 minutes.

Following the development of what we might call the classical theory of aberration formation propounded by Sax, a number of investigators devised methods for determining the proportion of breaks which restituted, the duration for which breakage ends remained available for rejoining, the distance over which breakage ends were able to interact, and other quantitative facets of the theory. The biggest impetus to the quantitative analyses which followed Sax's initial work were the studies using fast neutrons and alpha particles. With these densely ionizing radiations it was shown that all aberrations, including those which were two-hit with x rays, increased linearly with dose and were independent of intensity. Furthermore, fast neutrons were more efficient than x rays in producing aberrations and this was interpreted to mean that more than one ionization was necessary to produce a break (see Lea, 1955).

On the idea that a chromosome break is produced by a single particle, the number of primary breaks produced by a given type of radiation should be proportional to dose and independent of intensity. However, this situation would also pertain if a break was a cumulative effect of all the ionizing particles in the nuclear sap or cytoplasm. Similarly, the fact that interchanges resulting from two breaks induced by x rays increase approximately in proportion to the square of the dose is consistent with a target hypothesis, but is also consistent with an indirect or diffusion hypothesis. However, the fact that with neutrons the yield of interchanges is proportional to dose, and not to the square of the dose, can only be explained according to the view that the *same* ionizing particles cause *both* breaks.

The important characteristic of ionizing radiation in the target theory is, of course, the localized release of large amounts of energy; the energy dissipated per ionization (33 ev) being greater by almost an order of magnitude than the energies of a few ev (4.9 ev for a carbon double bond) associated with strong chemical bonds. Thus, the concept of the disruption of a chromatid thread following the release of a packet of energy within or near it seemed a natural one, and this concept was supported by Catcheside and Lea's (1943) studies on the effect of very soft monochromatic x rays on chromatid aberration frequency in *Tradescantia* pollen-tube nuclei. In these experiments it was shown that the 1.5-kev characteristic radiation of aluminium produced no aberrations, and this finding is supported by some unpublished observations made in our laboratory where we have obtained no aberrations with this radiation even with doses of up to 1000 rad. Catcheside and Lea explained the inefficiency of these x rays as due to the range of their secondary electrons in tissue being less than the diameter of a chromatid.

At this point I feel that I have spent enough time on the general

background of the localization of the events and the dose-yield kinetics, and I think this is where Dr. Wolff might like to stand up
and say something about the dose-squared relationship of interchange aberrations. I know that he has some interesting points that
he would like to raise and this is probably an opportune time to
make them.

Dr. Wolff: We have been doing some things in regard to the
theoretically expected two-hit kinetics for two-break aberrations.
The usual way to express the kinetics for these aberrations is to say
that the shape curve obtained by plotting the numbers of aberrations against the dose is represented by the formula $Y = kD^2$ or
that the yield increases as the square of the dose.

In point of fact, however, when experiments are performed by
irradiating sperm of *Drosophila* and checking the numbers of translocations induced in the sperm, it is found that the translocations
do not increase as the square of the dose but increase approximately
as the 3/2 power of the dose. This type of response is so uniform
that Muller has called this the 3/2 power rule.

As a first approximation, we might expect a dose-square relation
to occur if there is a certain probability p proportional to the dose
that a break will be formed. Then the probability for the simul-
taneous occurrence of two breaks will be p^2 and proportional to the
square of the dose. Muller explained the deviation in experimental
results from dose square as being the result of inviability that comes
about from inviable chromosomal combinations in cells with multiple
chromosomal breaks. At higher doses he would expect to find relatively more of these inviable combinations and this would cause the
curve to increase somewhat less than the square of the dose.

The usual result of similar experiments performed in *Tradescantia*
microspores or *Vicia faba* root tips is that the two-hit aberrations
here too do not increase as the square of the dose as would be expected on the basis of the simple target theory hypothesis, but that
they actually increase as the dose to the 1.5 power, 1.7 power, or
1.8 power, with an occasional experiment being reported at very
high intensities that did perhaps increase as dose squared.

In these latter experiments, although the aberrations observed in
themselves lead to lethality after many cell divisions, they are looked

at in the first metaphase before such lethality occurs. Therefore, the
explanation used for translocations in *Drosophila* sperm not increasing as the square of the dose cannot be used for the experiments on
Tradescantia and *Vicia*. Lea and Catcheside proposed that the deviation from dose square here might be accounted for by postulating
that some of the two-break aberrations were actually one-hit, that
is, the densely ionizing tails of the electrons projected by the dose of
x rays or gamma rays would break both of the strands that go into
an exchange. According to this concept the total yield of exchanges
would have both a one-hit and a two-hit component and might be
expressed as $Y = \alpha D + \beta D^2$. If this were the true formula, then
when the dose is doubled the yield would not increase by a factor
of four.

This formula, too, includes the approximation that the two-hit
aberrations increase as the square of the dose. We wondered if this
was an appropriate expression for the yield and for the theoretical
kinetics for two-break chromosome exchanges. We do know that
breaks are produced in direct proportion to the dose and we know
that they are produced at random in the cell. Consequently, we
derived what we think to be the proper theoretical expressions for
the kinetics of two-hit aberrations.

Later I expect that Dr. Atwood will talk about what we call the
site concept. The site concept in essence states that in any given
cell there are but a limited number of sites where the chromosomes
by chance come close enough to one another so that if broken the
ends can exchange, that is, there are but a small limited number of
places in the nucleus where the chromosomes are within the rejoining distance of one another. We were led to formulate this site concept because we realized that although breaks were induced at
random within the cell they did not rejoin randomly. This phenomenon was early noticed in neutron experiments performed by
Dr. Giles many years ago, in which it was found that the yield of
two-break exchanges increased not with multihit kinetics but in
direct proportion to the dose. With random rejoining, we would
expect a break produced by one proton projected by a neutron to
rejoin with a break produced by another proton and lead to some
two-hit kinetics. This is never observed. In addition, it is found that

the distribution of two-break aberrations induced in $G1$ of the cell cycle or in late $G2$ or prophase do not fit a Poisson distribution, that is, they are not randomly distributed. The deviation from the Poisson distribution is such that we always observe too few cells having multiple exchanges. We believe this to indicate that there are but a small number of regions where exchanges can be formed.

Knowing that breaks increase in direct proportion to the dose and are produced at random within the cell, we decide to see what the correct probability statement would be for getting two breaks in one of these sites where the chromosomes were within the rejoining distance of h microns. Since breaks are distributed according to a Poisson distribution, $e^{-kD} \cdot kD^r/r!$, the chance of not getting a break in a chromosome in a site would be equal to e^{-kD} or the first term of the Poisson distribution. The chance, therefore, of breaking a chromosome at least once so that once it could form an exchange would be $1 - e^{-kD}$. Consequently, the chance of getting two chromosomes broken at least once would be $(1 - e^{-kD})^2$. This, then, we believe to be the proper probability statement for the chance of getting two chromosomes broken and not kD^2.

If we look at this expression to see how it increases with dose, we find that at low doses, i.e., where kD is very small, when the dose is doubled, the value of the expression and consequently the yield of exchanges would increase by a factor of four (Table 1); but when

Table 1. Values of $(1 - e^{-kD})^2$ As Dose Increases[a]

kD	$(1 - e^{-kD})^2$	Ratio of $\dfrac{(1 - e^{-2kD})^2}{(1 - e^{-kD})^2}$	kD	$(1 - e^{-kD})^2$	Ratio of $\dfrac{(1 - e^{-2kD})^2}{(1 - e^{-kD})^2}$
0.001	0.000001	4	0.6	0.2036	—
0.002	0.000004	—	0.7	0.2534	—
0.01	0.0001	4	0.8	0.3073	—
0.02	0.0004	—	0.9	0.3521	—
0.1	0.0091	3.6	1.0	0.3996	1.9
0.2	0.0329	3.3	2.0	0.7477	1.3
0.3	0.0672	3.0	3.0	0.9029	—
0.4	0.1087	2.8	4.0	0.9637	—
0.5	0.1548	2.6	5.0	0.9866	—

[a] From S. Wolff, *J. Theoret. Biol.* 3:304 (1962).

kD is increased, we find that with a doubling of dose the yield does not go up as rapidly. For instance, in the range where the expression has values equal to 1 to 10 percent, doubling the dose does not increase the yield by a factor of four. You can see from the table that the value of the expression would saturate at one exchange per site.

In the biological range, for instance, in the usual *Drosophila* sperm experiment, one observes only up to 15 to 20 percent translocations. It turns out that in this range as the dose doubles the yield only increases by a factor of two to three. In other words, this expression alone would give something that resembles 3/2 power kinetics.

So far we have been talking about the yield at only one of the sites, but if the cell had n sites, then the yield per cell would be n times the yield per site and would be equal to $n(1 - e^{-kD})^2$. It should be pointed out, however, that when two chromosomes are broken in a site, the ends may not always rejoin to give rise to the type of exchange that is scored in the experiment. Part of the time they may give rise to asymmetrical exchanges, part of the time to symmetrical exchanges, and part of the time they may restitute.

The number of sites times the probability that these sites when broken will give the type of effect scored may be defined as N, the number of effective sites. This is all that can be scored in a given experiment. Therefore, the yield of exchanges would be

$$Y = N(1 - e^{-kD})^2. \tag{1}$$

In Table 2 we can see some *Tradescantia* data (collected in the main by Dr. Conger for Operation Greenhouse) that were fitted to this equation. As can be seen, the fit to this equation alone is quite good. In addition, we have a fit to another equation that takes into account that in addition to the two-hit exchanges there can be some exchanges produced by a one-hit mechanism. If the chance for producing an exchange by a two-hit mechanism in a site is equal to $(1 - e^{-kD})^2$, then one minus this quantity or $1 - (1 - e^{-kD})^2$ would be equal to the chance of not producing two broken chromosomes in a site by a two-hit mechanism. In addition, the chance of not producing two broken chromosomes in a site by a one-hit mechanism would be $e^{-k_2 D}$. The product of these two terms would be the chance of not getting a site suitably broken for exchange formation either by a two-hit or a one-hit mechanism, and one minus this product would,

Table 2. Fit of Numbers of Dicentrics and Rings Induced in Tradescantia *Microspores to Eqs.* (1) *and* (2) *with* $C = O$[a]

			Exchanges per cell		
D (in r)	Number of exchanges	Number of cells	Obs.	Exp., Eq. (1)[b]	Exp., Eq. (2)[c]
50	27	850	0.0318	0.0236	0.0332
100	62	592	0.1047	0.0871	0.0967
150	55	317	0.1735	0.1806	0.1850
200	167	550	0.3036	0.2964	0.2934
300[d]	483	900	0.5367	0.5705	0.5549
400	231	250	0.9240	0.8715	0.8549
600	596	400	1.4900	1.4680	1.4991

[a] From S. Wolff, *J. Theoret. Biol.* 3:304 (1962).
[b] Equation (1): $N = 3.64 \pm 0.68$, $k = 0.00168 \pm 0.00022$, $P = 0.25$.
[c] Equation (2): $N = 5.35 \pm 1.57$, $k_1 = 0.00117 \pm 0.00027$,
$k_2 = 0.0000601 \pm 0.000018$, $P = 0.60$.
[d] This row of data from S. Wolff, *Radiation Research, Suppl.* 1:453 (1959); rest of data from Conger (unpublished).

therefore, be the chance of getting the site suitably broken. The yield would then be equal to

$$N\{1 - e^{-k_2 D}[1 - (1 - e^{k_1 D})^2]\}. \tag{2}$$

We have fit to these equations the very extensive data of Dr. Parker on detachments of attached-X chromosomes in stage 14 oocytes of *Drosophila*. These fits are presented in Table 3. It may be seen that the data are fit extremely well by these equations. In addition, these extensive data show saturation at about 3½ percent detachments per cell. None of the approximations used previously, i.e., $Y = kD^2$, $Y = kD^{3/2}$, or $Y = \alpha D + \beta D^2$, would ever saturate. Not only does the biological data saturate, so does the theoretical yield expected from these equations. I might point out that in Dr. Parker's data the site number observed is very low, as would be expected from the nature of the exchange observed. Detachments have to occur in a very limited region of the attached-X chromosomes that is close to the centromere. In the *Tradescantia* case, the site number observed was 3.5, which was very close to the number 4 that Atwood and I had derived by entirely different methods.

It also should be pointed out that if in these formulae one writes not e^{-kD} but the expansion represented by this term, and then drops

Table 3. Fit of Numbers of Detachments of Attached-X Chromosomes in Stage 14 Oocytes of Drosophila[a]

				Detachments per cell	
D (*in r*)	Number of translocations	Number of cells	Obs.	Exp., Eq. (1)[b]	Exp., Eq. (2)[c]
0	2	5548	0.00036	—	—
100	10	5385	0.00186	0.00190	0.00169
200	27	4379	0.00617	0.00624	0.00616
250	42	5278	0.00796	0.00885	0.00890
400	47	2536	0.01853	0.01713	0.01749
500	88	3646	0.02414	0.02241	0.02280
800	29	811	0.03576	0.03509	0.03481
1000	21	596	0.03523	0.04081	0.03981

[a] From S. Wolff, *J. Theoret. Biol.* 3:304 (1962). Data from D. R. Parker and A. E. Hammond, *Genetics* 43:92 (1958).
[b] Equation (1): $N = 0.053 \pm 0.007$, $k = 0.002 \pm 0.00023$, $P = 0.85$.
[c] Equation (2): $N = 0.485 \pm 0.0075$, $k_1 = 0.00259 \pm 0.00055$, $k_2 = -0.00025 \pm 0.00022$, $P = 0.85$.

out all higher powers of D, the formulae reduce to an expression that is similar to that devised by Lea and Catcheside (1942). However, the quadratic expression does not saturate where the data really do, which leads us to believe that the approximation is not a proper way to express the theoretical yield for two-hit aberrations.

Dr. Conger: I want to insert something here because I think this is what people might want to argue about, namely, the dose-squared relationship for exchanges with x rays. I have never found that. In fact, I have always found less than the dose squared, even on this one big experiment that Dr. Wolff used as an example. But I have found that for radiation in the anoxic state—and for this I had two quite large experiments—I got an almost perfect dose-squared relationship for exchange yields.

Dr. Evans: Do you mean that in an experiment using anoxia you get a dose-squared relationship, but in the presence of air the dose exponent is less than two?

Dr. Conger: This is the simple equation $Y = \alpha D + \beta D^2$. The alpha or linear term could not be detected for anoxic irradiation; it was almost perfectly dose-squared, anoxically. This is the data.

Dr. Wolff: Were the yields the same in both experiments? In other words, on the basis of these equations, at low yields I would expect the yield to increase approximately as the dose squared anyway. At very low yields, i.e., when *KD* is very low in these equations, you get four times the effect when you double the yield.

Dr. Conger: I cannot remember the rate.

Dr. Evans: The square is a little better at low yields.

Dr. Neary: We get a more nearly linear response. If you have a relationship which is, as you say, less than the dose squared, then if you analyze it as a sum of linear and square terms, the linear must predominate at low doses.

For any class of aberrations, if the response is less than the dose squared, you can artificially separate the component terms.

Dr. Gray: I would like to make what I believe to be a summary of what Dr. Wolff has been saying, because I think there are two different things involved. One is that in the low-dose region you may have a mixture of one-hit and two-hit events which can either be expressed in a simple way at very low doses in that formula or can be treated more exactly in this way. This is at very low doses. You can formulate either way.

There is quite a separate point involved in what Dr. Wolff says, and this is that, owing to a very limited site number, at high doses you cease to get aberrations proportional to the square of the dose, but you get the kind of relation he was presenting.

Dr. Wolff: I might point out one other thing, that the fits we have observed are not too bad to the simple two-hit equation [Eq. (1)], ignoring the one-hit component. In other words, if we fit the data to just what we expect on a two-hit basis, the fits are good.

In the data that we fitted of Drs. Conger, Parker, Bender, and our own, on organisms from *Tradescantia* to *Drosophila* to humans, we don't have a very big one-hit component. This turns out to be true over the whole dose range. I think, therefore, that the total decrease observed from dose square cannot be attributed to a large one-hit component at all. I think the one-hit component is rather small, and the major decrease comes from the fact that the proper way to represent the two-hit component is given by Eq. (1).

Dr. Lindsey: Is it true that you get a linear component and that this must be in the yield at the high intensities as well?

Dr. Evans: We have performed some experiments (Neary, Savage,

and Evans, 1961) in which *Tradescantia* microspores were exposed
to gamma rays at high dose rates, 10-minute exposure times, or at
low dose rates, 48-hour exposure times, where the total aberration
yields in the two experiments are similar. In both experiments the
exchange aberration yield increases as something less than the square
of the dose and, of course, the dose exponent for the low-dose-rate
experiment is rather less than that for the high-dose-rate experiment.
If we assume that our exchanges are a mixture of one- and two-hit
events, i.e., yield $= \alpha(\text{dose}) + \beta(\text{dose})^2$, then we find that the one-
hit component (α) is not significantly different between the two experiments, and that the very much shallower slope of the dose-response curve in the low-dose-rate series is almost entirely due to a
reduction in the $\text{dose}^2(\beta)$ term. This type of result in a dose-rate
comparison experiment is the basis for the assumption of a one-hit
component.

Dr. Neary: We should be very careful here with terminology.
We talk about one hit, for example. It would be safer to talk about
linear dose response and square response, and this does not imply
anything about mechanisms.

Dr. Gray: Let's try to get the facts straight because there is some
dispute as to whether there is a linear component in the exchange-
type aberration. Dr. Conger suggested, and I think Dr. Wolff is
suggesting, that there is very little evidence for a linear component
in the dose relation for interchange-type aberrations.

Dr. Wolff: In Table 3, which is Parker's data for the detachments
of attached-X's in *Drosophila*, we see that at a low dose he observed
0.18 per cell; when the dose was doubled he observed some three
times the effect. Even here in Dr. Parker's data we are not observing
linearity. I assume the same is true for Dr. Conger's data.

In addition, the fits of this data to Eq. (1) for two-break kinetics
are as good as the best possible fits that we can get including the
linear term.

Dr. Parker: If you subtract the control frequency, 0.0036 from
each of those, you come up with figues of 0.0015 for 100 r and
0.0058 for 200 r, or nearly four times.

Dr. Atwood: I think we should settle the question of fact. Dr.
Wolff has shown that it is not necessary to assume a one-hit com-

ponent to explain the 3/2 power rule, provided that we are in a range well above the very early region where the approximation to dose squared is good without a linear component. On the other hand, the range in which that approximation is good is the range in which the data are hard to get because the aberrations are scarce. Now, can you say that in that range one must assume a linear component?

Dr. Neary: If you take any set of data and analyze it, you can show that the coefficient for the linear term is significantly different from zero.

Dr. Wolff: You are putting it on the basis of $Y = kD^2$ for the two-hit component, so as you depart from kD^2 you are emphasizing a possible linear component.

Dr. Neary: I would only say that you can take the data and analyze them by any hypothesis you like, and if you can get a statistically acceptable fit, then your interpretation is valid.

Dr. Atwood: It requires that the fit be distinctive, that is, it must distinguish between the two hypotheses in the dose range in which the two-hit component would be solely expressed if it is the only component. I do not know whether I have made that clear.

Dr. Wolff shows that here in this range (high yield) you can have 3/2 rule without a linear term. In this range (low yield), you cannot have a 3/2 rule without so assuming, but in the low-yield range it is very hard to get data, so what I wanted to ask is, are there data in this range that require a linear term to fit the curve in this region?

Dr. Wolff: Muller actually found that for translocations in *Drosophila* sperm at low doses he did get what he thought was dose square. Parker also has pointed out that if you subtract the control values, his data shows almost straightforward dose square in the low-dose range.

Dr. Neary: We got around this difficulty by doing experiments at low dose rate where the square term is much reduced.

Dr. Auerbach: At very low doses or dose rates, it should be linear.

Dr. Wolff: Dr. Muller argued that at low doses you should not get the extra breaks that decrease the multiple exchanges. He then irradiated at low doses and found he got a dose-square relation.

Dr. Gray: I wonder if we should pursue this in too much detail, for this reason: If we consider other radiations such as neutrons, there is no dispute at all about the fact that the same type of aberration is produced in part by mechanisms which lead to a linear dose-response relation, and there is no sharp distinction between x rays and neutron radiation. They are graded into one another, and I think that our discussion hinges on whether in any given person's experiment with a given radiation and a given dose rate he does or does not see the linear component. I do not know whether the mechanism is too important a point to be concerned with, since we are going to admit presently that the aberrations which involve two chromosomes can be produced by a single particle event. So, if we are going to agree later on, perhaps we should not spend too much time discussing other people's experiments. Is that agreeable?

Dr. Atwood: It will certainly come up again.

Dr. Caldecott: I would like to ask a purely biological question in regard to the data of Dr. Beatty which you put on the board. Were the cells in sufficiently synchronous stages that one can predict that there was a uniform distribution of hit sites within nuclei?

Dr. Gray: The experiments consist of giving only one dose, so no dose relation is involved. A single dose was given under different conditions of external oxygen tension. You notice that there is no difference between the aberration frequencies in the three zones in nitrogen, i.e., when there is no possibility of an oxygen gradient; nor is there in 100 percent oxygen when you have practically the same oxygen tension throughout the spore. At intermediate oxygen tensions I think you must, therefore, ascribe the difference in aberration frequency to differences in oxygen tension in different locations, and you cannot ascribe it to a lack of synchrony or anything else, because this would affect equally aberrations produced in oxygen and in nitrogen.

Dr. Caldecott: The synchrony influences the number of sites very much.

Dr. Gray: Yes, I wished to point out that there exist differences in oxygen tension, in different locations within the anther, and that this must be considered in evaluating all the data.

Dr. Swanson: May I ask if it is assumed that the site number is invariable as regards the stage of division? I ask this simply because as the dose is increased there will be a shifting of cell populations.

Dr. Wolff: We first arrived at the site concept because we observed that the numbers of chromosome exchanges in *Tradescantia, Vicia,* and *Hordeum* were not distributed according to the Poisson formula. In other words, they were not randomly distributed among the cells. There always were too few cells having multiple exchanges. By treating the data in terms of multihit survival curves, we calculated that for *Tradescantia* the site number was about four. Knowing this, we were then able to get the distribution that the data did fit.

Dr. Evans has looked at the distributions he observes in *Vicia* just before metaphase for chromatid exchanges. He observes a similar lack of randomness. The site number seems to be smaller. For *Vicia* we had a site number of two for *G*1 cells, Evans gets less than two for *G*2 or prophase. Carlos Garcia-Benitez has done a *Vicia* experiment not in *G*1 when the chromosomes are single, not just before metaphase when they are contracting, but in *G*2, and there he gets a Poisson distribution for exchanges. Therefore it looks like site number is perhaps increased after the chromosomes are doubled, but before they really contract, and is not constant.

Dr. Swanson: This means that in making comparisons between experiments the problem becomes very complex. You can, therefore, only state this as a generality which holds for a particular experiment at a particular time. Even under these circumstances the problem is very difficult, because if you have a variable site number as a function of stage, high doses are going to retard cells more than low doses. So what does site number really mean?

Dr. Gray: I expect Dr. Atwood is going to take this up presently.

Dr. Atwood: At least it means that if we did not know about it, we would be more confused than we are already.

Dr. Gray: I think we will presently get back to this point. It is an important one. At this stage, I would suggest we let Dr. Evans carry on.

Dr. Evans: Since Lea and Catcheside's important paper on target-theory analysis of aberration frequencies, published in 1942, Lea's calculations have been widely quoted, although following the discovery of the oxygen effect it has been realized that some of the calculations and ideas need modification. The target hypothesis is not vitiated by the fact that oxygen may influence the aberration yield induced by sparsely ionizing radiation, for the presence of oxygen might be envisaged as merely enlarging and possibly altering the shape of the target.

However, what is perhaps not widely realized is that when Lea and Catcheside developed their application of target theory to chromosome aberrations, they pointed out that the biological data

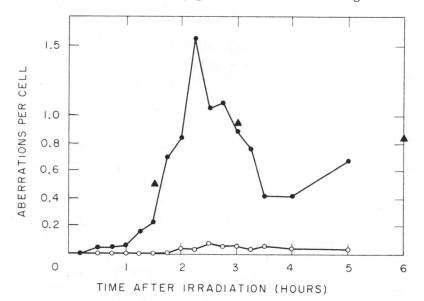

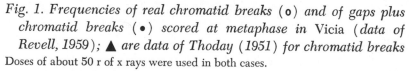

Fig. 1. Frequencies of real chromatid breaks (o) *and of gaps plus chromatid breaks* (•) *scored at metaphase in* Vicia *(data of Revell, 1959);* ▲ *are data of Thoday (1951) for chromatid breaks* Doses of about 50 r of x rays were used in both cases.

which they used was far from being ideal. In discussing chromatid breaks, which they mentioned were difficult to see and presented difficulties for accurate scoring, they stated: "There does seem to be a real discrepancy here since Sax states that these breaks are infrequent while the Cambridge data indicate that they are the most frequent aberration. We shall accept the Cambridge data while bearing in mind that the error in scoring may be considerable." The same discrepancy also existed for chromosome breaks which Sax again found to be rare events, whereas Catcheside and co-workers found them to be rather more frequent aberrations.

I want to direct our attention to these particular discrepancies because quite a number of the quantitative conclusions derived from the target-theory approach relied upon a knowledge of the true frequency of chromatid breaks. Recent data of Revell's and of my own on chromatid breaks in *Vicia* and *Tradescantia* (Evans, 1962), and incidentally Bender's (Bender and Wolff, 1961) data on mammalian

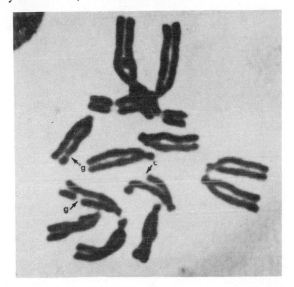

Fig. 2. Metaphase cell of Vicia *containing a number of chromatid aberrations*
Note the large and small gaps (g) and compare with the chromatid break (c).

cells, are more in agreement with the data of Sax. Looking back over the available published data, it seems reasonable to conclude that the high chromatid break frequencies scored by the Cambridge school were probably due to the classification of achromatic lesions or gaps as chromatid breaks. This difference between scores is not simply a factor of about two but is rather nearer a factor of 20 as may be seen from Fig. 1.

Since the frequency of true chromatid deletions is so important in the quantitative application of target theory, and since the gaps are the most abundant of the chromatid effects, I think we ought to discuss these gaps in some detail. An indication of the appearance of these gaps in metaphase chromosomes is given in Figs. 2 and 3.

What do we know about these gaps? First, I might say that in appearance they are a heterogeneous mixture since they come in different shapes and sizes. As may be seen from the slides, they are Feulgen-negative regions which may be similar in appearance to the normal nucleolar constrictions. However, they vary in length,

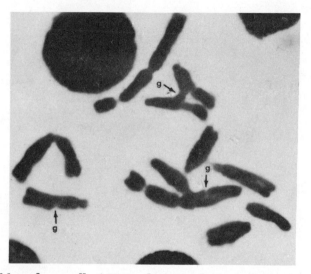

Fig. 3. Metaphase cell of Vicia *showing three gaps, one of which is at the point of exchange in an interchange aberration*

in some cases they may be wedge-shaped, and occasionally they do not completely traverse the diameter of the chromatid. Occasionally, the chromatid gaps are associated in pairs. The gaps are quite certainly not discontinuities, for when chromatids which have gaps pull apart at anaphase the gaps do not yield fragments (Fig. 4).

A second feature of these gaps is that their frequency appears to increase linearly with increasing dose. Furthermore, gaps induced by gamma radiation show a typical oxygen effect: the yield of gaps following a given dose in air being about 2½ times the yield at the same dose in nitrogen (Neary and Evans, 1958).

A third interesting feature of these gaps is the relation between their time of induction and stage in cell development. In *Vicia*, gaps can be induced in cells which are well into the prophase stage of mitosis, whereas true chromatid deletions and chromatid exchange aberrations cannot be induced in these cells. This is shown in the data in Fig. 1 where the first true chromatid deletions observed at metaphase are seen two hours after irradiation, whereas gaps are

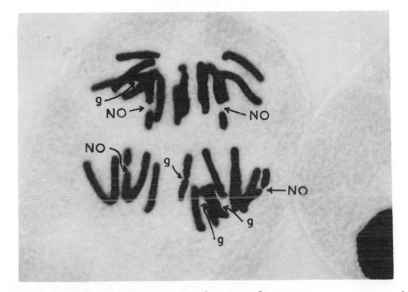

Fig. 4. Anaphase cell of Vicia *showing the continuous nature of chromatids containing gaps* (g)

Note the similarity between the appearance of the gaps and the normal nucleolar constrictions (*NO*).

observed at metaphase in the first half-hour following irradiation. Again, from the same figure, it is evident that the majority of the gaps are induced in late interphase. Very few gaps appear in cells which have chromosome-type aberrations, i.e., cells irradiated in G1, so it seems that gaps are mainly induced in those cells which have made their DNA prior to irradiation, i.e., G2 cells.

Gaps were observed many years ago by Nebel (1936), Sax (1938), and Carlson (1938) and it was suggested that they might be half-chromatid breaks. If this suggestion was correct, or even if the gaps were full breaks held together by a matrix, then we should expect that at the second mitosis following irradiation, i.e., the X2 division, these gaps should result in a large flood of chromatid or chromosome aberrations. As I have said, the gaps are by far the most frequent chromatid aberration, so that if they resulted in true breaks at the X2 division, the frequency of breakage at this division should be very much greater than the frequency of breakage observed at the first or X1 mitosis following irradiation. In fact we do not see anything like a large flood of aberrations in X2 divisions, so these gaps are obviously transient things. They can be repaired, and as their frequency is so low in G1 cells, it seems not unreasonable to suggest that they are repaired in the S phase as a result of DNA synthesis.

We would be very interested in knowing something about the nature of the structural change in the chromatid which is responsible for the appearance of a gap. I might say that in the mechanical sense the gaps are similar to the nucleolar constrictions, in that both these types of constrictions are weak points in the chromatid which can be broken when the cells are squashed during cytological processing. It is possible that a gap may be due to a localized despiralization in the chromatid, but I think that this explanation is an unlikely one because some of the gaps are very big and yet they do not appear to increase the length of the chromatid. An alternative explanation would be that the gap reflects a loss of material from the chromatid. Because gaps are Feulgen-negative, it is possible that there is a localized loss of DNA. If they are the result of loss of DNA, then there is a possibility that they might be mutational events, although they have a rather high frequency.

Dr. Conger: Have you confirmed these things about gaps not leading to fragments that fall free in anaphase in *Tradescantia?*

Dr. Evans: No, we have not done any anaphase studies in *Tradescantia*.

Dr. Conger: I have been impressed with how much more frequent gaps are in *Vicia* than in *Tradescantia*. I think we are arguing about gaps in *Vicia* rather than about those in *Tradescantia*.

Dr. Evans: Most of what I have said about gaps comes from our studies in *Vicia;* however, gaps are most certainly induced in *Tradescantia* chromatids. For instance, in my scoring of chromatid aberrations in *Tradescantia* pollen-tube chromosomes, the relative frequencies of gaps to true deletions is about the same as we find in *Vicia*.

Dr. Swanson might have something to say about this as I think he refers to gaps in his paper on subchromatid breakage in pollen-tube nuclei (Swanson, 1943).

Dr. Swanson: I used "gaps" in the same way as everybody else has, with a lot of confusion attached to it.

Dr. Moses: Could we establish a few morphological facts about gaps? Are they found only in squashes or are they also seen in sectioned material?

Dr. Evans: They are found in sectioned material also.

Dr. Moses: Can any material be visualized in the gap by phase or interference microscopy?

Dr. Evans: Yes, you can see something connecting the Feulgen staining material on either side of the gap.

Dr. Moses: Is there indication of a loss of some component?

Dr. Evans: Or a stretching?

Dr. Moses: If there is stretching, the material would appear pulled out and attenuated.

Dr. Taylor: I don't want to anticipate what I will say later because I will take this up in some detail, but I will say I think we do have evidence that gaps are in fact breaks in one subunit of the chromatid; and, in that sense, they could be stretched regions.

Dr. Evans: If they are a break in one subunit, then this break must always be repaired before the second postirradiation mitosis.

Dr. Taylor: Yes, they can be repaired.

Dr. Evans: I think it would be interesting to know how you can decide whether or not they are actual breaks. In answer to whether there are losses of material, at one time we thought there might be. I am sorry Zirkle is not here to comment on this point.

Dr. Wolff: Dr. Zirkle does find material in the paled regions.

Dr. Sparrow: How reproducible are these? In *Vicia* and *Tradescantia* do you see gaps in only an occasional experiment or an occasional slide? We assume that the phenomena that produces them occurs regularly, but can you see them all the time? I wonder if there isn't a wide spectrum of visibility of these things, depending on the species used and the environment during and after the exposure.

Dr. Evans: And also on the stage of cell development at the time of irradiation. For instance, if you are looking at metaphase chromosomes in meiosis or pollen-grain mitosis, and if the cells you observe were irradiated prior to the onset of meiosis or in the G1 stage in the pollen grain, then in either case there are going to be very few gaps.

Dr. Sparrow: As some of you know, in *Trillium* and in some other plants you can produce something that looks like these gaps by growing them at low temperature.

Dr. Evans: That is a point which I forgot to bring out. Exposure to low temperature may result in the formation of Feulgen-negative regions which are similar in appearance to some of the radiation-induced gaps. In both *Vicia* and *Trillium* these so-called "cold starved" regions are located in precise positions in the chromosome complement; they are in fact located at or near heterochromatic zones. Similar Feulgen-negative regions can also be produced in *Vicia* by treatment with certain base analogs. The radiation-induced gaps, however, are not localized to heterochromatic chromosome regions but are far more frequent and are randomly distributed.

Dr. Pollard: Are you going to give the dose relationships on the gaps?

Dr. Sparrow: Are the gaps highly reproducible?

Dr. Evans: Yes, they are just as reproducible as the chromatid-exchange aberrations. However, gaps are much more difficult to score as they range in size from regions which may be up to 1 μ or 2 μ in length down to very tiny scars which are difficult to resolve in the light microscope.

Dr. Revell: My rule has been to score them on the same basis I think would have been used when they were regarded as breaks. That is to say, when I score gaps, I get as near as possible to what I think used to be interpreted as chromatid breaks, and I leave out the ones below that.

Dr. Evans: I think an important observation is the fact that gaps are sometimes found at regions where chromatids have actually undergone exchange (Fig. 3). The mode of formation and structure of this sort of gap may be quite different from those gaps which are not associated with exchanges.

Dr. Atwood: Does the frequency of gaps associated with exchanges vary with the time between irradiation and fixation in the same way as for gaps not so associated?

Dr. Evans: That is a good point. I don't know.

Dr. Revell: I think they do. I think they are more conspicuous in exchanges that are induced in late interphases, that is, in early samples.

Dr. Lindsley: How commonly are gaps associated with the point of rejoining that forms a scorable rearrangement? Is this a common observation?

Dr. Evans: It is difficult to give a precise answer.

Dr. Revell: I would guess that in a quarter of the chromatid exchanges you have such gaps.

Dr. Evans: Gaps associated with exchanges raise another difficulty, in that if the gap is of a reasonable size, then it may be difficult to determine whether the exchange is a complete or an incomplete type.

I think that if we have completed our discussion on gaps I had better move on, but I must point out that spuriously high breakage scores which were used in target-theory calculations do not of course invalidate the target-theory hypothesis. Nevertheless, aside from the importance of the low frequency of true chromatid breaks to the exchange hypothesis, which we shall discuss later, these low scores lead us to a reconsideration of some of the basic tenets of the classical theory of breakage. As an example I might point out that the reasonable agreement between the results of three different methods described by Lea for estimating the primary breakage/cell/r and the proportion of primary breaks (f) which persist no longer exists. Although clearly one would expect that f is somewhat smaller than the 10 percent value normally accepted and is probably nearer 1 percent.

Perhaps we should now consider how big the target is and what sort of structural alteration must occur in the chromatid to result in breakage or exchange. In brief, it would appear that the chromosome, or at least the chromosome observed at leptotene, is a multistranded structure. There are opinions as to a possible single-stranded form, but there is a lot of evidence from electron-microscope studies and from considerations of the amount and arrangement of DNA in the nucleus which indicates that the chromatid may consist of 32 DNA double helices with associated proteins. Such a structure is about 0.2 μ in diameter, in other words, it is twice the diameter assumed by Lea and Catcheside in their target calculations. Read (1961) has recently drawn attention to this discrepancy and has shown that data obtained from alpha-ray experiments in *Tradescantia* does not, as was previously thought, indicate that the passage of an alpha-ray track through or near a chromatid has unit probability of breaking that chromatid. Using the new measurements on chromatid volume, and the existing aberration-frequency data, Read has concluded that a chromatid is broken only occasionally when traversed by an alpha particle ($p = 0.3$). These calculations again rely heavily on the knowledge of how many primary breaks are induced per r.

Another illustration of how a change in a biological parameter will lead to a large change in a much-quoted conclusion of Lea's is in relation to the finding that with x rays of wavelength 1.54 Å the minimum energy which dissipated in a chromatid is sufficient for the probability of breakage to approach unity is about 17 ionizations. If we repeat Lea's calculations, using the new value for chromatid size, we obtain a value of 46 ionizations, i.e., an approximate three-fold increase in the amount of energy necessary. The questions of chromatid size and of single- or multiple-stranded structures are fundamental to any sort of understanding of the process of formation of aberrations, and I think that we ought to discuss these questions now. Would you like to start the ball rolling, Dr. Steffensen?

Dr. Steffensen: Yes, there are a few people in the audience who might like to hear some of the evidence to follow. I am really paraphrasing their work.

First of all, I think the value for 0.2 μ of Read's is exactly the value one obtains from almost every electron micrograph of plant chromosomes I have seen and have included in a review (1961). The diameters of chromosomes at interphase or chromatids at a late interphase in *Tradescantia* come out to be 0.2 μ. A chromatid diameter at prophase of 0.2 μ agrees with electron micrographs of Ris at leptotene and the diameter of many higher plants.

I could not agree more with Read's agonizing reappraisal where he suggests that the chromosome could not be single-stranded DNA because of simple volume and geometrical calculations. Chromosome length and DNA value can also be calculated in *Tradescantia* by direct measurements and again correspond rather well with Read's evaluation. These objective methods indicate no essential disagreement for the dimensions of chromosomes in higher plants.

Dr. Wolff: It seems to me that Sax's measurement was for a prophase and that he came out with 0.1 μ. I should think that the interphase chromosome would be less rather than more than the prophase. Dr. Ris has some pictures which indicate to him that there are multistranded structures, and yet other electron microscopists have data which indicate that chromosomes are not multistranded structures. They, of course, can talk about that here, but I would like to point out something that Dr. Gall at Minnesota has been doing with lampbrush chromosomes, which consist of two paired chromatids. The loops come out bilaterally from the main axis. Gall treated these chromosomes with DNase. He found that if he produced breaks in the main axis he got four-hit kinetics. When you break DNA, which is a double-stranded Watson-Crick helix, with DNase you get two-hit kinetics, and when phage φX174 single-stranded DNA is treated with DNase it is broken with one-hit kinetics. If Gall breaks the chromosome loops where the chromosome is only one chromatid, he gets something like two- to three-hit kinetics.

In addition, Dr. Miller, who worked with Gall, has looked at these loops which ordinarily appear to be multistranded. If Miller treated these loops with just saline, it seems most of the strands disappeared, and he was left with a single-stranded fiber running through the loop axis.

Dr. Steffensen: Notice that my previous mention concerns large plant chromosomes. I didn't discuss lampbrush chromosomes because our target-theory discussions involved *Tradescantia*. I am sure Dr. Ris will be the first one to say that *Drosophila* or lampbrush chromosome might have two strands of DNA, but the calculations cannot be used as generalizations for all chromosomes. Long ago, cytologists pointed out that the strand number differs greatly, and nobody will disagree with Gall for the moment.

Dr. Moses: I think that we must recognize three levels of chromosome strands. In an operational sense, we are talking about a strand in a somatic chromosome which is of the order of 0.2 μ. In another sense, we are talking about a microfibril which can be seen with the electron microscope and is of the order of 100 Å. In a third sense, we talk about a strand as being a molecule of DNA. We would like to be able to relate these three and to view them as three successive hierarchies of organization starting with the DNA molecule, but I do not believe that we are presently in any position to do anything but guess about the relationship.

We know that the 100-Å fibrils are a part of the 0.2-μ strand of the somatic chromosome, as well as of the lampbrush chromosome and the primary spermatocyte chromosome that I have been looking at, but as yet the morphological evidence has not told us clearly the scheme by which the fibrils are organized to form the larger strand. Thanks largely to Dr. Ris there is presumptive evidence that the 100-Å fibril may be composed of two DNA protein strands, but Cavalieri has cast doubt on how many molecules of DNA there are in the functional units that Meselson and others study in cesium chloride gradients. There are thus uncertainties at all three levels that must keep them separate in our thinking until a testable unifying model is forthcoming. I do not think that we can talk about a generic strand until we have more information, and I think we are obliged to define operationally which strand we are talking about.

I would now like to ask what unequivocal evidence there is for a multistranded, i.e., multifibrillar somatic chromosome. Let's lay some facts on the table; is there an unequivocal answer?

Dr. Steffensen: Dr. Inoué at Dartmouth has studied the sperm heads of the cave cricket with ultraviolet polarization microscopy, and the picture he finds is as follows.

The plane of base orientation primarily determines the absorption efficiency of ultraviolet light. A periodic zigzag pattern of ultraviolet absorption follows a large spiral pattern, the diameter of this chromosome being 0.2 μ. It is a well-known fact in electron microscopy of sperm heads that chromosome fibrils are either in a loose, linear coil or completely linear. There is no evidence whatsoever for branches or side chains.

Dr. Evans: I think that the evidence that Dr. Moses is asking for is in relation to the somatic interphase chromosome.

Dr. Moses: I think we lack the experimental observations that can

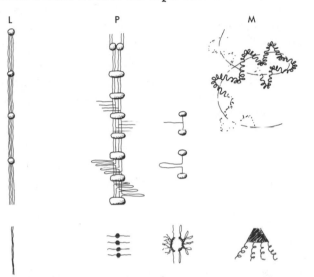

Fig. 5. Upper row: meiotic events in higher animals and plants interpreted schematically; lower row: certain characteristic features as seen in electron photomicrographs are redrawn

The bean-shaped structures are to suggest the protein links of Freese. $L =$ leptotene, $P =$ pachytene, $M =$ first meiotic metaphase. It is not yet decided whether the pachytene excrescences are loops or straight projections.

tell us unequivocally whether the chromosome is multi- or single-stranded.

Dr. Wolff: We are really interested in the backbone too.

Dr. Nebel: Concerning "strandedness" of the chromosome, electron microscopy has presented no material to overthrow the concepts developed in the 1930s by the students of Sharp. Thus, in the diagram (Fig. 5), I have drawn the univalent chromosome as entering meiosis with four strands (not fibers versus Ris). In zygotene these form one-half of the synaptinemal complex of electron microscopy and give rise to lampbrushlike side structures. These lateral projections or loops are retracted toward metaphase when three orders of coiling are seen in the electron microscope, not counting the Watson-Crick helices proper. Where the macromolecular findings of electron microscopy appear puzzling to some students of irradiation cytogenetics, it will be necessary to be patient until bimolecular forces are described which show how messages and events are transferred from the angstrom dimension to the micron level, i.e., from fiber to fiber bundle to chromatid or chromosome.

Note added in proof (*light-microscope observations*): A brief study was carried out in Mayaguez in December, 1961. Onion root tips were exposed to 341 r of gamma irradiation from fuel elements. The root tips were fixed and stained in aceto orceine 1 to 3 hours after exposure. Careful analysis of anaphase lesions only showed from 1 to 5 percent of these lesions affecting the two chromatids of the anaphase chromosome asymmetrically. It is thus clear that the somatic anaphase chromosome contains two chromatids which on rare occasions show differential response to irradiation. (Such lesions have not been reported to survive the subsequent S phase.) This work confirms earlier studies by Nebel and Ruttle (see Nebel, 1939), and more extensive modern work by La Cour and Rutishauser (1954), Sax (1957), Wilson, Sparrow, and Pond (1959), Wilson and Sparrow (1960), and Crouse (1961), all dealing with the existence of half-chromatids. Thanks are due to Dr. H. Teas and Dr. H. Warmke for accommodating the work done at Mayaguez.

Note added in proof (*electron-microscope observations*): Work done during the spring of 1962 at the Argonne National Laboratory with pigeon spermatocytes and Epon imbedding was recently presented at the Radiation Research Society meeting in Colorado Springs and is being prepared for publication in the journal *Chromosoma*. What concerns us here is that the evidence suggests that the chromosome does not consist of a hierarchy of 32 or 64 gene strings. The pachytene chromosome of the pigeon spermatocyte has lampbrush structure. The lateral loops consist mainly of DNA and are carried into the metaphase chromosome. Lateral loops also exist in somatic chromosomes, e.g., in the onion. This agrees with the model proposed by Schwartz (1958). We use the word "strand" for a cytogenetic gene string only. Thus the electron microscope shows only two strands, namely, the chromatids in the pachytene chromosome. Microfibrillae are for the most part components of the lateral loops, not parts of the main axes. While the details of strandedness for somatic chromosomes must still be worked out with the electron microscope, it seems predictable that not much will be added to the concepts of light microscopists. The electron microscope must however tell us how the lateral loops are arranged at all stages of the mitotic cycle and especially during S phase.

Dr. Ris: I would first like to say that in sections you can never be sure how many strands there are. In order to determine the number of strands, you need electron micrographs of high resolution of whole undistorted chromosomes, and this is rather difficult. I have seen only a few published. I have made some of *Tradescantia leptotene* chromosomes; most instructive are stereoscopic electron micrographs. In these pictures leptotene chromosomes of *Tradescantia* show many strands. One can argue that it is perhaps one strand going back and forth, and I cannot definitely answer this argument. We are trying to get a look at the ends of chromosomes where we should find either free ends or loops.

The assumption of a single strand going back and forth also leads us into difficulties if we consider the regions called "chromomeres." Such a strand would have to go back and forth between chromomeres several times. Any one chromomere would have to contain regions which, on the unraveled strand, would be far apart. It is difficult to see how a chromomere could correspond to a specific locus under these conditions. I have never observed braiding of strands. While this problem is certainly not solved, the morphological evidence favors a multistranded leptotene chromosome.

There is general agreement that chromosomes in anaphase and telophase (that is before replication) appear definitely double or even four partite in the light microscope. This is not an optical illusion since the subunits may be quite far apart and easily resolved. A chromosome can therefore not consist of a single continuous chromonema or a single continuous DNA molecule. In addition, as soon as we have to accept more than one strand we run into difficulties in understanding replication, mutation, and crossing over, and it makes little difference whether there are two, four, or more strands.

In lampbrush chromosomes, as was mentioned, Miller and Gall find a single submicroscopic strand per chromosome. My stereoscopic electron micrographs of intact loops in lampbrush chromosomes, however, suggest a multistranded structure. It should be stressed here that the chromosomes photographed by Miller had been treated with concentrated KCl. Now it is known that nucleohistones dissociate in concentrated salt and that the structure of somatic chromosomes is profoundly altered by it. I would therefore question the intactness of lampbrush chromosomes treated in this fashion.

Dr. Wolff: But he is left with a backbone, and it seems to me, in terms of aberration production, that if there is truly a backbone, perhaps of the type that Dr. Taylor published as a model some years ago, then this is what we are interested in.

Dr. Evans: I think that from the radiobiological point of view there are two big difficulties associated with a chromatid made up of 32 DNA double helices with their associated proteins. First, this is a fairly large structure to break, and, second, this multistranded structure raises all sorts of genetic difficulties which would arise on the expectation of a relatively high frequency of breakage and mutation in only a few of the strands.

Dr. Ris: One chromosome is not the same as another chromosome. If we compare early prophase, for instance, of *Drosophila* and *Tradescantia*, it is obvious that there is quite a difference in thickness and DNA content of these chromosomes. I would guess that we will find less strands per chromosome in *Drosophila* than in *Tradescantia*.

Dr. Moses: It is true that one chromosome is not similar to another, but we cannot neglect the fact that the lampbrush chromosome, or any other for that matter, must be compatible with whatever model is proposed. Thus it should be possible to derive a lampbrush chromosome from a somatic chromosome by simply realigning the elements and keeping the basic organization intact. Otherwise, it would be necessary to invoke a complete transformation of the basic structure with DNA becoming detached and reassembling in different ways. At the moment this seems to be unreasonable.

Dr. Taylor: I am sure we could not settle this question even if we talked all day, and I am sure we do not have enough information to settle it.

However, I think that as radiobiologists we ought to have some concept of chromosomal organization for interpreting results. Probably, as we find out more, the problem will become further complicated, because the chromosome is not a static structure, as I think is being brought out. It is a dynamic structure, and it has different properties at different stages of the cycle. Such changes will eventually have to be explained. Let me introduce a diagram here which will probably convince no one. However, I want to at least show some possibilities and indicate very briefly the kinds of evidence we will have to use. I hope that eventually the electron microscope will give us an answer, but there are other indirect ways of attacking the problem, for example, time of appearance of mutations induced by base analogs, distribution of tritium-labeled DNA, and the structural restrictions on reunion of the subunits can tell us something about the nature of the chromosome.

This is a model (Fig. 6) that Ernst Freese first suggested. These helices represent DNA, and we have connected them with sort of hypothetical linkers. I might say there is no definitive evidence for these linkers, and we might eventually have to eliminate them from the model, but in thinking about the organization they seem quite necessary to explain the properties of a chromosome.

I have proposed an additional type of linker which I have called an *H* linker, as well as the *R* linkers between segments of DNA. No specific types of chemical bonds are implied by the names; they could be polymers of some sort.

Now, you see, this could be a linear arrangement of single double helices with associated protein. At another time in the cell cycle it could be folded up accordion-wise to give quite a different structure. If the edges of this ribbon roll together and then it coils, a compact chromosome could be formed. With a model like this, you can visualize the changes that might occur in going from a lampbrush to a compact type of chromosome.

To obtain the side-chain model, which I proposed some time ago, the following changes could occur at least in replication. If the DNA

helices replicate according to the Watson-Crick scheme, an array
of helices with one free end would result. This will produce a side-
chain structure as a transitory form in its replication. To complete
the two chromatids, the ends would have to be united and the result
would be the tandem linkage of DNA helices which could remain

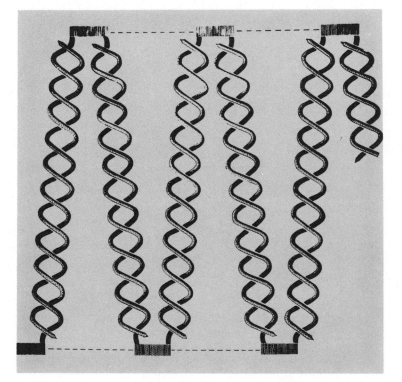

Fig. 6. Freese's chromosome model

folded accordion fashion or become extended. I submit this conceptual model for your consideration as we discuss radiation effects.

Dr. Evans: Before relinquishing the floor I would like to make one
point about chromosome structure and breakage. The true chromatid
discontinuities and exchanges which we observe at metaphase in
Vicia or *Tradescantia* are induced in *G2* cells. In cells which are in
prophase, i.e., about an hour or two removed from metaphase, no
true *chromatid* aberrations can be induced.

The structure and metabolic activity of a prophase nucleus is quite different from the structure and activity found in the interphase condition. It is difficult to define what sort of changes might occur in chromosome structure in the transition from interphase to prophase, but the fact that we cannot break these chromosomes suggests that it would be dangerous to extrapolate too much from the chromosome structure which we see or infer from studies on prophase nuclei. We must bear this in mind.

Dr. Moses: I think you have brought us back to the point. If there is time later on I would like to present some electron-micrograph evidence that I think will support your diagram.

Dr. Steffensen: One more point: again, I want to give a dissenting opinion on the side-chain hypothesis. From data of very excellent electron micrographs of spermatocytes of Drs. Ris, Grasse, and others, now in the literature, the strands are actually quite linear over a few microns as separate 100-Å nuclear-protein fibrils. This was my point about the observations of Inoué. The single chromosome is a fairly large structure made of several fibrils. The fibrils run essentially parallel and all of the evidence would seem to indicate that the fibrillar orientation is linear, just as everybody knows that genes are linear.

Dr. Gray: I think probably we ought to proceed a little further and come back to the structure problem. I certainly want to come back to it because even the question of what we call the chromatid is vitally important and, as Read has shown, the whole concept which requires that so many ionizations must be produced across the chromatid thread to break the thread—which really rests on the heavy-particle evidence—could be quite as easily or perhaps much better interpreted as a requirement that one cluster of ions must be left in each of two threads which are close together. Until we have gone into the question of whether real breaks are produced and examined the circumstances under which they are produced, I think we would be jumping too far ahead.

I would like at this point to ask Dr. Stanley Revell to give us his exposition because this may alter our ideas; it would be better to come back to the mechanisms which may be involved a little later. Dr. Revell obviously caused a great deal of rethinking to be done when he first observed the gaps—which we have spent quite a little time talking about already. His observations forced him to the conclusion that we should be looking at aberration production differently, and he will now tell us about his point of view.

References

Bender, M. A, and S. Wolff. 1961. Am. Naturalist 95: 39.

Carlson, J. G. 1938. Genetics 23: 569.

Catcheside, D. G., and D. E. Lea. 1943. J. Genet. 45: 186.

Crouse, H. V. 1961. Chromosoma 12: 190.

Davies, D. R., and E. Wall. 1961. Genetics 46: 787.

Elkind, M. M., and H. Sutton. 1960. Radiation Research 13: 556.

Evans, H. J. 1962. *In* International Review of Cytology 13, G. H. Bourne and J. F. Danielli, eds., 221. New York: Academic Press.

LaCour, L. T., and A. Rutishauser. 1954. Chromosoma 6: 696.

Lea, D. E. 1955. Actions of Radiations on Living Cells. 2d ed. New York: Cambridge University Press.

Lea, D. E., and D. G. Catcheside. 1942. J. Genet. 44: 216.

Nebel, B. R. 1936. Genetics 21: 605.

—— 1939. Bot. Rev. 5: 563.

Neary, G. J., and H. J. Evans. 1958. Nature (London) 182: 890.

Neary, G. J., J. R. K. Savage, and H. J. Evans. 1961. *In* Effects of Ionizing Radiations on Seeds. Vienna: International Atomic Energy Agency.

Read, J. 1961. *In* Effects of Ionizing Radiation on Seeds. Vienna: International Atomic Energy Agency.

Revell, S. H. 1959. Proc. Roy. Soc. (London) B150: 563.

Sax, K. 1938. Genetics 23: 494.

—— 1939. Proc. Natl. Acad. Sci. U.S. 5: 225.

—— 1940. Genetics 25: 41.

—— 1941. Cold Spring Harbor Symposia Quant. Biol. 9: 93.

Schwartz, D. 1958. Nature 181: 1149.

Stadler, L. J. 1931. Sci. Agr. 11: 557.

Steffensen, D. 1961. *In* International Review of Cytology 12, G. H. Bourne and J. F. Danielli, eds., 163. New York: Academic Press.

Swanson, C. P. 1943. J. Gen. Physiol. 26: 485.

Thoday, J. M. 1951. Brit. J. Radiol. 24: 572, 622.

Wilson, G. B., and A. H. Sparrow. 1960. Chromosoma 11: 229.

Wilson, G. B., A. H. Sparrow, and V. Pond. 1959. Am. J. Bot. 46: 309.

Chromatid Aberrations—The

Generalized Theory

Dr. S. H. Revell: Since we have been into this problem already, I hope that those of you who are not chromosome observers have not been throwing up your hands in despair about this gap business. It is a rather dirty problem. One cannot make an absolutely clear distinction, but I think Dr. Evans and I and anybody who has looked at these is quite certain that there is a very important essential distinction to be made.

In this paper I want to present the new hypothesis for chromatid aberrations which I have already published (1959*a,b*). However, I want to do this as quickly as possible, so as to leave space to consider a few of the implications of the hypothesis which I think are important. For this reason I am not going to give in detail the evidence which I think supports the hypothesis (as I've said, it's published), and I shall simply indicate the general nature of this evidence. Needless to say, I shall be very willing to discuss any detail of the supporting data that anyone feels should be expanded. But I particularly want to show that the interpretation I am suggesting for chromatid aberrations is entirely in accord with a *general form* of the theory for aberration induction as previously enunciated— and that there is no statistical contradiction involved.

The exchange theory I am proposing is essentially a theory for the interpretation of radiation-induced chromatid aberrations at *metaphase*. This is, of course, the earliest stage at which we can satisfactorily observe the structural consequences of the dose given in some part of resting stage, and we try to deduce from what we see at metaphase what the primary stages in aberration development were.

Figure 1 shows the aberrations that we see, divided into two kinds according to the conventional theory—the breaks which are thought according to this theory to be primary, and the secondary exchanges. It is assumed that these breaks, or discontinuities, are the survivors of a much larger number of breaks originally induced

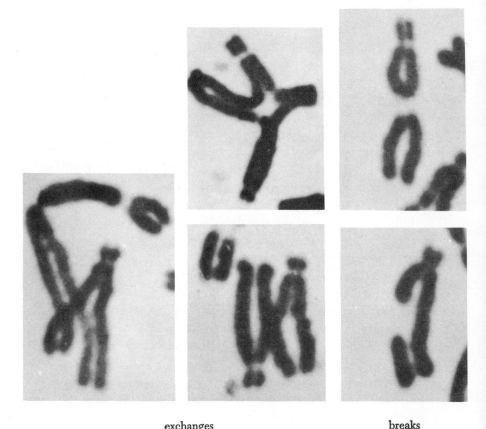

exchanges   breaks

Fig. 1. Types of aberrations observed

by single ionizing particles where and when they crossed interphase chromosomes. The exchanges between chromosomes are supposed to arise secondarily, by aberrant unions between primary breaks. I would like to emphasize that the only direct evidence we have for supposing that radiations can cause breakage where radiation has not caused exchange is the presence of these discontinuities. This was a very important point in Muller's 1940 paper and has already been raised.

Up until that point and through the history of Muller's 1940 paper, everybody seems to have had the very admirable and conservative attitude that they were talking about primary events and exchange events. Very great importance was attached up to that time, so far as I can make out, to the observations of Sax and others of actual discontinuities at metaphase.

Dr. Auerbach: Would that apply to all material? In maize, terminal breaks are frequent, and these would be true breaks.

Dr. Revell: I am not sure I understand your question.

Dr. Auerbach: You said that there had been no evidence for breakage without reunion. Now, what about the evidence for terminal breaks leading to fragments in plants that were observed cytologically and genetically?

Dr. Revell: I must say that on the spur of the moment I don't remember exactly how close the genetic check is in these cases on what happens at the so-called point of breakage. Is it certain, for instance, that some small structural change is not involved as well?

Dr. Evans: I do not think the evidence is good enough to say unequivocally that these terminal deletions are not the result of incomplete exchange, such as an intrachange of the inversion type, where an inverted region might exist either in the fragment or on the proximal side of the exchange.

I would like to say that to my knowledge the only absolutely firm evidence for a breakage which does not (at the time of breakage) involve any incomplete rearrangement at the breakage point is the observations on breakage-fusion-bridge cycles.

Dr. Auerbach: I believe there is genetic evidence for terminal deletions in the sporophyte of maize, where the breakage-fusion-bridge cycle does not usually occur.

Dr. Atwood: The loss of several linked markers that are all distal to unlost markers is reported as a single event.

Dr. Revell: My point was that, to exclude the possibility of there being a more complex structural change at the site of an apparently simple breakage and fusion, one would have to have very good genetics at the point of breakage.

Dr. Atwood: You seem to argue that an aberration interpreted genetically as a distal fragment could really be something else. What is that something else?

Dr. Wolff: I think it is important to get this point so that everyone will know what you are really trying to say here.

Dr. Evans: Perhaps I ought to draw a diagram (Fig. 2). In this

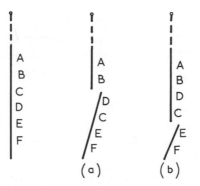

Fig. 2. Diagrammatic representation of an incomplete intrachange due to inversion of regions C and D

diagram, if we invert regions *C* and *D* and make the inversion incomplete, i.e., a typical radiation-induced incomplete intrachange, then, whether or not the incompleteness is on the proximal or distal side of the intrachange, the result, in the morphological sense, is an apparent simple terminal deletion. However, from the genetical viewpoint, if the incompleteness is on the proximal side of the intrachange (a), then the deleted fragment will contain an inverted region, this of course would not be spotted genetically—one would simply register the fact that regions *C, D, E,* and *F* were lost as an apparent simple terminal deletion. On the other hand, if the incompleteness was on the distal side of the inversion (b), then the inverted region is not lost. If this inverted region is large enough, it might be resolvable on the cytological level in salivary glands, or possibly by genetic methods, but it would have to be looked for.

Dr. Auerbach: Why should you get a loss?

Dr. Evans: The point is that we observe exchange and discontinuities. I think it is quite clear that a discontinuity which you observe need not be a simple break, but may be an incomplete exchange.

Dr. Conger: I don't understand what the confusion is.

Dr. Gray: I think Dr. Revell will clear this up in his paper because this is his theory, but we will make sure at the end that the maize is taken care of.

Dr. Revell: The only point I wanted to make is that in the simple interpretation the aberrations are divided into exchanges on the one hand and simple breaks on the other, where one has a simple break unaccompanied by any neighboring structural change. It is assumed that the rearrangement of the exchanges arises by secondary reunion between these simple primary breaks. Now, in the theory which I have proposed, all the same aberrations are interpreted as chromatid exchanges as shown in Fig. 3. It is assumed that aberrations previously interpreted as chromatid breaks and as isochromatid breaks actually arise from small intrachanges which unravel before metaphase is reached. There are four types of intrachange, depending on which combination of chromatids is exchanged.

A chromatid interchange, in its complete and in its two incomplete forms, is shown at the top of Fig. 3. The four types of intrachange in the lower part are shown in their complete and in their incomplete forms, and each is given in its earlier state (with chromatids entirely paired) and as it is supposed to appear at metaphase (that is, after chromatids have contracted and so lost their paired relationship within the intrachange).

Chromatid breaks are supposed to arise as incomplete intrachanges of types 1, 2, and 3, and isochromatid breaks are supposed to arise from intrachanges of type 4—the incomplete fraction being the sister nonunions.

Dr. Conger: You say that all of these result from exchanges as though breaks were not involved at all, and this is also true in your paper. I just do not see how you can make new connections, even if it is done in an exchange way, without breaking something or having a discontinuity exist at some moment.

Dr. Revell: That is true.

Dr. Conger: This is not in your paper. I want to make the point that two breaks must exist, but that they do it in an exchange region.

Dr. Revell: Yes, that is perfectly true, and it is in those papers of mine to which you refer. The point about this interpretation is, and

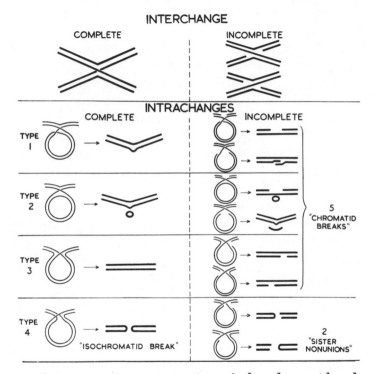

Fig. 3. *Diagrammatic representation of the chromatid-exchange hypothesis*

we will go into the details later, that the aberrations are not interpreted as providing evidence of what the primary event is, and there is no evidence on this hypothesis that discontinuity can occur except where exchange has occurred, and this is the main point of difference between the two interpretations of the metaphase changes.

This theory was already supported by some available evidence. Catcheside, Lea, and Thoday (1946) have already found that the proportion of incomplete chromatid interchanges was about the same as the proportion of isochromatid breaks showing proximal or distal sister nonunion. Dr. Conger (1955) found the same thing. There was, however, one apparent difficulty in the theory, this was that it could only account for a relatively low frequency

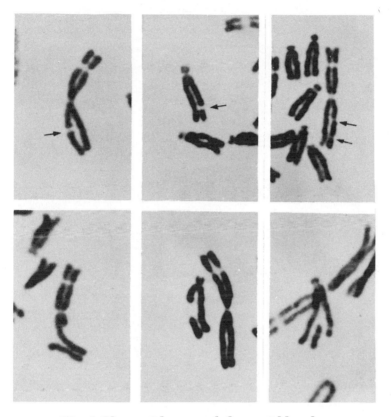

Fig. 4. Chromatid gaps and chromatid breaks

of chromatid breaks: if all the intrachanges are arising with about equal frequency, and if the likelihood of incompleteness is the same for all of them (incompleteness is usually found to be somewhere between 10 and 20 percent), then there should be only about five chromatid breaks for every two sister nonunions of isochromatid breaks. Of course, this is far too low to conform with

general observation. It could mean that chromatid breakage would
be at some value much below isochromatid breakage and not much
higher as is usually found.

Another aspect of this difficulty is that whereas isochromatid
breakage is found to rise by some intermediate power of the gamma-

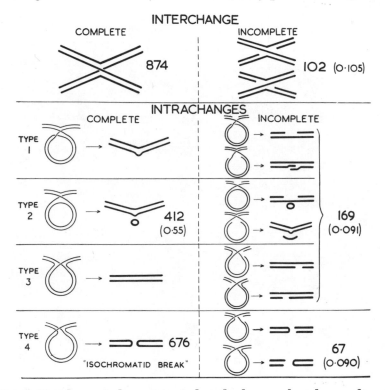

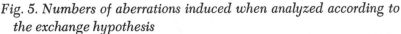

*Fig. 5. Numbers of aberrations induced when analyzed according to
the exchange hypothesis*

Total cells analyzed: 5000, cells with chromatid changes: 1919 (38.4 percent),
65 r 2–5 hours metaphases.

or x-ray dose (around dose "one and a half"), due to there being a
one-hit and a two-hit component, chromatid breaks are generally
considered to rise linearly, in accord with each chromatid break
being neither more nor less than one hit. Of course, if chromatid
breaks were really intrachanges as I am proposing, then they should

increase by the 1½ power or so of the dose, as do isochromatid breaks. In passing, I would like to remind you that the linear relation between single chromatid breaks and x- or gamma-ray dose is extremely important for the conventional breakage-first theory, but that evidence for this linearity is not nearly as plentiful or satisfactory as one would wish.

Now, I believe that this chromatid-break difficulty is resolved if one scores only real chromatid breaks. Figure 4 shows two kinds of radiation effect. The three top pictures are of radiation effects falsely scored as chromatid breaks. The three bottom pictures are true chromatid discontinuities, the fragment being lost at anaphase.

These real chromatid breaks do occur at about the low frequency to be expected according to the theory that they are incomplete intrachanges. That is to say, there are about five such real discontinuities for every two sister nonunions.

Figure 5 shows the results of one such experiment in which bean root meristem cells were given 65 r of x rays. In a total of 5000 cells there were 976 chromatid interchanges, of which 102 were incomplete—a proportion of 0.105. There were 743 isochromatid breaks, of which 67 were sister nonunions—a proportion of 0.090. There were 169 chromatid breaks.

If all four types of intrachange are equally frequent, and if the likelihood of incompleteness is equal in all four types, the frequencies of the eight incomplete intrachanges are identical. Hence, for every two incomplete intrachanges (of type 4) giving a metaphase appearance of sister nonunion, there should be a mean of five intrachanges (of types 1, 2, and 3 together) giving a metaphase appearance of chromatid breakage. (There are five and not six chromatid breaks because one of the two type-2 intrachanges has a broken ring and not a broken main chromatid.) The observed number of 169 chromatid breaks is close to the predicted value of 167.5, and is equivalent to 0.091 incompleteness for the total of intrachanges of types 1–3 postulated according to hypothesis. (Data from Revell, 1959a.)

This category of real chromatid discontinuity is also found to increase by about the ¾ dose power, the same rate of increase as is shown by isochromatid breaks (shown in Fig. 6). Thus, real chroma-

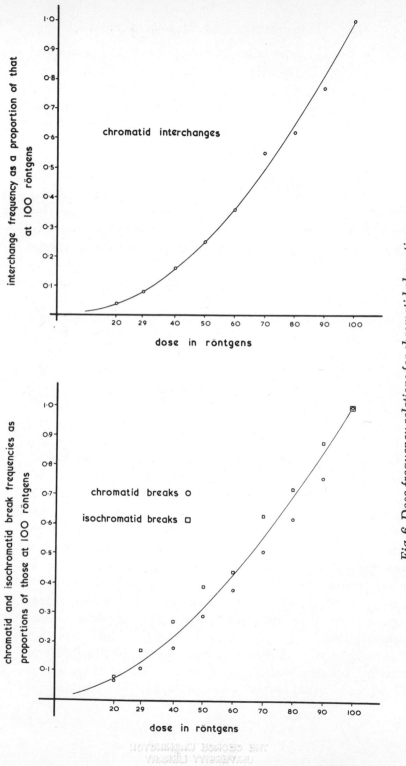

Fig. 6. Dose-frequency relations for chromatid aberrations

tid discontinuities seem to have a large two-hit component, and this strongly suggests that they are not as simple as they look—it suggests that they do arise as intrachanges. On the other hand, the achromatic lesions or "gaps" do show a rough linearity with dose, as shown in Fig. 7.

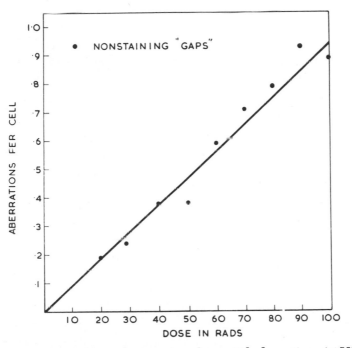

Fig. 7. *Frequency-dose relations for chromatid aberrations in* Vicia faba

Dr. Wolff: Have you ever done intensity effects on these to see if you get the same phenomenon that one gets with exchanges?

Dr. Revell: No.

Dr. Auerbach: In Fig. 6 what is the evidence? The lower part is not filled in. Where it is filled in there is a very good linear relationship. I do not really quite see the evidence that the dots do not increase directly with dose, because when one takes in the red dot down there, it seems to be a straight line.

Dr. Revell: It does not seem so to me.

Dr. Conger: What is the control?

Dr. Revell: Zero.

Dr. Conger: It is not at the intersection of the axes?

Dr. Auerbach: The line of green dots all through is curved and so is that of the crosses; but for the red dots the only basis for saying they do not form a straight line is that it would not go through the point of origin.

Dr. Gray: We are not discussing whether it is a straight line, but whether it is proportional to dose. If it is proportional to dose, you must include the origin.

Dr. Auerbach: It is only proportional at the very beginning.

Dr. Gray: You can analyze this into a linear term and a square term. He said that the aberrations as a whole varied with $D^{1.6}$, but both the isochromatids and the true breaks could be analyzed into a linear term and a D^2 term.

Dr. Auerbach: I can understand that, but wasn't the point that a similarity was to be found between the isochromatid breaks and the true chromatid breaks? I was struck by the dissimilarity, except at the lowest end, but at any other point if you double the dose you get twice as many breaks, which is not true for exchanges.

Dr. Revell: This is simply not so. It may look so from where you are sitting, but the figures do not show it.

Dr. Evans: It is not a square relationship at all; it is less than a square.

Dr. Revell: I am only saying that they rise as the dose $3/2$, not as the dose squared.

Dr. Auerbach: Is it necessary for your theory to assume that true chromatid breaks will behave like isochromatid breaks?

Dr. Revell: Yes.

Dr. Auerbach: I am struck by the fact that they behave quite differently.

Dr. Revell: I don't think we can go through this on the spot. I think we should go over the actual figures later, and I think you would be convinced that the isochromatid and chromatid breaks in fact both rise as about dose "one and a half."

The isochromatid breaks and the real chromatid breaks show a rate of increase that is about proportional to the dose.[1.5] It therefore seems that this exchange hypothesis does account for the relative frequencies of chromatid aberrations if we leave out the "gaps," which can be shown not to be chromatid aberrations at all in the conventional sense.

Now, it has been suggested, indeed asserted, to me that even if all the aberrations are chromatid exchanges by the time they reach metaphase, this does not affect the breakage-and-reunion theory—that all the chromatid exchanges, whether between chromosomes or within chromosomes, could all arise in just the usual way by breakage and reunion. But in fact it is almost impossible for this to be so. Although the primary effect of the tracks of ionization must be presumed to be in some way minutely destructive of biological order, afterwards these minute effects must be in some way canalized towards chromatid exchange *and nothing else*—this is what the hypothesis requires. This canalization towards chromatid exchange I have called the exchange process (Revell, 1959*a*). It is postulated that all the aberrations are chromatid exchanges by the time they reach metaphase, and that one would not get *only* chromatid exchanges from random breakage and random reunion. The primary event, which one must still undoubtedly accept as occurring when the ionizing particle crosses the interphase chromosome, cannot be breakage unless the exchange process has an almost fabulous system for reunion guidance. Figure 8 is meant to demonstrate this point.

This is intended to represent some resting-stage chromosomes. At some places they are close enough together for chromatid exchange to be possible between chromosomes. At some places they are looped close enough together so that chromatid exchange is possible within chromosomes, that is, intrachange. Now, if random chromatid breakage is the primary event that we identify by dose fractionation, then, clearly, if there is to be an appreciable likelihood of two breaks occurring at these sites of proximity where inter- and intrachange is possible, there must also be a very high likelihood of true isochromatid breakage. But, according to hypothesis, all the "isochromatid breaks" we score at metaphase are actually intrachanges (and my data agree with this also).

Therefore, if we choose to accept the exchange hypothesis, but wish also to retain the breakage-and-reunion theory for exchange formation, we must invoke an infallible "reunion guidance system." This system must invariably work in such a way that legitimate reunion (the restitution of chromatid *and isochromatid* breaks) always occurs unless one type of illegitimate reunion supervenes (chromatid exchange), but at the same time the system has to ensure that

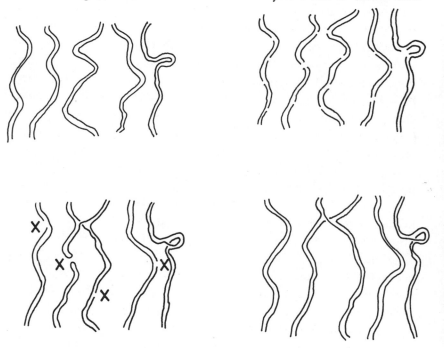

Fig. 8. Diagram illustrating the difficulty of reconciling the exchange hypothesis with random breakage followed by reunion

Top left: unbroken resting-stage chromosomes. *Top right:* the same chromosomes after random chromatid and isochromatid breakage. *Bottom left:* the situation after one chromatid interchange and one chromatid intrachange have occurred as allowed by the exchange hypothesis, but also showing reunion and nonrestitutions that are both forbidden within the requirements of the exchange hypothesis, as marked X. *Bottom right:* the situation after one chromatid interchange and one chromatid intrachange have occurred, as allowed by the exchange hypothesis, but with all other breaks perfectly restituted. To produce this result some reunion guidance system would have to ensure perfect restitution of chromatid and isochromatid breaks unless one type of illegitimate reunion intervened (that is, chromatid inter- or intrachange), but would also have to ensure that all other forms of illegitimate reunion, e.g., true sister union, never occur.

another type of illegitimate reunion (the sister union of isochromatid breaks) never supervenes. And this system of reunion guidance would always have to work perfectly, even in places where the chromatid geometry would otherwise make forbidden types of reunion (anything other than simple chromatid exchange) almost certain.

In the face of these difficulties it has seemed to me inevitable that if one accepts the exchange hypothesis one cannot also retain the breakage-and-reunion theory within it.

Dr. Sparrow: Why do you insist that sister reunion is not allowed?

Dr. Revell: I am merely pointing out the difficulties of having breakage and reunion as the first and second events within the exchange hypothesis that I am advocating for the aberrations at metaphase. I am not arguing in a general way at all, but within this hypothesis.

Dr. Sparrow: It seems to me you are saying that they do not occur because they are not consistent with the hypothesis.

Dr. Revell: No, that is not so. I think my wording has been quite explicit on this point. I have been attempting to explain the great difficulty of accepting my intrachange interpretation of certain aberrations at metaphase and of retaining the breakage and reunion interpretation of the two events that can be resolved in an x-ray dose fractionation experiment. I am not making a circular argument, I am merely asserting that, within the hypothesis, one cannot have breakage and reunion except according to this fabulous system of reunion guidance.

Dr. Atwood: What do these X's mean?

Dr. Revell: They are simple chromatid and isochromatid breaks that must all restitute perfectly, since according to my interpretation they never appear at metaphase. If one assumes that breakage is the primary event, then there must be a lot of breaks if there is to be an appreciable likelihood of their occurring at the sites of chromatid exchange.

Dr. Atwood: Yes, we all agree that there must be a lot of breaks.

Dr. Revell: The hypothesis says—and I am only talking within the hypothesis—that all the changes which at metaphase seem to be simple breaks are actually intrachanges.

Dr. Atwood: Your hypothesis says this?

Dr. Revell: Yes, according to the hypothesis one does not see any simple chromatid breaks. They are all the result of interchange.

Dr. Wolff: You have drawn the exchange and the interchange as coming from breaks. There are breaks at the places that do exchange. I do not see why you cannot get a sister reunion, which is what Dr. Sparrow asked.

Where you have an exchange or interchange you have four free ends, and you would have the same thing down where union occurs, but sister union was ruled out for some magical reason.

Dr. Conger: I want to ask a question. In all of your drawings and diagrams and papers, and so forth, you have all of these things occurring in a loop. In your thinking, is the loop required for the exchange events to occur which do lead to the aberration?

Dr. Revell: Yes.

Dr. Conger: Looking at this diagram here and listening to what you are saying is confusing. Do you say that the aberrations can only occur where a Revell loop occurs?

Dr. Revell: Yes.

Dr. Conger: There is only one on the right there and that is where a Revell exchange aberration could be initiated, but not on any straight part; is that right? Is that your thinking?

Dr. Revell: Yes.

Dr. Auerbach: This is then, in a different form, the old hypothesis of Serebrovsky. The additional assumption is that events leading to rearrangements take place only where two chromosomes are sufficiently close to each other. If we call these events breaks, is it then true that no breaks would be produced at all in regions where they do not lead to rearrangements?

Dr. Revell: That is right, as far as breakage is concerned.

I would like to emphasize that I am not dealing here with what I think really happens. I am dealing with what has to occur if one attempts to reconcile the chromatid-exchange hypothesis that I am offering with breakage and reunion as the two events that we identify in dose fractionation. If one feels that one must still identify these two events as breakage and reunion, then, within my hypothesis, one has to adopt this system of reunion guidance which, personally, I think is fantastic. You seem to think so too.

Dr. Atwood: I don't think you have to adopt it. I do not see that there is any guidance involved. You have shown reunions that occur. Where is the nonrandomness?

Dr. Revell: The nonrandomness is that one must only get reunions that give chromatid exchanges—others are forbidden.

Dr. Atwood: Don't you observe that type?

Dr. Revell: One observes an aberration which appears as a simple break, but the hypothesis rules out its occurring as a simple break.

Dr. Conger: It rules it out as happening in that way. It does not rule out the possibility of that thing appearing at metaphase, but it rules out the possibility of it happening in the way that we see in the second X from the left.

Dr. Wolff: Also, does not the hypothesis rule out the exchange, this X cross exchange in the middle pair of chromosomes? Does not the hypothesis equally well rule out its happening that way because you have drawn it as two separate breaks in the upper right-hand corner?

Dr. Revell: Yes, it does.

Dr. Wolff: But yet you have not X'd this off.

Dr. Revell: I see your difficulty with this diagram. The chromatid interchange and the chromatid intrachange are meant to be aberrations that, according to my hypothesis, one does see at metaphase, and the changes marked X are meant to be those one does not see.

Dr. Conger: Do you think perhaps that the chromosome is mostly little Revell loops; then you would not have the difficulty of canalizing initial events into them? Do you think it is mostly your loops that would allow the exchanges to happen? That would make it work.

Dr. Revell: I am not quite sure that I understand what you are saying.

Dr. Conger: Almost all the chromosome is loops.

Dr. Revell: I would suspect that it is.

Dr. Auerbach: According to the old contact hypothesis, one event produced a rearrangement.

Dr. Revell: There are two events, because we know that there are two ionizing particles sometimes needed for the aberrations interpreted as isochromatid breaks, even with x rays and gamma rays. Although the site contains chromosomes that are close enough together to exchange, to induce the exchange you sometimes need two tracks.

Dr. Conger: For a chromatid deletion in metaphase you require only *one event* in your loop, but it involves *two breaks*. Is that not so?

Dr. Revell: It involves one chromatid exchange, but it sometimes needs two tracks to initiate the exchange.

Dr. Auerbach: Why, if they are not breaks, could not one track initiate this exchange?

Dr. Revell: Because they are sometimes too far apart or one chromosome is missed.

Dr. Gray: In fact, it is a mixture.

Dr. Revell: That's right; it is sometimes one track, even with x rays and gamma rays, because they do rise by an intermediate power of the dose.

Dr. Neary: May I raise a point about this loop concept? According to the loop concept, would you not expect intrachanges to be very much more numerous than interchanges? There are many more sites for intrachange than for interchange.

Dr. Evans: This is in fact what is observed. The work of Atwood and Wolff and also some of my own work has shown that the distribution of intrachanges between cells fits a Poisson distribution. In this sense there are therefore more sites.

Dr. Neary: More sites, but not more aberrations. The number of intrachanges and interchanges are comparable.

Dr. Evans: Yes, that is true, but I think that the real answer to your question is that quite a fair proportion of the chromatid intrachanges cannot be detected cytologically, whereas all the chromatid interchanges can be detected.

Dr. Swanson: I would like to ask—and there are a lot of cytologists here who looked at a lot of chromosomes—whether this concept is consistent with cytological evidence in terms of the way the chromosome is arranged in the nucleus. This was brought up by Dr. Spar-

row. You would get a very changing picture from time to time as
the chromosome condenses, of course, but I cannot remember from
any observations of chromosomes that we get the type of formation
that would be necessary for the Revell loops to be sufficiently numerous to meet the situation described. There is no appreciable movement of chromosomes in the interphase nucleus. An opening out of
the coiling system occurs, but where are the loops in this system?

Dr. Revell: Couldn't they be the coils, for instance?

Dr. Swanson: I don't think so.

Dr. Valencia: These could be coils themselves.

Dr. Revell: There is an observational point here. Minutes can be
induced by irradiation throughout interphase, and one gets double
minutes from $G1$ and single ones from $G2$. For instance, during the
time in interphase when irradiation causes chromatid exchanges in
Vicia, one also gets a lot of bent chromosomes with single minutes.
I do not know how you interpret these, but Catcheside and others
have previously interpreted them as intrachanges, as I suggest. Sometimes you see an actual ring.

Dr. Sparrow: That is your claim, too?

Dr. Revell: Yes.

Dr. Swanson: This should be consistent with the number necessary to produce isochromatids.

Dr. Revell: They are not very different.

Dr. Swanson: I got 412 to 460, which is a fair discrepancy.

Dr. Revell: That is true.

Dr. Swanson: Is this a discrepancy on the basis of observation?

Dr. Revell: Yes.

Dr. Swanson: Why?

Dr. Revell: Because in *Vicia* minutes are nearly always very small.
Some of those that one does succeed in seeing are very small indeed,
and it seems to me entirely reasonable to assume that one cannot be
seeing every one. A serious objection to my hypothesis would be
introduced if one saw *more* minutes than isochromatid breaks, but
this never happens. The frequency that one gets varies from ½ to ¾
of the isochromatid break frequency, which I think is a very plausible short fall, considering the scoring difficulty.

Dr. Evans: I think that this debate about the presence or absence of loops in chromosomes is not only relevant to the exchange hypothesis, but also to the breakage hypothesis. Whatever mechanism we might invoke to account for the intrachanges, a fair proportion of them appear to have a looped or ring structure.

Dr. Swanson: I think you would agree that this is not the way we tend to visualize a chromosome in its uncoiled state.

Dr. Revell: I would not insist upon the fact that there have to be actual loops, but at least there has to be some chromosome condition in irradiated interphase that can give intrachanges.

Dr. Conger: Do you mean after the thing has happened?

Dr. Revell: Yes, after the time during which you can get aberrations initiated. Whatever theory one adopts, there has to be a phase in which chromatid intrachange can occur.

Dr. Auerbach: What is this?

Dr. Revell: This is a normal chromatid.

Dr. Valencia: It could be one-hit deficiency. There could be two hits, but usually not.

Dr. Revell: What is the point you are making?

Dr. Conger: That there is confirmation that this does happen with reasonable frequency.

Dr. Auerbach: In plant chromosomes all you see is a loop, but in *Drosophila* chromosomes you can see the order of the bands in a loop, and you may find that it is reversed in one part of a duplication in relation to the other. Now, how can you get this without actual breaks?

Dr. Revell: There are two quite separate questions here, if I have understood you correctly.

First of all, there is the question of whether the primary event that we undoubtedly identify in our dose-fractionation studies is chromatid breakage. This is one question.

The second question is whether breakage or some sort of discontinuity is involved in chromatid exchange itself. The answer to this second question is obviously "yes": chromatid discontinuity must exist at some stage for the exchange to occur, but this is quite a separate question from whether chromatid breakage is the primary event which occurs as the track crosses the chromosome.

Dr. Auerbach: May I draw something here? In *Drosophila*, an irradiated or chemically treated sperm chromosome may give rise to a reverse repeat, where a small sequence of bands in the salivary chromosomes is repeated in reverse order. The complementary chromosome has a corresponding deficiency.

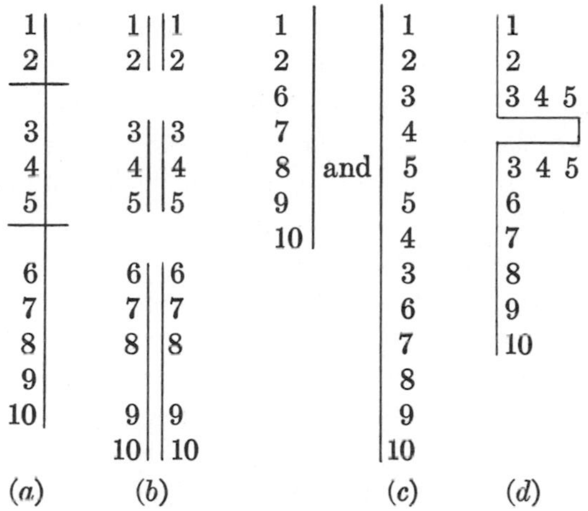

```
 1|      1| |1        1|        1        1
 2|      2| |2        2|        2        2
 ——       —  —        6|        3        3 4 5
 3|      3| |3        7|        4        ┌─────
 4|      4| |4        8| and    5        3 4 5
 5|      5| |5        9|        5        6
 ——       —  —       10|        4        7
 6|      6| |6                  3        8
 7|      7| |7                  6        9
 8|      8| |8                  7       10
 9|                             8
10|      9| |9                  9
        10| |10               10

(a)      (b)                  (c)       (d)
```

Fig. 9. *The production of reverse repeats according to breakage-first hypothesis*

This is quite easily understood in Fig. 9. The original chromosome has received two hits initiating breakage (a). In the ovum, when the chromosome splits into chromatids (b), the broken pieces fall apart and a piece of one chromatid is inserted in the wrong direction into one of the breaks of the other chromatid (c). The second break in the recipient chromatid restitutes. What I want to know is how you can explain such a situation without chromosome breakage.

Dr. Evans: I think that is fine. You have induced three breaks and this is the point. You have three breaks to produce the intrachange. What Dr. Revell is talking about is one exchange.

Dr. Auerbach: Where does the breakage occur?

Dr. Evans: You must have two exchanges. You put a second exchange in. It is a question of semantics, really.

Dr. Auerbach: I would like to see what method you can suggest for producing such a reverse repeat without a break which is open and into which a piece can be inserted. I have asked this question very often but I have not yet found anybody who could answer it.

Dr. Evans: Can you in fact tell me what the dose response is for that sort of aberration?

Dr. Auerbach: No, it happens much more frequently with chemicals, but Bauer in one of his papers mentions that he got reverse repeats with x rays. Unfortunately, details were not published.

Dr. Revell: I am not sure how close these markers were.

Dr. Auerbach: This was cytological work. The bands are very closely paired like this (d). In fact, Slizynska once got a triplication.

Dr. Revell: Then the answer is that one could not get the aberration simply by having one chromatid exchange. Discontinuity must always be involved in the exchange.

Dr. Auerbach: You just said that your exchange could not be based on breakage.

Dr. Revell: No, I pointed out that there were two quite separate questions. One was whether chromatid breakage was the primary event that we identified by dose fractionation, and I said that this was very difficult to reconcile with the exchange hypothesis.

The second question was whether a breakage, or more strictly a discontinuity, is involved in chromatid exchange, and the answer to this was "yes." These are, however, two quite separate questions.

Dr. Auerbach: The discontinuity follows as a result of the exchange.

Dr. Revell: No.

Dr. Auerbach: Make a diagram.

Dr. Revell: I can't on the spur of the moment make a diagram of the combination of intrachanges which would give the aberration you describe. I'd have to work it out, but if you like, we can sit down afterwards—

Dr. Auerbach: I wish you would, because with chemicals reverse repeats are quite frequent.

Dr. Giles: What are the relative frequencies? Is it easy to get the second type?

Dr. Auerbach: I cannot say that for x rays, because Bauer never published his data in detail. I would say that chemicals produce about two to three times as many ordinary as reversed duplications.

Dr. Conger: This is a plea I have been making for years. I think this will help in avoiding confusion. I think we should keep a very clear distinction between breaks and aberrations. The English school are the biggest offenders in this but they are not the only ones.

The important point is this: the break is an event, or it is an idea. We are talking about the idea now, so let's say that it is an idea and that the aberration is the thing that we see, the observed thing. You call this sort of seeing event, Stanley, a chromatid *break*. I object to that.

Dr. Revell: No, I don't call it a literal break.

Dr. Conger: You do in your papers.

Dr. Revell: I call it a discontinuity.

Dr. Conger: Let's call it an aberration. If our theory is that it comes from a break, it is all right in a way to call it a break, but we are trying to touch on these points and sort them out, and we are confusing ourselves. Let's restrict the use of the term *break* to the event or the idea and not use it for the aberration which results therefrom. As an isochromatid thing, which some of us might call an isochromatid break, but which is not really a break, let's call it a deletion. This is the consequence, the seen thing. It may or may not involve this idea, but I make this plea, I have done it in the past to no avail but maybe this is the time for it. There are many processes involved and breaks may not result in deletions by the simple expedient of having a break rejoined, or all of the other consequences.

Dr. Revell: I am delighted that you have said this, but it is what I have been arguing for and pleading for for years.

Dr. Auerbach: How do you see intrachromosome rearrangements?

Dr. Evans: This is one of our many cytological difficulties, for the scoring of both intrachromosome and intrachromatid rearrangements is inefficient. For instance, a complete exchange of the inversion type cannot be detected if the inversion involves only one chromosome arm.

Dr. Auerbach: I don't see why you cannot assume that those gaps you get correspond to what we call minutes in *Drosophila*, that is, small one-hit events that give the phenotypic effect called minute. You need not then be too surprised if you do not find them at the next generation, because Dr. Revell just said that some of these minutes are so small that they can hardly be seen.

Dr. Evans: You are suggesting that the *Drosophila* minutes are equated to gaps? I don't think so, because the frequency of gaps that we get is extremely high and, if each gap did represent a genetic loss, then one would expect to find a much higher yield of mutations or cell death if death is a consequence of such loss.

Dr. Auerbach: This is a diploid.

Dr. Evans: As I remember from the graph which I showed earlier, at 50 r the peak frequency of gaps is about 1.5 per cell. In other words, at quite low doses almost all cells have radiation-induced gaps.

Dr. Auerbach: You don't know whether there are. You don't have so much segregation, and there might be.

Dr. Evans: What we really need in order to answer this question is some information on gap frequency in pollen or sperm, and parallel information on the frequency of recessive lethals. However, from the available observations, it would appear that these gaps are repaired.

Dr. Auerbach: In *Drosophila* there are these very small deficiencies, and it is surprising that you don't get them.

Dr. Evans: Gaps may be very large in size and if they represent losses we should certainly see the displaced region. I think it reasonably certain that we are not missing interstitial deletions comparable in size to the nonstaining zones.

Dr. Sparrow: This is partly asking for information. In *Trillium,* when your chromosomes disappear at anaphase, you can count the number of gyres and you know exactly what they look like. Statistically, at the earliest prophase, you can also count them and you find about the same number of gyres. This means that they go through interphase with all of the same number of gyres. By the time you get to the middle prophase, you don't have these recognizable spirals any more; you have long, snaky things.

On the basis of a Revell loop, you should get a frequency of your interchanges that is different if you irradiate when the spirals are present from that obtained during midprophase or late prophase. Has anybody looked for this kind of information? There should be a difference with stage in the aberrations you get.

Dr. Revell: You don't get any chromatid aberrations from irradiations in prophase, not as defined visually at that metaphase. There are no chromatid aberrations induced by irradiation within two hours of metaphase, and we know that this two hours represents the whole of visible prophase.

Dr. Wolff: In the irradiated cell taking into account mitotic delay?

Dr. Revell: Yes.

Dr. Sparrow: Then *Vicia* is very much different from *Trillium.*

Dr. Evans: I think once again I can refer to Dr. Swanson's experiment with *Tradescantia* pollen-tube chromosomes. In pollen tubes irradiated at different times after sowing of the pollen, up until about seven hours prior to metaphase the whole spectrum of chromatid aberrations was induced. But in cells which were, I think, about seven or less removed from metaphase, no interchanges were observed and a reduced frequency of deletions was noted. These deletions are the ones which I earlier questioned as being possible gaps. I think that this situation is comparable to what we find in *Vicia,* where as you get nearer to metaphase you suddenly come upon a phase where you can no longer induce true chromatid aberrations, but only gaps and subchromatid events. I think that the same is true of Sax's experiments in *Tradescantia* where suddenly at some time prior to metaphase you can't induce—

Dr. Sparrow: I am talking about the middle prophase. If you irradiated there in *Trillium,* I am quite sure that gaps would occur in late prophase, but by anaphase they are fragments. So, they do occur at prophase.

Dr. Evans: No question; they do not appear at the following metaphase after a prophase irradiation, at least in mitotic nuclei.

Dr. Sparrow: There should be a size relationship here, too, because most of these things should be comparable to the size of the spiral loop or gyre.

Dr. Revell: What information is there on this? Dr. Evans and I think that G2 in *Vicia* corresponds with what has been called prophase in many radiation studies. So far as I can see, prophase has often been defined as the period in which you get chromatid aberrations induced if you give an x-ray dose. This seems to be a rather arbitrary way of identifying prophase.

Dr. Evans: I think that we must clear this up, as this is once more a question of semantics. Sax, in his 1941 paper, defines as prophase in *Tradescantia* that stage where the chromosome reacts as double to x rays. Other cytologists have used the classical term prophase in the visual sense, to define that stage where the chromosomes first become visible; the classical term has therefore nothing to do with a radiation response. This difference in definition is the reason for the complications. The chromosome in an interphase nucleus which has made DNA and is in the G2 phase reacts as double to x rays, but the nucleus is not visibly in prophase. If we use metaphase or anaphase as a reference point, we might refer to the paper by Sax and King (1955) which showed that in *Tradescantia* microspores irradiation given six hours or less before anaphase results only in subchromatid aberrations and in no true chromatid aberrations. Chromatid aberrations cannot be induced in the six to eight-hour period prior to anaphase. The *Vicia* results parallel this observation (K. Sax, and E. D. King, 1955).

Dr. Sparrow: Do you mean that they are completely resistant to aberration induction by ionizing radiation?

Dr. Evans: They are resistant to aberrations at the metaphase of that mitosis. What happens at the X_2 division in *Vicia*, we don't know.

Dr. Lindsley: I would like to ask a question. Maybe it will clarify the exchange hypothesis in my mind. Does the exchange hypothesis state essentially that we can think of the nucleus as having sites as proposed by Wolff and Atwood, and that within these sites everything behaves essentially according to breakage hypothesis, but that outside of the sites there are never any breaks?

Dr. Revell: That is a good question. You might, but you would have to assume that the sites had a differential sensitivity. You would have to assume that by virtue of being in a site the chromosome was breakable.

Dr. Evans: The answer is yes.

Dr. Revell: If I might take this point a little further, it does not seem to be a very plausible idea biologically, because different chromosome regions enter into sites in different nuclei.

Dr. Lindsley: According to this rather artificial way of looking at the problem, the only thing that makes the strands within a site more sensitive than those outside is their proximity to each other, which by definition of a site must be sufficient to allow exchange.

Dr. Revell: Yes, it helps me to compartmentalize it this way.

Dr. Conger: Only a small fraction of the chromosome is not in loops.

Dr. Auerbach: At the other regions, nothing happens?

Dr. Evans: These things only occur at sites.

Dr. Gray: The gaps occur.

Dr. Revell: I hope I have made it clear that in talking about reunion guidance I am discussing the question of whether it is possible to reconcile the chromatid-exchange hypothesis that I am offering with breakage and reunion as the two events that we identify in dose fractionation. I think it is very difficult to combine these two things because it leads to all these difficulties of some kinds of reunion being allowed and some not. These difficulties are so great that if one accepts the exchange hypothesis it seems to me one must abandon the interpretation of the two events as chromatid exchange and reunion.

Let us deal with the implications of this. If the first event that we resolve by x-ray dose fractionation is not breakage, then the second event that we resolve in such an experiment cannot be chromatid reunion. Thus, when we measure "rejoining time" (in conventional parlance), we are not measuring the time that breaks stay open, but we are measuring the time that *primary events stay available* to combine with other primary events. Pairs of primary events associate in some way to give an *exchange initiation,* as I have called it. This, you see, is simply a more general statement of the special theory usually adhered to. The "kinetics" are the same. Figure 10 is intended to show the essential difference between the two concepts.

There is an important difference, I think, between these two concepts which, frankly, I am disappointed that more people have not taken up, although I have drawn attention to it in two publications. (I suppose you all have one or two important points in your own work too which everybody ignores, mine is this.) If reunion is already really complete at the end of "rejoining time," then the exchange is already determined irreversibly—it must appear at metaphase. Thus, any effect of a treatment given after irradiation—such as an inhibitor of oxidative phosphorylation or an infrared exposure or whatever it may be—*must be within "rejoining time"* because breakage-and-reunion theory commits us to the view that it cannot possibly be later. Now, according to the exchange hypothesis, one does not commit oneself to the view that "rejoining time" marks the

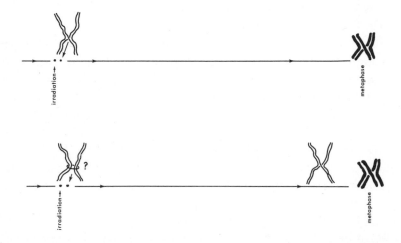

Fig. 10. *Diagram to illustrate the difference of interpretation of dose-fractionation experiments that is imposed by the exchange hypothesis*

Top: If the two events (. .) resolved in an x-ray dose-fractionation experiment are chromatid breakage and reunion, then the chromatid exchange itself is formed at the end of "rejoining time," and must be irreversible from then on. *Bottom:* But if the two events (. .) resolved are not chromatid breakage and reunion, then the end of "rejoining time" only marks the completion of exchange initiation—a state between chromosome parts predisposing to later exchange. This conception does not dictate that chromatid exchange formation is irreversibly determined by the end of "rejoining time."

end of the development of the aberration. Exchange initiations, though they fix the primary events in pairs, need not themselves be irreversible. So we do not have to commit ourselves to believing that all experimental treatments subsequent to irradiation must act within "rejoining time."

In what I've published about the exchange theory, I have deliberately avoided calling the primary event anything but a labile tendency to pair with another primary event—the exchange initiation being the result. I've kept it abstract like this because I did not want to saddle the exchange theory with any particular physicochemical theory for what these two events actually were—my results do not give any positive information on this. But, of course, one need have no shortage of conjectures about it, and I hope very much that there will be some speculation in this direction now, with suggestions for experiments.

Dr. Auerbach: There is one very general question which I want to ask. We have heard quite a lot of things which have to be reconciled with this theory, but what are the facts which cannot be reconciled with the conventional breakage-first theory?

Dr. Revell: It is not impossible to reconcile the observations from broad-bean cell and other experiments with the breakage-first theory, but if the proportions of aberrations are as I observe and, in particular, if the relative frequencies of chromatid breaks and isochromatid breaks are as I and Dr. Evans find, then these frequencies are better accounted for by the hypothesis that I have proposed.

Dr. Auerbach: I have always felt quite happy with the breakage-first hypothesis. In fact, I do not want to abandon it without knowing why I should. Is it the doubtfulness of the interpretation of the gaps, or what else should force me to look for other things?

Dr. Revell: There are two facts. One is that real chromatid breaks are very much less frequent than has been generally supposed (I am calling them breaks in conventional parlance here).

Dr. Conger: Call them aberrations.

Dr. Auerbach: Free fragments. This is then based on the doubtfulness of how to interpret the chromatid gaps.

Dr. Gray: It is based on that, but the community might accept the point being made that there is this distinction. He is quite correct. It assumes that, i.e., we can distinguish between gaps and breaks. This is absolutely vital.

Dr. Auerbach: Could I repeat what I wanted? Assuming that the gaps are not real chromatid breaks, you have too few breaks. Is this the first point against the breakage-first theory?

Dr. Revell: Yes.

Dr. Auerbach: But couldn't it be that most broken chromosomes restitute if they do not form rearrangements? The breakage-first theory makes no assumption about the proportion of breaks that rejoin.

Dr. Gray: I think it does, Dr. Auerbach, because it derives this from the incompleteness of the exchanges. It says that the tendency to remain open is derivable from an observation of incompleteness either of interchanges or of isochromatids.

Dr. Revell: I think that I have clearly shown that there is a very low frequency of chromatid discontinuities relative to isochromatid discontinuities.

The second fact which I think is very difficult to account for in terms of conventional theory is that these real chromatid discontinuities go up as the ³⁄₂ power of dose. How does one reconcile this rate of increase with the fact that isochromatid breaks also rise by the ³⁄₂ power if one is single breakage and the other a double breakage?

Also, how does one reconcile the fact that these single discontinuities go up as the ³⁄₂ power of the dose if chromatid exchanges go up only as dose squared?

Dr. Auerbach: That is exactly what you find in *Drosophila;* rearrangements go up as the square of the dose, and small deficiencies, which I take these to be, go up at an intermediate rate between proportionality and dose squared.

Dr. Revell: I am very glad to hear this!

Dr. Auerbach: The frequency of the minutes goes up at some value between $dose^1$ and $dose^{3/2}$, probably because some are one-hit events and others two-hit events.

Dr. Revell: How are they scored?

Dr. Auerbach: Genetically.

Dr. Revell: So here the whole question of viability effects supervening between irradiation and scoring arises?

Dr. Auerbach: No, only very large ones are lost through viability.

Dr. Lindsley: There is a whole spectrum associated with viability. Deficiencies may range in size from very small ones to ones that include practically an entire chromosome arm. Their effect on viability ranges from very little to complete dominant lethality.

Dr. Revell: The aberrations scores that we make in materials such as *Vicia* are from the first mitosis following the radiation, and therefore I think one must regard them as providing the best data for comparison with radiation dose.

Dr. Auerbach: Why couldn't a mixture of one-hit events and two-hit events give you the ⅔ power relation with dose?

Dr. Revell: This is what I am in fact suggesting, that every real discontinuity which we see at first metaphase is in fact a manifestation of an intrachange, which may be complete or incomplete. Every time we see a simple discontinuity at metaphase I am suggesting that we are in fact seeing an unraveled exchange, and that these are a mixture of one-hit and two-hit intrachanges.

Dr. Auerbach: There is nothing in this which causes me to abandon the breakage-first theory.

Dr. Evans: Except that if you accept that these breaks increase as the 1½ power of dose, then you must also say that the interchanges must go up in relation to the cube of the dose. If these morphologically single exchanges are mixtures of one- and two-hit events, then for interaction of these single observational exchanges—

Dr. Atwood: There is a way out of that. You can say that if the break is a real one in the sense that the chromatid has rotated, then it requires two adjacent real gaps that overlap to give the appearance of one gap.

What I am saying is this: with a certain frequency, since you have so many gaps, two will be so close together that it is a big gap now, and for some reason that we do not know the chromatid will rotate, whereas with the minimal size gap it will not rotate, thus the so-called real breaks will have a higher hit number.

Dr. Revell: It is not simply a matter of their appearance at metaphase which has caused us to call these real breaks.

Dr. Atwood: Their later appearance—

Dr. Revell: It is the fact that there is only a fragment loss at anaphase from the real breaks—the gaps don't yield fragments.

Dr. Atwood: You could have a further explanation. If you have a gap so big as to require more than one hit, then usually the fragment does fall off at anaphase.

Dr. Auerbach: I would just like to make one more point. There are several facts which speak against any relationship between the effects of chemicals on aberration frequency and on crossing over.

For one thing, Linnert made a list of effective chemicals in *Oenothera*, in regard to their ability to change chiasma frequency and to produce chromosomal aberrations, and there was no correlation whatever.

Second, she observed chromosome breakage by urethane in cells in pachytene, in which crossing over was already completed. Third, in my own work and Sobel's on *Drosophila*, there also has been a lack of correlation between the ability of formaldehyde to induce crossing over, which it does mainly in spermatogonial cells, and to produce rearrangements, which it does mainly or only in spermatocytes. Finally, Miss Sonbati found that in *Drosophila* treated with mustard gas there is the expected correlation between lethals and translocations, but not between lethals and crossovers.

Dr. Parker: Dr. Revell, it seems to me that there is an inconsistency in your argument. You say that you do not have enough simple breaks, but you are arguing for a relationship between breaks that neither restitute nor rejoin and those which are involved in detectable exchanges. You hold that on the breakage-first hypothesis there should be a predictable ratio of unpaired breaks to breaks that do rejoin in a specified way. I do not see how on the basis of either hypothesis you could make a prediction of how many unrejoined (and unrestituted) breaks you should have.

Dr. Revell: You mean that all one would have to do, in the case of there being the small frequency of chromatid discontinuities that I see, is to assume that restitution is more efficient? I think this is a very difficult assumption because the frequency of real chromatid discontinuities fits so closely with their interpretation as incomplete intrachanges, as I have shown.

Dr. Auerbach: Maybe it is more efficient with some kinds of exchange.

References

Catcheside, D. G., D. E. Lea, and J. M. Thoday. 1946. J. Genet. 47: 113.
Conger, A. D. 1955. J. Cellular Comp. Physiol. 45, Suppl. 2: 309.
Revell, S. H. 1959a. Proc. Roy. Soc. (London) B150: 563.
—— 1959b. Erwin Baur Memorial Lectures, Abhandl. deut. Akad. Wiss. Berlin, Kl. Med. 1960: 45.
Sax, K., and E. D. King. 1955. Proc. Natl. Acad. Sci. U.S. 41: 150.

Numbers of Nuclear Sites
for Aberration Formation and the
Distribution of Aberrations

Dr. K. C. Atwood: I would first like to show the kind of observation that led Dr. Wolff and me to suspect that there must be a limited number of sites at which exchanges can occur. In Table 1 may be

Table 1. *Number of Cells Containing 0, 1, 2, or 3 Chromosome Dicentrics and Rings*[a]

Material	Radiation and dose		Number of cells with indicated number of aberrations per cell				X^2 test
			0	*1*	*2*	*3*	
Tradescantia	x ray, 300 r	Observed[b]	153	131	16		$X^2 = 24.1$
		Expected[c]	174.3	94.5	31.2		$n = 2$,
							P 0.001
Tradescantia	x ray, 300 r	Observed	155	127	18		$X^2 = 19.8$
		Expected	174.3	94.5	31.2		$n = 2$,
							P 0.001
Tradescantia	x ray, 300 r	Observed	162	120	17	1	$X^2 = 9.17$
		Expected	178.5	93	24.3	4.8	$n = 3$,
							P 0.02
Vicia seed	x ray, 700 r	Observed	314	89	1		$X^2 = 12.17$
		Expected	342	73.5	8.5		$n = 2$,
							P 0.01
Vicia seed	Neutrons, 70 rep	Observed	411	134	5		$X^2 = 13.51$
		Expected	423	110.4	11.6		$n = 2$, P
							approx. 0.001
Barley seed	x ray, 30 kr	Observed	399	98	3		$X^2 = 6.21$
		Expected	407	84.6	8.9		$n = 2$,
							P 0.05

[a] Data of K. C. Atwood and S. Wolff, in S. Wolff, *Radiation Research, Suppl.* 1:453 (1959).

[b] Experimentally observed number of cells with the stated number of aberrations.

[c] Number expected from the Poisson distribution.

seen the distributions of the numbers of two-break aberrations per cell induced in *Tradescantia, Vicia,* or barley. In each case the actual distribution of aberrations is compared to the expected Poisson distribution, and is found to be non-Poisson. The multiple exchanges, i.e., two or more, are fewer than expected, and some central class is always too large. The data represented in Table 1 are just a few examples; many other distributions of chromosome dicentrics and rings showed the same anomaly—a decreased dispersion. The variance is less than the mean, whereas in the Poisson distribution the variance and mean are equal.

In the four experiments with the highest average numbers of aberrations per cell this effect was most pronounced. This leads one intuitively to consider that perhaps we have some severe limitation on the number of interchanges possible within a cell. The deficit in multiple aberrations could be explained if we assume a preexistent deficit of cells with high number of sites. A site is just a place where chromosomal regions are close enough together to allow an interchange.

The model under consideration, then, has the following features:

An interchange cannot occur unless the points of interchange are very close together.

Points on different chromosome arms are seldom close enough together to permit an interchange.

In the time interval between irradiation and the establishment of interchanges, adjacent points on proximal and distal fragments usually remain very close together.

According to this model, the configuration that results from rejoining is dependent solely on proximity of broken ends. The second assumption above follows naturally from the first: two randomly chosen breaks will seldom be very close together; hence, the number of interchanges will be much less than the number of breaks. The third assumption is needed to explain the relative scarcity of terminal deletions. It means that breaks that are not in sites will ordinarily restitute, since the proximal and distal broken ends will be within rejoining distance of one another.

The question at issue now is what number and distribution of pre-existing proximity sites would result in the observed distributions of interchanges. As yet, I have not been able to answer this question satisfactorily, but certain limitations can be stated.

First, the distribution of sites cannot be Poisson; if it were, then the distribution of aberrations would also be Poisson. More generally, the variance of the site distribution must be less than its mean. To illustrate this we let E_s and Var_s represent the mean and variance of the site distribution, and E_x and Var_x the corresponding values for a distribution of interchanges. Then we have

$$E_x = E_s p \tag{1}$$

and

$$Var_x = E_s p(1 - p) + Var_s p^2, \tag{2}$$

where p is the probability of interchange at a site. From Eqs. (1) and (2) it follows that

$$\frac{Var_x}{E_x} = p \frac{Var_s}{E_s} + (1 - p). \tag{3}$$

Hence, for $Var_x/E_x < 1$, as is observed in the experiments, Var_s/E_s must also be less than unity.

As to the number of sites per cell, it is possible to estimate an upper limit. We can see that in Eq. (2) Var_x would be minimized if $Var_s = 0$, that is, if all the cells had exactly the same number N of sites. If we assume $Var_s = 0$, then $E_x = Np$ and $Var_x = Np(1 - p)$; hence,

$$N = \frac{E_x}{1 - (Var_x/E_x)}. \tag{4}$$

The values of N from Eq. (4) are probably meaningful upper limits for E_s only when the aberration yields are fairly high, say, one or more per cell. Under these conditions N was found to range from 3.0 to 3.5 for *Tradescantia*.

As was mentioned earlier, von Borstel suggested that E_s might be estimated from the equation

$$P_0 = [1 - (1 - e^{-kD})^2]^n, \tag{5}$$

where P_0 is the proportion of cells having no interchanges, k is a break constant, and the individual sites are assumed to obey two-break kinetics. The value of n obtained by some method of curve fitting is then an estimate of E_s. The application of such a method to a dose-effect curve for *Tradescantia* gave the best fit with four sites per cell.

Dr. Lindsley: Do you ever get more sites per cell?

Dr. Atwood: Not for the average yield, but for individual cells, yes. Such instances would be expected occasionally if the distribution of site number is such that a few cells do have large numbers of sites. An occasional cell may occur having a chromosome configuration with many proximities.

Dr. Auerbach: Do you score each aberration as an aberration, however complicated? If you have one between, say, three chromosomes—

Dr. Wolff: When we see a tricentric, it counts as two dicentrics, which is how it arose.

Dr. Atwood: In the data we have examined, the complex aberrations are not frequent enough to make trouble for the site theory.

Now, if we consider a region of proximity, with breaks, the strands may rejoin in three different ways. They may rejoin asymmetrically to form a ring or dicentric; they may rejoin symmetrically to form a translocation, or they may restitute and restore the original configuration. With no special assumptions, the probability of asymmetrical rejoining, which is the type scored, might be thought to be one-third. The estimation of a site number of, say, four from the dose-effect curve involves a choice of whether there are really 12 sites, each with probability one-third of forming an exchange when appropriate breaks are present, or whether there are just the number of sites that seem to fit the data. It turns out that you cannot explain the low variance of the distribution of abberations if you assume 12 sites. In order to have the site numbers inferred from Eqs. (4) and (5) fall within the same range, the activated site must be defined as a member of the set of break pairs each of which will inevitably produce an interchange. This may go against intuition or not, depending on your individual bias. I found it a little surprising, but see no reasonable alternative at present. In a sense it is a deterministic philosophy of aberration formation, as opposed to a probabilistic one.

Dr. Lindsley: Is there no problem in assuming as you must have that there is another set of sites that produce symmetrical interchange?

Dr. Atwood: Yes, one must assume that as soon as the break points are established the result is fully determined. This does not mean, however, that a given region of proximity cannot possess all of the potentialities, perhaps in interspersed fashion, before irradiation. It means that each pair of points within the region is associated with only one rejoining pattern, and the site is the summation of those that are associated with the scorable pattern. It should be emphasized that this can all be based on the detailed geometry of the site; it does not necessitate the assumption of other qualitative differences.

Fortunately, it is not necessary to specify the fine structure of sites in order to use the concept of site number to advantage, but before we see how this concept is useful it is necessary to talk about the numbers of primary breaks as opposed to aberrations. We have made an adaptation of Lea's methods of relating the numbers of primary breaks to the numbers of aberrations. First, consider a dose of neutrons that projects a total path length of D microns within the nucleus, and causes n_1 primary breaks. The breaks are distributed along the paths so that the probability that a given break is within a given micron of path is $1/D$. The probability that another given break is within the rejoining distance, h microns, of the first is $2h/D$, since one break can be on either side of the other. Thus each of the $n_1(n_1 - 1)/2$ pairwise combinations of the n_1 breaks has the probability $2h/D$ of forming an exchange. The yield is approximately

$$Y_1 = \frac{hn_1(n_1 - 1)}{D} .$$ (6)

For the x-ray yield we have approximately

$$Y_2 = \frac{h^3 n_2(n_2 - 1)}{2R^3} ,$$ (7)

where R is the radius of the nucleus. This expression is derived on the basis that the probability of a pair of breaks being within a sphere of radius h is proportional to the ratio of the volume of this sphere to the volume of the nucleus.

Dr. Pollard: In calculating these, did you allow for deltas along the path of the protons?

Dr. Atwood: I do not recall whether such allowance was made. Dr. Randolph did the calculations of *D*.

Dr. Pollard: Are these all fast neutrons?

Dr. Wolff: These are 14 Mev neutrons generated by the DT reaction in a linear accelerator.

Dr. Atwood: Do you expect a big difficulty here in assessing the delta-ray effect?

Dr. Pollard: I suspect that you will get many effects like x-ray effects.

Dr. Atwood: The only thing we can do to make sure that this is not the case is watch the kinetics. If they remain first order, then our assumptions seem reasonable for what we are trying to do.

Dr. Pollard: So long as they do not ask for absurd physics, we are in good shape.

Dr. Atwood: Aside from the estimation of *D*, we did not look at it from that viewpoint. We were simply looking for a self-consistent hypothesis that would have to be reconciled with physics later.

Dr. Evans: There are other biological unknowns; for instance, in these nuclei 20 percent of the nuclear volume is occupied by the nucleolus. This nucleolar volume must be regarded as an inactive sphere within the nucleus itself.

Dr. Atwood: You would have to subtract its volume from the nucleus, therefore our nuclear volume may be wrong. We can make the point that *h* is small, however, even with large errors in these constants.

One further necessary assumption is that *h* is the same regardless of the type of radiation. As you can see from the equations, *h* and *n* are interrelated so that at constant yield, say 0.1 exchanges per cell, if *h* became smaller *n* would increase. I have a slide here that I borrowed from Dr. Wolff (Table 2) which will serve two purposes, to illustrate this and also the next thing that I shall try to explain. In Table 2 we see that as we assume successively lower values of *h*, the number of primary breaks (as we call them) increases with both kinds of radiation, but it increases much more with x rays than with neutrons.

Table 2. The Numbers of Breaks Necessary to Produce a
Yield of 0.1 Chromosome Exchanges per Cell [a]

h	Neutron n_1	x ray, n_2	n_2/n_1
1	5.78	7.64	1.32
0.5	7.68	19.6	2.55
0.4	8.45	27.0	3.20
0.3	9.59	41.0	4.27
0.2	11.5	75.5	6.57
0.1	15.8	206.0	13.0

[a] From S. Wolff, *J. Cellular Comp. Physiol.* 58, *Suppl.* 1:151 (1961).

It is possible to estimate h by a method that makes use of the site number. The first step is to use the x-ray yield Y_2 and the site number N to calculate the number of x-ray breaks that are in sites. We assume that the frequencies of sites with 0, 1, and 2 x-ray breaks are binomially distributed, so that the aberration yield is proportional to N and p^2, where p is the probability of a break in one site component. Thus,

$$p = (Y_2/N)^{1/2}. \tag{8}$$

The number of sites per cell with single breaks is $2Np(1 - p)$; hence, the total number of x-ray breaks per cell that are within sites is

$$X = 2Y_2 + 2Np(1 - p). \tag{9}$$

Now we derive X again from an independent assumption; namely, that the ratio of the number of breaks within sites to the total number of breaks equals the ratio of the (summed) chromosome length within sites to the total chromosome length. The neutron irradiation induces n_1 total breaks per cell, and $2Y_1$ per cell are within sites. (It is important to note the implication here that sites with single breaks are negligible when the yield is linear with dose.) The proportion of the strand length that is within sites is then $2Y_1/n_1$. Now, if n_2 breaks are induced by x rays,

$$X = \frac{2Y_1n_2}{n_1}. \tag{10}$$

Dr. Lindsley: What does that equal again?

Dr. Atwood: X is the number of x-ray breaks within sites. It is the total number of x-ray breaks n_2 multiplied by a fraction $2Y_1/n_1$ which is the proportion of the total genome length or strand length inside the sites.

Equation (10) expresses the ratio of the total x-ray to neutron breaks in terms of known quantities: $X/2Y_1 = n_2/n_1$.

In the example to be shown, with the values $Y_1 = Y_2 = 0.1$ and $N = 4$, we find X from Eqs. (8) and (9) and note that $X/2Y_1 = 6.35$. From Eqs. (6) and (7), n_1 and n_2 are obtained for various values of h. As shown in Table 2, n_2/n_1 is close to 6.35 when h is 0.2 μ.

Dr. Evans: You are assuming that the sites are the same with the two radiations?

Dr. Atwood: Yes, the method depends on that assumption.

Dr. Revell: Are they the same volume?

Dr. Evans: This is a constant, too. One assumes that they are the same size and the same entities in both situations. This is a basic assumption.

Dr. Gray: This is an assumption in the sense that the radiochemical reactions initiated by the two radiations may be different. I think we should recognize this.

Dr. Atwood: Whatever those differences may be, some interactions will involve preexisting features of the sites.

Also, I understand that another estimation has been made by the regular target theory. What was the basis of this?

Dr. Wolff: It was to check the numbers of cells without exchanges following various doses of neutrons. They decrease exponentially according to the formula e^{-NkD}; assuming N is 4, you find out what k is and relate it to a sensitive volume.

Dr. Atwood: By that method 0.18 μ was the value for h. That, fortuitously perhaps, is similar to the other value. We had still another value I think of 0.3 μ.

Dr. Wolff: It came from the noninteraction of neutron breaks with x-ray breaks.

Dr. Atwood: Oh, yes, this method has been published. It gives an upper limit. In any case, all of these values are in reasonable agreement and we could not get the value of 0.2 μ in Table 2 without having the numbers of sites deduced from the numbers of cells not having an exchange, and also fairly consistent with the way the aberrations are distributed among the cells.

Thus, the whole structure holds together in that a fairly constant site number can be deduced by different methods and a fairly constant value for h can be deduced by several different methods. It looks as though the concept of site number would be useful in some other respects. For example, there are ways that one could imagine the number of sites being influenced by external agents or changing in the course of the cell cycle. One imagines that the number of sites would be part of the explanation of differences in yields among cells that have very different numbers of chromosome arms or very different intranuclear configurations. I think these things remain to be explored.

I have tried quite hard to derive a distribution of sites in the cells of *Tradescantia* microspores based on some reasonable assumptions. At the present time I can only say that the distribution will require that there be a restriction in the formation of sites such that if an arm of a chromosome participates in a site, there will be a greatly decreased probability that the same arm will participate in another site. With this assumption, you can see that in *Tradescantia* in which there are 12 chromosome arms there are 66 possible pairs of these 12 arms with which a site can be formed. If, however, one site is formed, then there are only 45 possible pairs of arms to form the second site; and, if this second site is formed, then there will be only 28 pairs remaining, and so on. The formation of the first site, given none, can be regarded as 66 times more probable than the formation of the sixth, given five. This may seem a little artificial but I think that it lies somewhere near the truth, and I think that the distribution, if it is found on this basis, can be tested experimentally.

Dr. Pollard: Is it correct that you have taken four sites and that these have chromosome arms 0.1 to 0.2 μ apart? I am just trying to get it fixed in my mind.

Dr. Atwood: Yes, you spoke of the physics of the situation. Another thing that is very disturbing about this, I suppose, is that with this distance of 0.2 μ, in order to be sure that first-order kinetics are maintained with neutrons, you have to assume that the site dimensions are such as to be nearly always completely within the radius of influence of a particle that gives that kind of kinetics. That is, if you think of a particle path as a cylinder traversing the cell, its radius of influence must be larger than 0.2 μ. I do not know whether this is true.

Dr. Pollard: No, it certainly is not. If you are thinking about a single proton aside from the secondary radiation and aside from a delta ray, it is very doubtful whether you will get any reaction at all, except maybe 8 to 10 Å. What you are saying, which is not at all unreasonable, is that you have a density of secondary electrons. So in essence you said that the physics of this process is that you have many irradiated electron tracks which are doing a job and that this is the problem of the recoil of the proton to the neutron. It is a very interesting thing to say. I think you are probably right that this is what is happening. I don't think that this particle is such that you can spread ionization around it.

Dr. Neary: Can I suggest an alternative? You may with neutrons get an exchange between the chromosomes or the chromatids when only one of them has been damaged by a neutron, and this would immediately explain the noncombining of neutron- and gamma-ray damage.

Dr. Atwood: You are right. That would explain the effect. But when you make a structure that holds together fairly well, it is hard to reject it on an assumption that at the outset seems unreasonable; that is, that the nature of the damage with one kind of radiation should be so different that it should have a completely different type of interaction with unbroken chromosomes. If you want to say that this is true, then you open up a field for investigation.

Dr. Lindsley: This is true for alpha rays.

Dr. Atwood: There is some evidence that alphas lead to nonrejoins, but not that damaged chromosomes rejoin with undamaged.

Dr. Wolff: There are certainly far fewer rejoins when you hit with alphas, but there are some.

Dr. Revell: The general pattern of aberrations is the same as for x rays, but the difference is that you get much more incompleteness.

Dr. Atwood: This could have another kind of explanation, namely, that the broken ends are qualitatively the same, but the gap is greater in extent. For example, if a gap is so large that the distance h is exceeded to begin with, then you would get a nonrejoin. Also, if there is shattering within a short region, then there would have to be multiple rejoining throughout the shattered region in order to result in complete rejoins. The joint probability of many rejoinings may become very small.

Dr. Pollard: Are there any data at all on slow neutrons?

Dr. Atwood: I have not looked at any in this context.

Dr. Pollard: A slow proton gives you small ionization and the distribution around it is quite different, therefore, you could have a very nice check of your whole theory. It is a very interesting new distribution and it is very good to do this, and if you believe that you are correct, why don't you try it?

Dr. Conger: Slow neutrons give you too much variation.

Dr. Pollard: Three percent is not from the slow-neutron capture. It is a good cross section and the only comparable one is Lea's reaction of slow neutrons with protons in the amount of radiation, but the proton is predominantly from the nitrogen in the cell.

Dr. Conger: I agree, but my recollection is not that the rest was only 3 percent.

Dr. Pollard: That would be true. You can take the cross sections and figure it out. The problem is that it is not easy to get a slow neutron volume that is devoid of fast neutrons or gamma rays. You must have only things that capture slow neutrons. There are a few which biologically predominate—nitrogen[14] which gives you carbon[14], and another is the capture to form deuterium with 2-Mev gammas. The actual ionization it produces is due largely to the first, which has a considerable cross section.

Dr. Atwood: Dr. Conger has found something different.

Dr. Pollard: Of course, if you put boron in that is another matter.

Dr. Atwood: You can't get rid of it.

Dr. Pollard: Can't you feed them boron[11]?

Dr. Conger: You not only can but Dr. Hollaender paid me for about three years to do that.

Dr. Pollard: That is boron[11], get the 10 out of it.

Dr. Auerbach: Do you think that by drying the cells you could get differences? Would the sites be closer together?

Dr. Atwood: I don't know what a dried cell would be like with respect to sites.

Dr. Wolff: We know that by centrifuging after radiation the yield is increased. What we are attempting now is a kinetics study to see whether the increase in yield is what we expect in terms of a site-number increase caused by postirradiation centrifugation moving chromosomes around.

Dr. Auerbach: You would have to use both types of irradiation. This was one of the assumptions.

Dr. Wolff: This is an assumption that has been made right along. In the beginning when Lea first thought of h, he would solve for h with x rays and then throw the value into neutron equations.

Dr. Auerbach: You would also have to see whether this assumption still holds.

Dr. Evans: In addition to this, Herskowitz (1959) has shown that if you dehydrate *Drosophila* females for 12 hours and then irradiate, you get an increase in crossoverlike rearrangements, and I think he concluded that this was due to a shrinking of the nucleus.

Dr. Steffensen: I would like to submit very seriously that the distance h varies as cellular conditions change. Without giving a long story, let's give this simple summary. If you assume that the exchange of the dicentrics and centric rings is completely random, then their ratio should be 10:1. We are considering the 12 arms of the *Tradescantia* microspores. According to Lea, if an exchange were completely random, then the distance h should be large; if nonrandom, h is small. An analysis of random versus nonrandom exchange was made by following the ratio of dicentrics to rings. A ratio of 6 was the highest observed, while 2.3 was the lowest. We owe the neutron data to Drs. Conger and Giles. It turns out that the one-hit line with x rays where only one electron track will break two chromosomes corresponds to a ratio of 2.3. Also, the same value is obtained with neutrons. If one raises the temperature or the state of metabolism, the ratio increases (more random). If the temperature is low or metabolism is stopped, the ratio is reduced. I contend that one cannot assume a constant distance for h; on the contrary, h will vary, depending upon conditions. Furthermore, slight variations in radius h will greatly alter radiosensitivity.

Dr. Atwood: If the distance h varies, it should lead to an apparent change in the number of sites.

Dr. Steffensen: All I am saying is that I think that the site hypothesis is fine as far as it has gone. The site number can increase or decrease, depending on the diameter of h. The facts are that ratios of inter- to intraexchanges can be varied. Since the exchange volume varies as a cube of h, a slight difference in radius h will produce a large effect. At high temperatures, h will have a larger radius and more sites will be present, and at low temperatures the site number will be at a minimum.

Dr. Atwood: If you think you are getting an increase in h, you can check it by also seeing that the site number is higher, which means that the distribution will become more dispersed, while at the same time the yield for a given dose will be higher. On the other hand, if the yield increases without increased dispersion, then increased primary breakage would be implicated, rather than site number.

There are two more things I wanted to say. One is that I was interested to hear that the intra-arm aberrations do not show the distributional anomaly. This is what we would expect if our hunch as to the cause of a narrowed distribution is true, because the formation of an intra-arm site in a given arm will not change the probability of forming such a site in another arm, whereas sites involving two different arms will to some extent be mutually exclusive. The second thing is that this morning a new way of finding the number of primary breaks suggested itself. It is the so-called gap method.

Dr. Conger: We can call this a Newfound gap.

Dr. Atwood: We define a quantity g which is called the gap ratio and is the total number of aberrations divided by the number showing gaps. In the very same material we simply count the total gaps and multiply it by the gap ratio and then we have the total number of primary breaks. The assumption here is that a primary break will have the same probability of forming a gap whether or not the break is involved in an aberration. If this should turn out to give similar results to other ways of finding the numbers of primary breaks, then I would say that we have created another fortuitous coincidence which must be explained.

Dr. Evans: This is certainly true, but I should think that you could make the ratio anything because the scoring of gaps is so difficult.

Dr. Atwood: I was assuming that the persons scoring would have similar scoring efficiency for gaps in and out of aberrations.

Dr. Evans: The efficiency is very, very poor, even looking at gaps with aberrations. If you get an incomplete aberration, it is very difficult to say that it is incomplete or has a gap. Certainly, in practice, it is very difficult to score this sort of change in an objective manner.

Dr. Wolff: The percentage of incompleteness is not too outrageously high, so it would not make too much of a difference.

Dr. Lindsley: I thought that it was one-quarter of all aberrations.

Dr. Evans: In my opinion one-quarter is a very high value.

Dr. Revell: This would be the very highest.

Dr. Lindsley: You should score at an optimum time when you have the best gap revolution.

Dr. Evans: This is another difficulty, in that gaps do vary enormously in frequency with time, far more than do aberrations.

Reference

Herskowitz, I. 1959. Genetics 44: 329.

Part 2

Biochemical Nature of

Induced Aberrations

Introduction

Dr. J. Totter: A year and a half ago when there was a similar meeting here, one of the main themes was the bringing together of physical and biological time gaps. The physicists deal with an event that begins to take place in about 10^{-5} seconds, and then everything that happened during the absorption of the energy, everything that is of interest of physicists, takes place in about a millionth of a second, although it takes him considerably longer to discuss these events. Now there is a similar gap to consider here. We have considerable chemical knowledge about genetic material, DNA, protein, and so forth, on a molecular basis. On the other hand, there is a lot of cytology and biology on a dimension which is reachable with the microscope, and one of the main themes of this afternoon's program is the attempt to bring these things together somewhat. I do not anticipate that this gap will be closed much better than the other one was, but Dr. Swanson is going to review some of the methods which are used to help understand the chemistry of the larger chromosome.

Survey of Work on Chemical Bonds
Involved in Aberrations

Dr. C. P. Swanson: I will restrict myself insofar as I can to chromosomes in higher organisms; most of the fragments of information which we possess have been derived from studies of this sort.

In trying to visualize some of the chemical bonds that may be broken by radiation, it would be nice if we could have an active atom or a molecule present which would tie these broken ends up at the moment they were made. This would enable us to isolate, count, and examine them; unfortunately, we do not have such a mechanism at the present time and, consequently, we must approach the problem by various indirect means.

It seems to me that there are four sets of information to which one can refer. Let me go through the four points I think worthy of our consideration.

One is the enzyme work relating to the digestion of chromosomes. Much of this has been the work of Dr. B. P. Kaufmann. We heard earlier that Gall's work indicated that DNase could under certain conditions and with certain kinetic relationships fragment the lampbrush chromosomes, but other work has indicated that neither the proteases nor the nucleases, when used alone, will break the chromosomes down into particulate matter. One can remove the RNA and DNA and still leave a recognizable chromosome. If this residual chromosome, as it is called, is then subjected to some of the proteases, it may or may not resist dissolution, all of which leaves us with very little idea as to what the chromosome is made of, how it is put together, and what bonds are broken in separating strands and inducing fragments.

It can, of course, be pointed out that there are four kinds of molecules here: RNA, DNA, the histones, and the nonhistone proteins, but insofar as they are woven into a molecular fabric to form a chromosome, about the only thing that we can do at the present time is to go along with Kaufmann and say that it is a type of fabric in which no single molecule is totally responsible for the linear integrity of the chromosome. This means that we could be dealing with many kinds of chemical bonds and, even if we knew them all, we would not know which one had to do with the integrity of the chromosome.

Some very interesting work has been done with the possible role of divalent ions, which should be discussed by Dr. Steffensen, but since I have been given the charge, let me see what I can do with it. Correct me if I do not handle your data correctly, Dr. Steffensen.

It has been shown by Steffensen that calcium deficiencies cause an increase in the spontaneous fragmentation of chromosomes and markedly increases their x-ray sensitivity. When deficient, magnesium also causes an increase in fragmentation but no increase in sensitivity. It was suggested in the papers that Steffensen has published that possibly these ions were linked to DNA in some manner, but the work of Mirsky and Naora in Mirsky's laboratory would suggest that the calcium is somehow bound to the histones or other proteins in the chromosome and very probably not associated with DNA, and that magnesium was bound to the DNA at the phosphate groups. What this information allows us to derive in terms of the bonding type of structure in the chromosome is very difficult to say. I should point out that Mazia, in using versene, showed that the salivary-gland type of chromosome could be fragmented or dissolved into 250-Å blocks; this removal of calcium led to fragmentation of the chromosome into small units and gave some indication of the size of the blocks of which the chromosome was made. This work has not been accepted by Kaufmann, but I have been unable to follow all the details of argument.

Apart from this, there are two other pieces of evidence which seem to me to be very important in relation to this kind of work. One is the fact that Wolff has shown that the rejoining process—and here I am going along with the breakage-fusion hypothesis, at least for the sake of argument—must be accompanied by a synthesis of proteins.

Then, there is the work of Kirby-Smith which shows that the signals one gets from the radiation of chromosomes are essentially those from proteins rather than from DNA. I am wondering, therefore, whether we are not dealing, in the breakage phenomena, with a process that is much more related to proteins than it is to the DNA.

I am not sure how all of these varied pieces of information fit together, but it seems to me that they are significant in pointing to the proteins as a kind of molecule whose manner of fragmentation and possibly of resynthesis should be understood more thoroughly if we are to understand breakage phenomena.

In another piece of work attempting to get at the problem of chemical bonding and being no more successful than the previous investigators, Cohn, in Giles' laboratory, showed that there was a very fast uniting series of breakage points in addition to a very slow uniting component. In an effort to distinguish between these two kinds, Cohn tried to make a possible distinction between them on the basis of their response to CO aftertreatment, and I believe that they responded very much alike. Consequently, he was unable to distinguish them on this basis. Yet, it does appear that at least in root tips there are two kinds of breaks. Whether this means two kinds of bonds, one of which unites rapidly and another which unites somewhat more slowly, remains somewhat problematical.

Dr. Hollaender: The same sort of phenomenon seems to occur in solutions of nucleic acid and protein. One will dissolve much faster than the other.

Dr. Swanson: Which one?

Dr. Hollaender: It can be shown for nucleic acid and nucleoproteins.

Dr. Swanson: Is there any knowledge here of the studies done on this system?

Dr. Hollaender: There is one which dissolves easily and one which takes a day or two. Butler tried to analyze this. I do not have the details.

Dr. Gray: I think that in this connection one of the more important pieces of work (just recently published) is that of Peacock who studied the effects of radiation on calf-thymus DNA protein. The DNA protein is irradiated in solution, and it is probable that the total effect is partly direct effect on the nucleoprotein molecule and partly due to radicals.

From the kinetics of the change in the molecular weight and change in the gyration of the molecule, Peacock observes that with increasing dose the molecular weight (which starts at 22 million) falls right down to about one-tenth of the original value, but the radius of gyration which measures the length of the molecule does not fall at all quickly, and it is only after a considerable dose that you start to get a fall in the radius of gyration. He concludes from this that the first action on the nucleoprotein is to strip off small bits of protein without actually breaking the backbone, and it is only when you have stripped off a lot of protein that the radicals begin to attack the DNA core. Thereafter, the kinetics go in the usual way for the breakup of the DNA molecule. I think that this might be very important because in the cell we are dealing more with DNA protein than with DNA.

Dr. Pollard: Were the doses very large?

Dr. Gray: No, the doses were from 10,000 rad upwards, which, for the irradiation of a nucleoprotein in solution, is not a high dose. Proportionately, it would mean that a dose of about 100 rad might be stripping off perhaps a few percent of the protein from the DNA protein molecules. A few percent stripped off could be pretty damaging, I would imagine, to a chromosome.

Dr. Hart: The work on proteins is quite well known and you do remove amine groups. This work of Peacock's seemed to me to be explained by a stripping off of reactive groups such as NH_2 from an outer shell of this compound. For simple amino acids, ammonia is a very prominent product of irradiated aqueous solutions.

Dr. Chu: I think it is pertinent to the point Dr. Swanson just made regarding the protein and the chromosome structure to mention some of our recent observations of ultraviolet radiations on chromosomes. We have so far tried two wavelengths: one is the 2804 and the other is 2652. Chromosome aberrations are produced at both these wavelengths. At 2804, in addition to the regular type of aberration which we see, we also induce chromosome fuzziness and shattering. At this time, I would not be able to say anything about the chromosome structure or bonding. We do not know whether we have hit the structural protein or destroyed the enzymes which affect the repair mechanism. In another experiment in which cells are irradiated with uv at 2652 Å in the presence of chloramphenicol, we can also induce chromosome shattering which was not induced by either uv at 2652 Å or chloramphenicol alone. These very preliminary results seem to indicate that protein is intimately involved in maintaining the integrity of chromosomes.

Dr. Swanson: The only other thing I would like to mention with the chemical mutagens is that they exhibit a pattern of selective action. I believe most of us here are familiar with the mutagens that have been used and with the fact that the aberrations produced are not randomly distributed over the chromosomes. How you can interpret this in terms of chemical bonding is, of course, open to question. We tried to get at the problem using radioactive mutagens, in the hope that they would either be selectively absorbed and consequently selectively active or randomly absorbed but still selectively active, but we were unsuccessful in getting anything out of this.

However, in the fractionation of exposures either with mutagens or with radiation, we do find different patterns of activity. For example, if one does an x-ray-x-ray fractionation of moderate dose, say a total of 300 r, there is a period of one or two hours during which total interaction is observed.

We also find interaction between breaks induced by x rays and those induced by the mutagens that we have used. We have worked particularly with maleic hydrazide, and here one finds that the time of interaction is reduced to 30 minutes. If we separate the two agents by longer periods than this, the aberration frequency is additive, and there is no indication that they might be interacting with each other.

Once again, we can ask whether these data indicate differences of bonding. Here I think we can only leave the subject with a very big question mark after it. We do know that the chromosome reacts differently with different agents. Again, I think this is meaningless insofar as chemical bonding is concerned and as it relates to the knowledge we have at present of the structure of the chromosome.

Dr. Auerbach: Which did you use first?

Dr. Swanson: Either one. It can be done in either direction with the results being roughly the same.

Dr. Hollaender: Did you try any ultraviolet?

Dr. Taylor: To what cell or organism does this one hour apply?

Dr. Swanson: We apply these treatments to *Vicia* root tips. In summing things up, it seems to me that we must focus somewhat more on the proteins than we have to date. The DNA molecule has tended to dominate much of our thinking. I would not say that I think this emphasis is due to pass, but I think we should give more attention to the proteins in trying to visualize how the chromosome is made up and how it is hooked together by the various bonds broken during treatment with damaging or modifying agents.

We do know, of course, that there are other divalent ions besides calcium and magnesium that may enter into chromosomal structure and integrity. The iron atom in particular is very rapidly taken up by nuclei that have been on an iron-deficient medium, and it soon becomes very heavily concentrated in the nucleus. Whether this is associated with enzyme activity or with the chromosome itself is not known.

I realize in speaking as I have that I have left you with no profound notions as to what might be involved in the problem of chemical bonding as this relates to the rupture and repair of chromosomes, but I think that the literature reveals very little of a positive nature that we can latch on to and say: "Here we have a piece of information which gives us a good point of departure." We still have not reached this point in our knowledge of what radiation does in its alteration of the linear continuity of the chromosome.

Dr. Atwood: Has anyone tried the reduction of disulphides?

Dr. Swanson: I think a fair amount of this has been done, and it is a confused picture.

Dr. Totter: Was there not recently some work by Mazia on this?

Dr. Steffensen: I don't think that there is any good evidence, at least in plants, about sulphur amino acids in chromosome protein. I think that the best evidence comes from histone studies in general. Metallic ions are now proposed to stabilize protein-nucleic acid complexes, binding arginine groups to phosphates. There is no clear data as to the exact kinds of metal bonding. Evidence is lacking on the precise nature of secondary- and tertiary-bond structure in chromosomes.

One point on iron, I think you can show that a good share of iron will follow the course of RNA metabolism. It goes in with the amino groups, concentrates in the nucleolus, and later appears in the cytoplasm. Undoubtedly, iron will attach to ribosome particles because RNA is single-stranded and because iron has a preference for the amino groups. Again, most of the evidence is indirect and much has still to be deciphered.

Dr. Yerganian: Recently, Hampar and Ellison of the College of Physicians and Surgeons, Columbia University, demonstrated that the Herpes simplex virus causes chromosome aberrations during the first 40 hours of infection *in vitro.* Whether the breakage was due to the direct action of the virus particle or an immediate antimetabolite arising upon introduction of the virus in the culture medium remains to be ascertained. Even more striking is the fact that breakage is observed in only one mutant line (MCH) of FAF28, an adult fibroblastlike derivative from the Chinese hamster, *Cricetulus griseus* (Yerganian and Leonard, 1960). In our hands, the same strain of Herpes simplex virus obtained from Hampar and Ellison resulted in cytopathologic effects (CPE) when used to infect the classic diploid parental FAF28, quasidiploid and aneuploid clones, and a number of embryonal derivatives, in sharp contrast to the carrier state and high cellular proliferation retained by the MCH subline of Hampar and Ellison. The MCH subline is unique in that the heterochromatic X_2 chromosome has undergone translocations onto autosomes and the resulting chromosome breakage and lack of CPE may be the expression of a position effect.

Dr. Swanson: I was interested in this because it reaches a peak very quickly and then fades out.

Dr. Yerganian: After 40 hours the relationship of the virus to the MCH cell is that of a carrier state in the absence of further aberrations.

Dr. Giles: Do they rejoin or what?

Dr. Yerganian: Yes, typical exchanges and deletions are noted, as in so many now classic reports on plants and animals following exposure to radiation and radiomimetic compounds. An array of one-hit and two-hit aberrations of both the chromosome and chromatid forms occurred.

Dr. Evans: There are certainly some triradials in the picture as I recall it.

Dr. Pollard: Is that the only virus he worked on?

Dr. Yerganian: To date, Herpes simplex is the only virus reported to cause chromosome breakage. Newcastle's disease virus (NDV) and Vaccinia are being studied presently in our hands with a wide range of single-cell clonal isolates featuring distinct chromosome markers.

Dr. Gray: I wonder if Dr. Steffensen could tell us what the calcium story is. As far as I understand, it is that in the meiotic chromosomes a calcium deficiency leads to more spontaneous breakage, but not in the case of mitotic chromosomes.

Dr. Steffensen: Not in the mitotic chromosomes of *Tradescantia*. I studied calcium-deficient root tips, so deficient that they were almost dead. Still, no fragment increase appeared above spontaneous levels. Meiosis is a labile process and we already know that mitosis is reasonably stable. The deficiency of calcium increases chromosome sensitivity to radiation in at least two or three species in mitosis. It works in barley seeds and *Tradescantia*. A good share of the problem with chelating agents (EDTA) was due to the failure of workers to realize that the heavy metals are preferentially bound. A series of metal chelates should have been employed. To my knowledge the usually twofold increase in sensitivity to *Tradescantia* chromosomes grown calcium-deficient is *the only* modifying factor that is independent of the oxygen effect (Steffensen, 1958).

Dr. Gray: Do you have autoradiographic evidence that the calcium content of the chromosomes is small at the time that the chromosomes are more sensitive? Can you correlate sensitivity with the actual calcium content of the chromosomes by autoradiographic methods?

Dr. Steffensen: We did it in a lily where I was happy to show that calcium-45 did not exchange in chromosomes and nuclei, and I do not have the heart to do it quantitatively.

Dr. Swanson: We confirmed Dr. Steffensen's studies, in that mitotic chromosomes will not fragment when there is a deficiency of calcium. We have grown roots on a deficient medium; they die abruptly, but before they die they do not exhibit any aberrations.

Dr. Moses: Cytochemical methods are relatively insensitive in demonstrating chemical and physical changes in DNA or protein after radiation. However, there are two which can be used. One, I believe, could be profitably exploited, but has not been, while the other has. At one time methyl-green stainability was mistakenly thought to be an index of degree of polymerization *in situ*. It is in fact a much better measure of association between protein and DNA. After a fairly high dose of 20,000 r, the one change that can be demonstrated is an increase in methyl-green binding. That was reported some time ago in the context of showing lack of polymerization (Sparrow, Moses, and Dubow, 1952). The results do not indicate a change in polymerization (opposite to that expected) but more likely a change in the protein of DNA relationships resulting in the availability of more dye-binding sites on the DNA.

The other method which I think could be profitably used might reveal DNA denaturization *in situ* and consists of looking for a hyperchromic effect in the ultraviolet in nuclei before and after irradiation. I don't believe this has been done, but I think it would be worth trying.

Dr. Gray: How long after exposure to 1000 r was the methyl green given?

Dr. Moses: It was given 24 hours after irradiation with 20,000 r.

Dr. Gray: I may mention that in *Vicia faba* metaphase figures stained with Feulgen 20 seconds after irradiation are indistinguishable from controls even when the dose is as high as one million rad delivered in a few seconds.

Dr. Moses: We also found in our experiment that the Feulgen values of the irradiated nuclei were indistinguishable from the controls, but that the methyl-green staining had increased.

Dr. Ris: Mirsky and myself, some years ago, made a study on isolated calf-thymus chromosomes which showed that DNA and the nonhistone-type protein are both essential for structural integrity of the chromosome. Histone, on the other hand, could be removed from the chromosomes without destroying their structural continuity. Certain sperm nuclei, however, do not contain any nonhistone-type protein and apparently there only the DNA is involved in the structural continuity of chromosomes. It might be interesting to compare radiation effects on sperm of this kind (for instance, trout) with sperm of the sea urchin in which the chromosomes both chemically and in their ultrastructure resemble those of somatic nuclei.

Thus, both the protein and the DNA have to be necessarily intact for their structures to be intact.

Dr. Swanson: So you have the idea, as does Dr. Kaufmann, that this is essentially a fabric with both the protein and the nucleic acid contributing to a longitudinal integrity?

Dr. Ris: I think both, but we don't know whether it is a sequence of protein DNA or how it is interlocked. However, the work of Norman Anderson seems to indicate that there is a sequence of DNA protein; he isolates nuclear proteins and also finds that DNA is linked to a protein with covalent bonds, and if he breaks these bonds then the viscosity of the extracted protein does go down very rapidly, so that there seems to be a large fiber that contains protein and DNA linked together contributing to viscosity.

Dr. Hollaender: It has a response to radiation that is as small as 5 rad.

Dr. Totter: Has that work been discontinued?

Dr. Hollaender: Fisher took it along to Syracuse. I don't know what he has been doing with it recently.

Dr. Totter: This is a completely different order of sensitivity from anything else connected with chromosomes. Thank you, Dr. Swanson, for a survey of the work on chemical bonds. Next is a paper by Dr. Kihlman, entitled "Aberrations Induced by Radiomimetic Compounds and Their Relations to Radiation-Induced Aberrations."

References

Steffensen, M. 1958. Nature 182: 1750.

Sparrow, A. H., N. J. Moses, and R. J. Dubow. 1952. Exptl. Cell Research Suppl. 2: 245.

Yerganian, G., and M. J. Leonard. 1960. Science 133: 1600.

Aberrations Induced by Radiomimetic Compounds and Their Relations to Radiation-Induced Aberrations

Dr. B. A. Kihlman: The title given to me for my contribution covers a very wide field. I have chosen to concentrate on three topics with which I am particularly familiar or which to me appear of particular interest. These topics are: (1) the distribution of aberrations within and between nuclei after treatments with chemicals, (2) delayed and nondelayed production of chromosomal aberrations, and (3) the influence of oxygen on the production of chromosomal aberrations by chemicals. The distribution of radiation-induced aberrations has been discussed already by Dr. Atwood. What I intend to do is point out some characteristic differences between the distribution of aberrations induced by chemical compounds on the one hand and by radiation on the other.

The distribution of aberrations with and between nuclei after treatments with chemicals

The distribution of aberrations within nuclei will be influenced by many factors, some connected with the target, the cell nucleus, and others with the aberration-inducing agent. In the case of radiations, such as gamma rays and 200-kvp x rays, the most important factor will be the structural and spatial organization of the nucleus. When the agent is a chemical compound, its penetration, chemical reactions, and affinity for various nuclear constituents are the factors most likely to be responsible for the markedly nonrandom distribution of aberrations which is usually obtained (Table 1).

Table 1. *The Frequencies and Types of Localized Isolocus Breaks Obtained in the* M-*Chromosome at Various Times after Treatments with 8-Ethoxycaffeine (EOC) and Maleic Hydrazide (MH)*[a]

Chemical treatment	Time between treatment and fixation (in hours)	Localized isolocus breaks (percent of total i.b.)	Locus affected in the M-chromosome
EOC (10^{-2} M, 1¾ hr,	4	23.5	
20° C, pH 7.6)	6	66.7	
	12	88.2	
	16	95.2	
MH (2×10^{-4} M, 1 hr,			
20° C, pH 6.2)	26	89.7	

[a] The frequencies are expressed as a percentage of the total number of isolocus breaks (i.b.).

Table 1 shows how extremely localized the aberrations may be after treatment of *Vicia faba* root tips with chemical compounds. The two agents chosen as examples are 8-ethoxycaffeine (EOC) and maleic hydrazide (MH), and the type of aberration, isolocus breaks. Column 3 indicates the percentages of aberrations located at the particular locus. For both compounds the aberrations are concentrated in the nucleolar arm of the metacentric M-chromosome. After EOC treatments, the isolocus breaks are localized to the nucleolar constriction (Kihlman and Levan, 1951), after MH treatments to a heterochromatic segment close to the centromere (McLeish, 1952). For EOC, the degree of localization increases with increasing time between treatment and fixation, i.e., the localization is most extreme in cells treated in early interphase, when over 90 percent of the aberrations may be concentrated in the nucleolar constriction (Kihlman, 1961c). The duration of the recovery period does not influence very much the localization of isolocus breaks induced by MH, which is inactive in later interphase.

It seems very likely to me that the markedly nonrandom distribution of EOC-induced isolocus breaks reflects an equally nonrandom distribution of EOC within the interphase nucleus. Since EOC has a high surface activity, it is reasonable to assume that its concentration is high on the surface of the nucleolus. The nucleolar constriction is in contact with the nucleolus during the interphase, and would hence be exposed to higher concentrations of EOC than would other

Table 2. *The Number of Cells Containing 0, 1, 2, 3, etc. Interchanges Obtained after Irradiation and Treatments with Radiomimetic Chemicals, Expected Values Calculated Assuming a Poisson Distribution*

Treatment	Interchanges per 100 cells	Distribution	Frequencies of cells with indicated number of interchanges						Cells with 1 interchange / Cells with 2 or more interchanges	X^2
			0	1	2	3	4	5		
70-r x rays (110 r/min); oxygen, fixation 18 hr	34	Observed	68	30	2	—	—	—	15.0	
		Expected	71.5	24	4	—	0.5	—	5.3	3.1
70-r x rays (7 r/min); oxygen, fixation 10 hr	35	Observed	68	29	3	—	—	—	9.7	
		Expected	70.5	24.5	4.5	—	0.5	—	4.9	1.7
Light-acridine orange, $4 \times 10^{-4}\ M$ cupferron, ½ hr; nitrogen, fixation 26 hr	33	Observed	77	17	4	1	—	1	2.8	
		Expected	72	23.5	4	—	0.5		5.2	6.6
$10^{-3}\ M$ Methylphenylnitrosamine, 1 hr; oxygen, fixation 26 hr	31	Observed	78	16	4	1	1	—	2.7	
		Expected	73.5	22.5	3.5	—	0.5		5.6	6.7
$10^{-4}\ M$ Nitrosomethylurethan, 1 hr; nitrogen, fixation 26 hr	28	Observed	78	16	6	—	—	—	2.7	
		Expected	75.5	21	3	—	0.5	—	6.0	3.1

chromosome regions. A high concentration on the nucleolus and nucleolar constriction would also be expected on the basis of the high affinity of EOC towards lipoids (Kihlman, 1951), since both the nucleolus and the nucleolar constrictions are known to be rich in lipoids (Albuquerque and Serra, 1951).

As extreme a localization as that found for EOC and MH is not often observed after treatments with radiomimetic chemicals. On the other hand, a random distribution is even more unusual. The aberrations are usually concentrated in heterochromatic regions, but the particular heterochromatic regions affected may vary considerably.

A nonrandom distribution between cells of x-ray-induced exchanges was observed by Atwood and Wolff (Wolff, 1959) and by Evans (1961) in experiments with *Tradescantia paludosa* and *Vicia faba*. They recorded an excess of cells carrying one exchange and a deficiency of cells carrying more than one.

In Table 2, the distributions of interchanges obtained after treatments with N-methyl-phenylnitrosamine, N-nitroso-N-methylurethan, and the light-acridine orange system are compared with those obtained after a dose of x rays producing about the same number of interchanges. Expected values, assuming a Poisson distribution, are included. As can be seen, the distribution obtained in the experiments with the radiomimetic chemicals appears to be nonrandom. In contrast to the x-ray experiments, after the chemical treatments there are *more* cells than expected containing two or more interchanges and *less* containing one aberration. However, because of the low number of aberrations, the difference is not statistically significant.

Table 3 shows the distribution of the sum of isolocus breaks and exchanges, which was obtained after treatments with x rays and chemicals. The radiomimetic agents are the same as in Table 2, except that light-acridine orange has been replaced by adenine. It is evident that an even more nonrandom distribution is obtained after chemical treatments when the isolocus breaks are included. The ratio of cells with one aberration to cells with two or more aberrations is always much smaller than expected after treatments with the radiomimetic chemicals, and larger than expected in the x-ray experi-

Table 3. *The Number of Cells Containing 0, 1, 2, 3, etc. Aberrations (Exchanges + Isolocus Breaks) Obtained after Irradiation and Treatments with Radiomimetic Chemicals, Expected Values Calculated Assuming a Poisson Distribution*

Treatment	Aberrations per 100 cells	Distribution	Frequencies of cells with indicated number of aberrations					Cells with 1 aberration	Cells with 2 or more aberrations	X^2
			0	1	2	3	4			
3×10^{-2} M Adenine, 2 hr; nitrogen, fixation 28 hr	44	Observed	74	14	8	3	1	1.2		18.4[a]
		Expected	64.5	28.5	6	1			4.1	
70-r x rays (7 r/min); oxygen, fixation 18 hr	45	Observed	61	33	6	—	—	5.5		1.2
		Expected	64	28.5	6.5	1	—		3.8	
10^{-3} M Methylphenylnitrosamine, 1 hr; oxygen, fixation 26 hr	64	Observed	64	16	15	3	2	0.8		16.7[a]
		Expected	52.5	33.5	11	2.5	0.5		2.4	
70-r x rays (7 r/min); oxygen, fixation 10 hr	59	Observed	48	45	7	—	—	6.4		7.9[b]
		Expected	55.5	32.5	9.5	2	0.5		2.7	
10^{-4} M Nitrosomethylurethan, 1 hr; nitrogen, fixation 26 hr	84	Observed	57	15	20	6	2	0.5		20.1[a]
		Expected	43	36.5	15	4	1.5		1.8	
81-r x rays (110 r/min); oxygen, fixation 18 hr	78	Observed	45	37	14	3	1	2.1		0.2
		Expected	46	35.5	14	3.5	1		1.9	

[a] Highly significant.
[b] Significant.

ments. For the radiomimetic chemicals, the X^2 test shows the difference to be highly significant. This type of nonrandom distribution is very commonly found after treatments with chemicals, although I am not prepared to say that it is characteristic of all radiomimetic agents.

Again, it seems reasonable to assume that the nonrandom distribution of aberrations between cells, in conformity with the nonrandom distribution with the nucleus, is due to an unequal distribution of the chemicals in question, but in this case within the root.

Delayed and nondelayed production of chromosomal aberrations

When root tips have been irradiated with ionizing radiations, such as x rays, aberrations of the chromatid type begin to appear in metaphase as soon as this stage is reached by the cells which were irradiated in late interphase. This takes about two hours for *Vicia faba*. Between two and four hours after irradiation, x-ray-induced chromatid exchanges occur with a maximum frequency.

On the other hand, after treatments with most radiomimetic chemicals, no cells with aberrations appear until about eight hours after the treatment. This is true even when the treatments do not affect the rate of cell division. The peak frequency of aberrations is usually 18–36 hours after the treatment. Because of this difference in time interval between treatment and the appearance of the induced chromosomal aberrations, the effect of the radiomimetic agents in question is said to be delayed, whereas that of ionizing radiations is nondelayed. When the effect is of the delayed type in *Vicia*, the aberrations are always of chromatid type, irrespective of the mitotic stage at which the cells were treated. In contrast, ionizing radiations produce aberrations of the chromatid type in the late and middle stages of interphase, and aberrations of the chromosome type in early interphase. In visible prophase, agents with nondelayed effects produce aberrations of the subchromatid type.

I said that most radiomimetic chemicals have delayed effects. Only for N-methylated oxypurines, such as 8-ethoxycaffeine (EOC), has the effect definitely been shown to be nondelayed (Kihlman, 1955*b*).

The types of effects obtained after treatments with x rays, EOC, and the alkylating agent N-nitroso-N-methylurethan (NMU) are illustrated in Fig. 1, where the frequencies of isolocus breaks and exchanges are plotted against the time (in hours) between treatment and fixation. The x-ray data are taken from a recent publication by Revell (1960), the EOC and NMU data are my own. The cells are

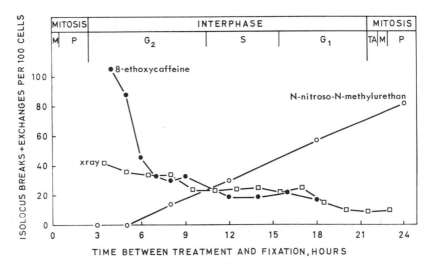

Fig. 1. *Frequencies of aberrations obtained at various times after treatments with x rays (50 r), 8-ethoxycaffeine (10⁻² M, 1¾ hr, 20°C), and N-nitroso-N-methylurethan (10⁻⁴ M, ¾ hr, 19°C)*
The x-ray curve is based on the data of Revell (1960). X rays: —□---□—; 8-ethoxycaffeine: —•---•—; N-nitroso-N-methylurethan: —o---o—.

scored in metaphase. The later in interphase the cells are treated, the shorter the time between treatment and fixation.

The period of interphase during which deoxyribonucleic acid (DNA) synthesis is assumed to take place is also indicated in Fig. 1. Since histone apparently is synthesized at the same time as DNA (i.e., Alfert, 1954; McLeish, 1959) the synthesis of histone also occurs within S, S being the name given to the synthetic period by Howard and Pelc (1952). The duration of S, the duration of the presynthetic period G1, and of the postsynthetic period G2 have been calculated on the basis of recent estimations by Howard and

Dewey (1960 and personal communication) and by Neary and collaborators (1959). The mitotic delay caused by the treatments in
question is as far as possible taken into account. According to these
calculations, the duration of interphase is 19 hours, of which eight
hours are spent in $G2$, five in S, and six in $G1$.

The x-ray curve indicates that cells irradiated in $G2$ are about four
times as sensitive as those irradiated in $G1$. The difference in sensitivity to EOC treatment is even more striking. The same EOC dose
produces about six times as many aberrations in $G2$ as in $G1$. Both
after EOC and x-ray treatments, the number of isolocus breaks is
fairly constant during the whole interphase period, the difference
in sensitivity being due mainly to a difference in the frequencies of
chromatid interchanges (Revell, 1961; Kihlman, 1961c).

In contrast to x rays and EOC, NMU appears to be entirely inactive in very late interphase. In NMU experiments, the majority of
the aberrations were found in cells treated before they entered the
S period. Although cells treated in $G2$ contain few or no aberrations
in the first division after the treatment, their daughter cells may contain a high frequency of aberrations in the following division. Thus,
the period sensitive to NMU and other agents with delayed effects
comprises, apparently, not only $G1$ but also a considerable part of
the preceding mitotic cycle.

These facts indicate that agents with nondelayed effects, such as
ionizing radiations and N-methylated oxypurines, do not produce
chromosomal aberrations by interfering with DNA and chromosome
synthesis (Thoday, 1954; Kihlman, 1955a, 1961c). However, the
synthetic period may be of some significance for the transition from
chromosome to chromatid aberrations, since these agents induce
chromatid-type aberrations when the cells are treated in $G2$ and
chromosome type after treatments in $G1$.

The situation seems different for agents with delayed effects. They
apparently are unable to produce any chromosomal aberrations after
the completion of DNA (and histone) synthesis and this indicates
that they act on chromosome precursors, rather than on the chromosomes themselves (Revell, 1952). However, since the aberrations are
always of the chromatid type, they are probably formed during S
or $G2$. This is not so difficult to understand, since the products

formed by the reaction between the chromosome precursor and the radiomimetic agent are expected to produce aberrations in connection with the reduplication process.

Influence of oxygen on the production of chromosomal aberrations by chemicals

Finally, I would like to say a few words about the effect of oxygen on the production of chromosomal aberrations by chemicals. It is now well known that oxygen enhances the production of chromosomal aberrations by x rays (Thoday and Read, 1947). It is believed that this is because of the reaction of oxygen with radiation-produced radicals (e.g., Gray, 1958; Howard-Flanders, 1958). On this basis an effect of oxygen on the production of aberrations by chemicals would not *a priori* be expected. Nevertheless, oxygen influences the effects of several radiomimetic chemicals.

As shown in Fig. 2, the radiomimetic effects of EOC, potassium cyanide, the visible light-acridine orange system, maleic hydrazide, and methylphenylnitrosamine are greatly affected by oxygen tension. With the exception of maleic hydrazide, the agents are entirely inactive in the absence of oxygen. The slopes of the curves are not always the same: for EOC the maximum effect is obtained at an oxygen concentration as low as 10 percent in the gas phase, in the other cases the effect increases with increasing oxygen concentration up to 100 percent.

Oxygen does not always enhance the effects of the radiomimetic chemicals by the same mechanism. For EOC and maleic hydrazide, the effect is inhibited by respiratory inhibitors and uncoupling agents as well as by anoxia (Kihlman, 1955*b*, 1956), which indicates that oxidative phosphorylation is required for the activity of these two chemicals. The effect of methylphenylnitrosamine is inhibited by anoxia and by respiratory inhibitors, but not by uncoupling agents (Kihlman, 1961*a*). This suggests that the effect is not produced by methylphenylnitrosamine per se, but by some decomposition product, probably a peroxide or a free radical, formed in the presence of oxygen and a heavy metal-containing enzyme. The oxygen dependence of the potassium cyanide effect has been attributed to the mediation of the radiomimetic effect by peroxides. These are believed to accumulate in the cell as a result of the inhibitory effect of cyanide on cytochrome oxidase and peroxide-destroying enzymes (Lilly and Thoday, 1956). In the visible light-acridine orange system, as in the case of x rays, nitric oxide seems to be able to replace oxygen as an enhancing agent (Kihlman, 1959*a*, 1959*b*). It seems likely, therefore,

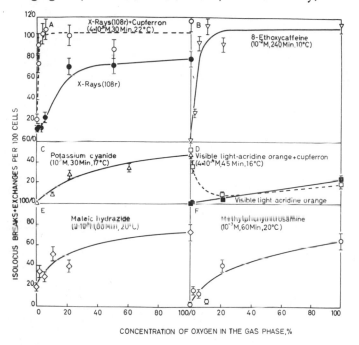

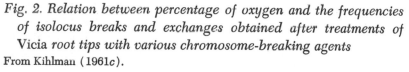

CONCENTRATION OF OXYGEN IN THE GAS PHASE,%

Fig. 2. Relation between percentage of oxygen and the frequencies of isolocus breaks and exchanges obtained after treatments of Vicia *root tips with various chromosome-breaking agents*
From Kihlman (1961*c*).

that oxygen enhances the effect by reacting with free radicals produced in the cell by the radiation (Kihlman, 1961*b*), i.e., by a mechanism similar to that believed to be responsible for the effect on x-ray sensitivity.

In Table 4, which summarizes what I have said before, I have attempted to classify the chromosome-breaking agents. Vertically in Table 4, I have divided the agents into two main groups on the

Table 4. Classification of Chromosome-Breaking Agents[a]

Type of effect	Effect inhibited by anoxia				Effect not inhibited by anoxia
	Inhibited by respiratory inhibitors		Not inhibited by respiratory inhibitors		
	Inhibited by uncoupling agents	Not inhibited by uncoupling agents	Oxygen can be replaced by nitric oxide	Oxygen cannot be replaced by nitric oxide	
Delayed	Maleic hydrazide,[b] ethyl alcohol[c]	N-Methylphenyl-nitrosamine[d]	Visible light-acridine orange[e]	Potassium cyanide[f,g]	Alkylating agents (nitrogen mustard[m]) dieproxypropyl-ether,[b] N-nitroso-N-methyl-urethan,[i] Myleran,[j] β-propiolactone[k] Mitomycin C,[h] adenine[l]
Not delayed	N-methylated oxypurines[m] (e.g., 8-ethoxy-caffeine, 1,3,7-tetramethyl-uric acid)		X rays[n,o]		Alpha rays,[p] ultra-violet light[q]

In [a] case of x rays the nonrandom distribution applies only for interchanges. For chemicals the isolocus breaks show an even more nonrandom distribution, but the exchanges are nonrandom in the same direction.
[b] B. A. Kihlman, J. Biophys. Biochem. Cytol. 2:543 (1956). [c] R. Rieger and A. Michaelis, Monatsber. deut. Akad. Wiss. Berlin 2:290 (1960). [d] B. A. Kihlman, Radiation Bot. 1:43 (1961). [e] B. A. Kihlman, Exptl. Cell Research 17:590 (1959). [f] L. J. Lilly and J. M. Thoday, Nature 177:338 (1956). [g] B. A. Kihlman, J. Biophys. Biochem. Cytol. 3:363 (1957). [h] T. Merz, Science 133:329 (1961). [i] B. A. Kihlman, Exptl. Cell Research 20:657 (1960). [j] A. Michaelis and R. Reiger, Züchter 30:150 (1960). [k] C. P. Swanson and T. Merz, Science 129:1364 (1959). [l] B. A. Kihlman, Exptl. Cell Research, in press. [m] B. A. Kihlman, Hereditas 41:384 (1955). [n] J. M. Thoday and J. Read, Nature 160:608 (1947). [o] B. A. Kihlman, Exptl. Cell Research 17:588 (1959). [p] J. M. Thoday and J. Read, Nature 163:133 (1949). [q] J. S. Kirby-Smith and D. L. Craig, Genetics 42:176 (1957).

basis of whether or not the effect is inhibited by anoxia. The effects of the alkylating agents, which include such powerful radiomimetic chemicals as nitrogen mustard and nitrosomethylurethan, are independent of oxygen tension, and so is the effect of Mitomycin C. Oxygen inhibits, rather than enhances, the effect of adenine. Radiations, the effects of which apparently are independent of oxygen tension, are alpha radiation and ultraviolet light. All of these agents form one of my main groups. The other main group consists of agents whose effects are inhibited by anoxia. These can be divided into subgroups on the basis of whether or not the effect is influenced by respiratory inhibitors, uncoupling agents, and nitric oxide.

Horizontally in Table 4, I have divided the chromosome-breaking agents into agents with delayed and nondelayed effects. As you see, the rule appears to be that radiations have nondelayed effects and radiomimetic chemicals delayed effects. The two exceptions are N-methylated oxypurines and the visible light-acridine orange system. The latter system may behave like a chemical, rather than like a radiation, because of the fact that it is dependent on the localization and chemical reactions of the sensitizing substance, acridine orange (Kihlman, 1961a). I find the radiationlike effect of the N-methylated oxypurines most interesting and would like to find another group of chemicals similar in this respect. Finally, Table 4 clearly shows the different natures of the radiomimetic effects of an N-methylated oxypurine such as EOC, on the one hand, and of adenine on the other. The effect of adenine is not enhanced by oxygen and is of the delayed type (Kihlman, 1962), whereas EOC is active only in the presence of oxygen and has a nondelayed effect. In contrast to the radiomimetic effect of EOC, that of adenine could well be due to an effect on DNA and chromosome synthesis.

Dr. Wolff: You mentioned that you thought that because when you treat with some of these agents many hours before metaphase and you only get chromatid aberrations, that when metaphase comes you are looking at cells being treated in G1 when the chromosome reacts to radiation as though single. This period is before DNA synthesis, so we expect that the chromosome is single.

Davidson, however, looked at a similar agent, azaserine, which gave similar effects and came to the opposite conclusion. He found that if he treated with azaserine and waited 48 hours, only chromatid aberrations were induced; whereas if he x rayed and waited 48 hours, chromosome aberrations were present. So, he wondered whether he was affecting the same type of strand in both cases or whether there was a delay of some sort. He therefore x-rayed his *Vicia* roots and also treated with azaserine. Well, when he looked in 48 hours, he found cells with chromatid aberrations that the azaserine produced, and also cells with chromosome aberrations that the x rays had produced. A cell with chromosome aberrations never had chromatid aberrations. He concluded that the cells that were damaged by x rays in G1 showed chromosomal effects, but that these same cells in G1 were not being affected by the azaserine. He thinks that the azaserine probably produces aberrations in S or G2 and that the cells it affects are delayed. Therefore, in 48 hours, you would not be looking at cells that were in G1 at the time you treated them.

Dr. Kihlman: As I said, we don't know exactly at what stage these agents are effective. Experimental results indicate that they apparently do not produce aberrations in G2 and S but that they could be effective earlier than G1. I mean that in order to produce aberrations with some of the chemicals, the cells should be treated in the preceding mitotic cycle.

Dr. Wolff: In the cells that do have chromosome aberrations induced by the x rays, you would also expect to get some chromatid aberrations induced by the chemical when this chemical was azaserine, which works the same in many ways, at least as far as time of action is concerned. He did not get these.

Dr. Taylor: Has anyone ever found both types of aberrations in a single cell of *Vicia?*

Dr. Wolff: With x rays you do. If you happen to pick a graded series after treatment, you will find some cells that will show a mixture. On a lucky slide there will be a lot of them and on others there will not.

Dr. Evans: At the moment we are doing experiments on these lines using cells which contain both chromosome and chromatid aberrations in the same cell. These cells can be obtained in reasonable frequency, provided the x-ray dose used is high enough.

I think the question that Dr. Wolff raises is very pertinent, because most people using chemical treatments have come to the conclusion that the chemicals appear to be ineffective in $G2$, but nevertheless yield chromatid breaks. Now we have in our laboratory measured the delay in the arrival of cells at mitosis following exposure to maleic hydrazide (MH), and our results suggest that treatment with a 0.25 mM solution of MH for two hours has a tremendous effect on the cell-development rate. An average duration for a normal mitotic cycle in *Vicia* roots is about 20–24 hours, but following MH treatment the cycle may take up to four days. We do not know whether any particular part of the mitotic cycle is inhibited by MH treatment, but should soon have an answer to this question as we have gone ahead and given combination treatments with MH and tritiated thymidine.

Dr. Taylor: You can distinguish the damage that occurred before, during, and after synthesis of DNA?

Dr. Atwood: When you have mixed cells, is there positional relationship with respect to the centromere? For example, do the tids tend to be distal?

Dr. Evans: I do not know. An attempt at answering a question which has a direct bearing on this, namely, does the chromosome respond as a double structure to x rays only after it has made DNA, has been made by Dr. Wolff, and also by Mr. Savage in our laboratory at Harwell. In these experiments, cells were exposed to tritiated thymidine and x irradiation in various combinations, and the type of aberration, chromosome or chromatid, induced in a given nucleus was noted in relation to the presence or absence of label in that nucleus. It is difficult to draw a precise conclusion from this type of experiment because we know that DNA is made over a fairly longish period of time, so that part of the chromosome could react as a single strand and part as a double strand. I think that the best way to attack the question is not to look at the different aberration types and to note simply whether the nucleus is labeled, but rather to look for the presence or absence of label in those regions of the chromosomes which are involved in aberrations.

We are currently carrying out this sort of experiment and, as I mentioned a moment ago, we are trying to use cells in which there are both chromosome and chromatid aberrations in one and the same cell. In the average sort of x-ray experiment, the number of these cells is usually very small, but I think that there is a simple reason for this. Normally, when one is scoring chromatid aberrations the x-ray dose used is quite low, for if the chromatid aberration frequency is too high, then the cells are difficult to score. However, the frequency of chromosome-type aberrations may be one-third to one-quarter of the frequency of chromatid-type aberrations at the same dose level, so that at a dose which gives a reasonable frequency of chromatid aberrations the chance of getting cells containing both a chromatid and a chromosome aberration is very low. One would therefore expect that if one increased this "reasonable dose" by a factor of three or four, then the frequency of cells carrying both types of aberrations should be very much increased, and this appears to be the case.

Dr. Yerganian: Our efforts to clarify observations induced by triethylene melamine (TEM) in Chinese hamster chromosomes have been somewhat hampered because of the fact that alkylating agents are most effective at the time sister strands are being formed. Since the greater mass of autosomes are composed of euchromatin which replicates early in the synthesis period, these sites are susceptible to breakage early in the cycle, leaving the heterochromatic sex elements intact. In asynchronous cultures, where TEM is applied for 10–20 minutes during the latter part of the synthesis cycle, lesions are restricted to sex elements and particular (heterochromatic) loci along certain autosomes. Therefore, there are two classes or periods of breakage and rearrangements, depending upon whether the broken ends are euchromatic or heterochromatic in nature. Alkylating agents, such as TEM, cause many breaks and rearrangements in mammalian systems.

Dr. Auerbach: We used TEM a lot. It is an excellent chromosome breaker but, when it comes to the interpretation of rearrangements, one must also consider the effect of the treatment on rejoining.

Dr. Yerganian: For this purpose, the synthesis period may be split into two phases: the first restricted to autosomes and the second to sex elements. When there is a preponderance of aberrations and rejoining of autosomes, the sex elements remain undisturbed, and vice versa.

Dr. Auerbach: I see that, but it might have something to do with the time of rejoining rather than the time of breakage.

Dr. Yerganian: More possibly they are related to the synthesis period.

Dr. Auerbach: Yes, one has to consider that.

Dr. Trotter: Do you have any other comments Dr. Kihlman?

Dr. Kihlman: It may be that cell division is delayed considerably by radiomimetic agents such as maleic hydrazide and azaserine. But a delay of mitosis cannot be the whole explanation for the difference between agents with "delayed" and "nondelayed" effects. The first two hours after treatment of *Vicia* roots with moderate dosages of agents with nondelayed effects, i.e., agents such as EOC and x rays, stickiness and subchromatid exchanges are found in cells fixed in metaphase or anaphase. Between two and 14 hours after the treatment, the aberrations are almost exclusively of the chromatid type. After recovery periods of more than 14 hours, aberrations of the chromosome type can be found. When agents with delayed effects are used, the divisions appear quite normal during the first eight hours after treatment. Very little stickiness and no subchromatid breakage is found. The aberrations obtained after treatments with these chemicals appear always to be of the chromatid type and they occur with a maximum frequency between 18 and 36 hours after the treatment. The EOC-induced aberrations occur with a maximum frequency at four hours after the treatment, although EOC reduces the mitotic rate much more than, for instance, nitrogen mustard, which has a delayed effect.

Dr. Evans: I think that it is very suggestive, but I think that we have to get some measurements in order to be conclusive.

Dr. Auerbach: I wanted to ask something in relation to your statement. Your first slide on locus specificity was remarkable. But the mutagens producing specific types of breaks also seem to act at different times in the cell cycle. Is there any indication that mutagens which act, say, late or early in the cycle tend to produce breaks in different regions?

Dr. Kihlman: Most radiomimetic chemicals have delayed effects and they all seem to produce localized breakage, although the localization is not as extreme as that found after treatments with EOC and maleic hydrazide. EOC is an exception because it is able to produce aberrations in very late interphase. However, the aberrations produced in very late interphase by EOC are not localized to any appreciable extent. When the period between treatment and

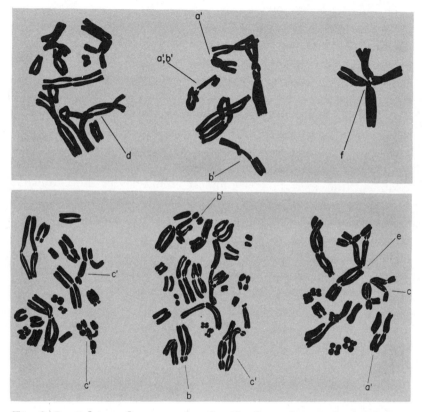

Fig. 3. *Partial complements of endoreduplicated metaphases and resulting breaks and reunions*

Centromeric break, (*a′*); unpaired break or deletion, (*b′*); paired break or deletion, (*b*); dicentric formation, (*c′*); multicentric fusions, (*c*); translocation featuring centromeric breaks and fusion, (*f*); and a multiradial configuration, (*e*).

fixation is increased, more and more aberrations are localized in the nucleolar constrictions, until we finally end up with almost all aberrations in the constrictions.

Dr. Auerbach: That may have more to do with the stage in the cell cycle at which it acts. You said that EOC acts in interphase and that there was no overlap of time with the other mutagens.

Dr. Kihlman: That is possible, yes.

Dr. Yerganian: May I take a moment to illustrate a variation in

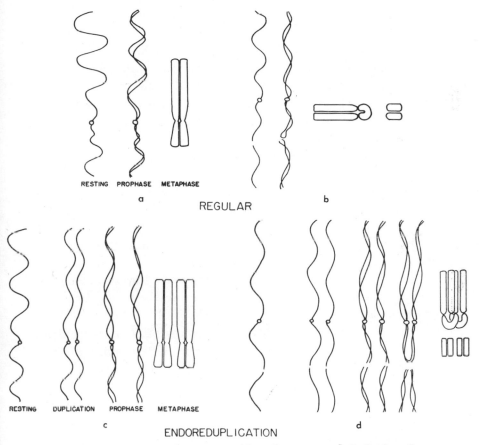

Fig. 4. Comparison of chromosome break in normal diploid and en-doreduplicated cells

mitosis which restricts the types of rejoining that occur with tri-ethylene melamine (TEM)? Figure 3 illustrates various breaks in endoreduplicated cells, a cell type that has yet to be employed rou-tinely in chromosome-breakage studies. In this instance, an ascites fibrosarcoma of the Chinese hamster was treated with TEM (0.025–0.05 mg) and cell fixations were delayed 48–72 hours to alleviate the inhibitory effects of the drug. In addition to breaks and reunions, a 40-fold increase in the frequency of endoreduplication took place (Yerganian, 1957). In order for endoreduplication to occur at such a high frequency, the replicating single-stranded chromosome would have to experience longitudinal separation at the centromere during replication (Fig. 4c). Subsequently, the two single strands replicate once again to give rise to juxtaposed homologues in metaphase. It is difficult to explain just how the parental strand could replicate twice in such a brief period of time without involving polyteny and yet appear so normal in the absence of TEM. The juxtaposed homologues actually consist of two chromatids and two sister half-chromatids; the latter having been elevated to the position of chromatids in the immediate division cycle.

The usual course of events following radiation of normal cells is seen in Fig. 4b. When *naturally occurring* endoreduplications are exposed to x-irradiation, uv, or TEM, paired sister reunions, as seen in Fig. 4d, are quite prevalent. However, in the case of *TEM-induced* endoreduplications, this type of sister reunion has never been noted (Fig. 3). There is some difficulty in trying to explain the absence of paired (isolocus) reunions when TEM causes both breakage and endoreduplication in the same cell.

Two of the four chromatids may undergo restitution or reunions but never with the broken ends of their homologues, thus reflecting some degree of immaturity or incompetence to realize the closeness of this attractive possibility.

Dr. Wolff: In Fig. 4b are you showing sister union when you irradiate in G1?

Dr. Yerganian: This is G1.

Dr. Evans: Is this a single strand and are you certain that it is G1?

Dr. Yerganian: Yes, and the configuration seen in metaphase (Fig. 4d) represents what occurs in *naturally occurring* endoreduplications, but not in the case of *TEM-induced* endoreduplication.

Dr. Wolff: Look at the bridge at metaphase.

Dr. Yerganian: These are paired acentric fragments in Fig. 4d.

Dr. Wolff: It looks like a dicentric to me.

Dr. Evans: There is an important distinction here. All the information we have indicates that if we hit a cell in G1 when it is single and we see this cell in mitosis, this gives us a chromosome-type effect.

Dr. Yerganian: That would be the case under normal circumstances as shown in Fig. 4b.

Dr. Wolff: No, that is not the normal sequence. If you break in G1, you don't get sister union; you get apparent terminal deletions that don't unite either proximally or distally.

Dr. Evans: We don't find that in G1.

Dr. Yerganian: I am talking about a mammalian system where we do get this.

Dr. Wolff: Dr. Chu and Dr. Bender don't.

Dr. Evans: Not in G1, but only in G2. In Fig. 4b, if you take away the right-hand single strand, we would agree with you.

Dr. Yerganian: The breakage action of TEM is effective when the chromosome is single stranded or in the early process of replication, but never thereafter. This should be contrasted to the breakage effect of x rays and uv, where midlate prophase chromosomes break more readily. A break induced by TEM is compounded from a single break to four after the double replication. Even though the breaks on each of the homologues are isolocus, they fail to undergo reunions with one another, but either restitute, remain open, or take part in independent reunions. The paired chromatids act as if single strands, i.e., units of two instead of four independent broken ends.

Dr. Taylor has had some experience with a similar situation among sister chromatid exchanges induced in *Bellevalia* with tritiated thymidine (Taylor, 1958).

Don't consider one but two replications following the induction of the break. I would like to restrict our attention to the observations that reunions can occur between the endoreduplicated homologues, as in Fig. 2d, only when naturally occurring endoreduplications are exposed to x rays, uv, or TEM, but never among cells forced to undergo endoreduplication by TEM. Do you follow me now? When a single strand undergoes two replications in the same cell, each of the paired sets undergoes independent restitution or takes part in reunions with other nonhomologous ends. Endoreduplicated homologues do not have the capacity to "seek" one another when the extra replication is enforced (precociously) upon them.

Dr. Moses: Are you not saying that there are two replications in one cycle?

Dr. Yerganian: Initial endoreduplications appear as paired homologues during the immediate cell-division cycle. Thereafter, they give rise to ordinary polyploid metaphases having scattered homologues.

Dr. Moses: Do you have any other evidence that two replications are actually occurring.

Dr. Yerganian: Nothing else has been done using tritiated thymidine.

Dr. Totter: Is this evidence of addition to one end of the break of some part of the molecule which is inducing the break?

Dr. Yerganian: It is possible that sister half-chromatids need to "mature" by going through one cell cycle. Since these chromosomes were forced, in some undisclosed manner, to undergo a 40-fold increase in endoreduplication, there may have been a limitation in precursoral substances or information essential for the maturation of sister half-chromatids to the status of a fully developed sister chromatid. In contrast to each normal chromosome having two chromatids, each of the endoreduplicated homologues has a chromatid:sister half-chromatid relationship.

Dr. Chu: Can you tell me what the time sequence is of a normal cell cycle, say G1 and G2, in relation to the time when the endoreduplication takes place?

Dr. Yerganian: This is most difficult to assess, primarily because this work was done before the present introduction of the G1, S, G2 scheme. The interpretation given above is based upon classical considerations and appearance of the chromosome type of breaks and reunions. About 90 percent of the mitosis in the tumor employed had regular mitoses.

Dr. Auerbach: How do you know that the TEM does not bring about duplication?

Dr. Chu: I would have to know the timing of the endoreduplication.

Dr. Auerbach: In general, chemicals only break one strand.

Dr. Yerganian: The frequency of endoreduplication rose from a negligible amount to one involving 20 percent of the metaphases after TEM.

Dr. Auerbach: Do you always get two loose ends and two joined ends?

Dr. Yerganian: Representative aberrations are shown in Fig. 1. Unfortunately, I do not have photographs as this study was done in 1953 and a camera lucida was all that was available. The main interest here is that aside from transverse breakage of the single strand the influence of TEM was also reflected longitudinally by precocious separation of the centromere during or after sister strand replication. In Fig. 3 a number of configurations illustrate the restitution of only one of the paired homologues (b^1), while others show open breaks (b). The centromere is also readily broken transversely (a^1). Which of the two strands represents the sister half-chromatids, I would not know. We hope to clarify this point using more modern approaches.

Dr. Auerbach: You get this quite frequently when you treat sperm with any of these alkylating agents. When the broken chromosomes split into chromatids, each of them may or may not form a rearrangement. They may also form different rearrangements which, incidentally, I think is against Dr. Revell's theory. So in your case, too, you might get a break in the original strand followed by endoreduplication.

Dr. Yerganian: That is principally what I tried to illustrate.

Dr. Auerbach: This is quite frequent with chemicals.

Dr. Yerganian: We don't know whether the parental strands are rejoining or remaining open.

Dr. Auerbach: It is difficult to say which one.

Dr. Yerganian: Dr. Taylor in an earlier study mentioned the inability of newer strands to exchange with one another following breakage by tritiated thymidine in *Bellevalia* (1958).

Dr. Taylor: I suppose I have to enter into this discussion, but I really think we are talking about two different things. What we showed with the exchanges in tritium-labeled chromatids was a restriction on the union of the two subunits which compose a chromatid, and not a restriction on the reunion of the two chromatids. I am not sure that I understand whether this type of restriction is involved here. To develop the full story takes quite a while (Taylor, 1958), but if we assume that only like strands can unite, unlike strands cannot unite unless a piece is turned around. There is a certain way that they can fit together and another way they cannot.

References

Albuquerque, R. M., and J. A. Serra. 1951. Portugaliae Acta Biol. Sér. A 3: 187.

Alfert, M. 1955. *In* Symposium on Fine Structure of Cells, 157. Groningen: P. Noordhoff Ltd.

Evans, H. J. 1961. Genetics 46: 257.

Gray, L. H. 1958. *In* Lectures on the Scientific Basis of Medicine 7: 314.

Howard, A., and D. L. Dewey. 1960. *In* The Cell Nucleus, J. S. Mitchell, ed., 155. London: Butterworths & Co. Ltd.

Howard, A., and S. R. Pelc. 1953. *In* Symposium on Chromosome Breakage, Suppl. Heredity 6: 261. London and Edinburgh: Oliver and Boyd.

Howard-Flanders, P. 1958. Advances in Biol. and Med. Phys. 6: 553.

Kihlman, B. A. 1951. Symbolae Botan. Upsalienses 11: No. 2.

—— 1955*a*. Exptl. Cell Research 8: 345.

—— 1955*b*. Hereditas 41: 384.

—— 1956. J. Biophys. Biochem. Cytol. 2: 543.

—— 1959*a*. Exptl. Cell Research 17: 588.

—— 1959*b*. Exptl. Cell Research 17: 590.

—— 1961*a*. Radiation Bot. 1: 35.

—— 1961*b*. Radiation Bot. 1: 43.

—— 1961*c*. Advances in Genet. 10: 1.

Kihlman, B. A., and A. Levan. 1951. Hereditas 37: 382.

Lilly, L. J., and J. M. Thoday. 1956. Nature 177: 338.

McLeish, J. 1952. *In* Symposium on Chromosome Breakage, Suppl. Heredity 6: 125. London and Edinburgh: Oliver and Boyd.

—— 1959. Chromosoma 10: 686.

Neary, G. J., H. J. Evans, and S. M. Tonkinson. 1959. J. Genet. 56: 363.

Revell, S. H. 1952. *In* Symposium on Chromosome Breakage, Suppl. Heredity 6: 107. London and Edinburgh: Oliver and Boyd.

—— 1961. *In* Effects of Ionizing Radiation on Seeds. Vienna: International Atomic Energy Agency.

Taylor, J. H. 1958. Genetics 43: 515.

Thoday, J. M. 1954. New Phytologist 53: 511.

Thoday, J. M., and J. Read. 1947. Nature 160: 208.

Wolff, S. 1959. Radiation Research, Suppl. 1: 453.

Yerganian, G. 1956. Proc. Intern. Genet. Symp., Suppl. Cytologia, 206.

Radioisotope Studies on the Structure

of the Chromosome

Dr. J. H. Taylor: I was supposed to talk about chromosome structure, but I have in addition a related topic I would like to present. I wish to include some data which relates to an earlier discussion, i.e., the mechanism of breakage, or perhaps the mechanism of rejoining. I will proceed with the first task of talking about chromosome structure.

To save time—at least I will give this as an excuse—I will give you the hypothesis or at least the reasons for my coming to the conclusion that a chromosome is essentially a single DNA double helix folded together in some manner.

I have not always had this concept as a working hypothesis because when we began the experiments with tritium in 1956, I was convinced that a chromatid was a multistranded structure at the molecular level. I think this was the classical picture held by most cytologists. I think everything that has happened since then points in the other direction.

I will show you a photograph of the model that has become known as Freese's model (Fig. 1). I am certainly not committed to any particular model, but we have to have some conceptual picture to work from.

The essential part of this model is that the DNA is arranged in a linear sequence or as tandem segments along the axis of the chromosome. Certainly, to pack this strand into the dimensions of a chromosome, it would have to be folded very well.

We have two types of hypothetical linkers which I will talk about later. One type, designated *R*-linker, is essential to maintaining the linearity, and another type, designated *H*-linker, would supposedly be involved in the folding.

J. H. Taylor

As I mentioned yesterday, I cannot visualize these as single chemical bonds, although they might be. As I said, we might have to eliminate them altogether and have the DNA run all the way through as an uninterrupted strand. However, I would think of these linkers,

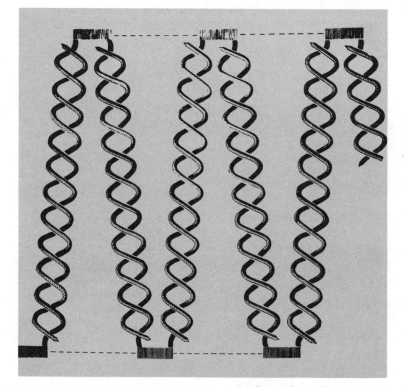

Fig. 1. *Diagrammatic representation of the hypothetical organization of DNA in a small segment of a chromosome*

The DNA molecules (units of replication) are joined end to end by R-linkers. The structure is folded and held in that position by H-linkers. In a condensed chromosome the units of replication would be folded or coiled and the whole ribbon-shaped structure would be distorted and coiled into a chromatid visible with the light microscope (from Taylor, 1957).

at least for the present, as some sort of polymer linking the pieces of DNA, perhaps very short and not necessarily inserted as part of the linear axis.

Now, let's look at Fig. 2a with the idea that first we will consider

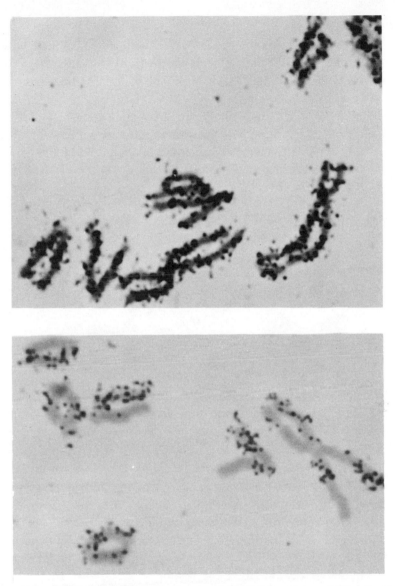

Fig. 2. Autoradiographic demonstration of the pattern of distribution of DNA labeled with thymidine-H⁰ during a single replication in root cells of Vicia (× 3000)

(a) All chromatids are labeled at the first division; (b) only the new DNA of each chromatid is labeled, for these labeled chromatids produce at the next replication a labeled and an unlabeled daughter if the second replication occurs in the absence of the thymidine-H³.

the segregation of labeled DNA. Most of you are familiar with this pattern, I am sure. Beginning with the original thymidine experiments (Taylor *et al.*, 1957), we have always found the semiconservative distribution.

If you label a chromosome during one replication, all of the chromatids appear labeled at the first division following that replication. The rationale is that a chromosome is composed of two subunits, similar to the Watson-Crick double helix. I will come back to

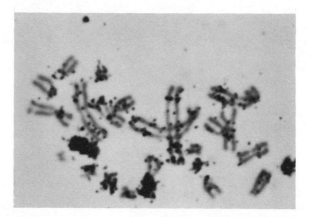

Fig. 3. Autoradiogram of a cell of Chinese hamster from culture
The cell was labeled by a 10-minute pulse of thymidine-H³. Asynchronous replication of chromosomes and semiconservative distribution of DNA are indicated. The Y chromosome and the long arm of the X are intensely labeled (× 1850).

that later. These you can visualize as replicating and forming two chromatids.

These are chromatids or daughter chromosomes that we see labeled (Fig. 2a). At the next division, on the basis of this type of replication, each daughter chromosome should pass all its label to one of its daughters and all of the unlabeled material to the other. Figure 2b shows this kind of segregation which occurs at the second division following a single replication in thymidine-H³. We have looked at a number of species now, although we have not exhausted the possibilities. We and others have looked at five or six species of plants, all of these with large chromosomes, and all distributing their DNA in this way.

Then we have looked at two species of mammalian cells—Chinese hamster and human cells. Figure 3 shows this semiconservative distribution of material. This is a hamster cell at the first division after labeling. In some instances the chromatids are more or less obscured by the silver grains.

Dr. Wolff: Is there any significance to that unlabeled chromosome?

Dr. Taylor: Yes, they are asynchronous in replication; I will come back to that later.

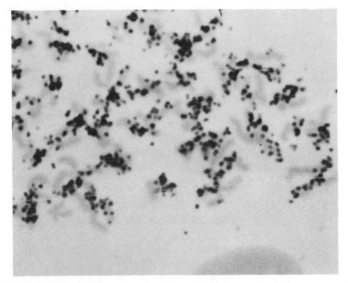

Fig. 4. Autoradiogram of a human cell (HeLa) at the second division after one replication in thymidine-H³ (× 3000)

As in *Vicia* the segregation of labeled DNA is consistent with the semiconservative scheme. Chromatid exchanges occur, but are less frequent than in chromosomes of *Vicia*.

Figure 4 shows the second division in the human cell (HeLa), and you can see quite clearly at least in some of the chromosomes that there is one unlabeled chromatid and one labeled chromatid just as we saw in the large plant chromosomes. It is not possible to do the kind of quantitative study with these smaller chromosomes which we did with *Bellevalia* (Taylor, 1958), at least we have not been able to yet, but the distribution of labeled DNA appears to be regularly semiconservative.

Dr. Pavan: For all chromosomes?

Dr. Taylor: Yes, the second division following one replication always segregates a clean chromosome from a labeled one. This is consistent with the idea that there are two subunits. There is an old and a new unit in each chromatid, and then at the next replication when these two subunits separate one contains all of the tritium.

The second point that I would make is that these two subunits in the chromatid are unlike in their ability to rejoin with one another. I cannot develop the arguments fully on this point because it would take too long, but the basis of the analysis was the sister chromatid exchanges which can be detected at the second division following one labeling cycle. Sometimes they do not occur in a particular chromosome, but they do occur with what we could consider to be high frequency, one per chromosome per cell cycle for the large chromosome in *Bellevalia*. The exchanges often occur in pairs in the sense that the two daughter chromosomes derived from the original one in which the event occurred have exchanges at the same locus; we call these twin exchanges.

The twins would occur with the frequencies observed only if complete breakage and reciprocal exchange between whole chromatids occur during interphase when the tritium is incorporated. I will quickly draw a diagram in which one subunit has this directional sense and the other the opposite (Fig. 5). One is labeled and the other unlabeled in each chromatid. If a break and reciprocal exchange occurs, only one kind of union can occur. A labeled subunit is joined to an unlabeled subunit. This type of union will occur in both chromatids if only like strands can unite. When these chromatids replicate the next time we will see the exchange.

Dr. Auerbach: There should not be any unpaired ones?

Dr. Taylor: Yes, you will only get paired ones from the first interphase if the restriction on reunion is obtained. However, by the time they can be analyzed at the second division you will also see exchanges which occur at the interphase after labeling (second interphase). At the second interphase, exchanges can occur which will not be paired because they are independent events in separate chromosomes. The frequency should be one twin pair for each two single exchanges. One finds the predicted number (Taylor, 1958).

Dr. Ris: Are there single exchanges between the double units?

Dr. Taylor: If they occur, we have not been able to detect them. They do not shift the predicted ratio to an appreciable extent.

Dr. Ris: Are the strands which you indicate the twin chains of a double helix?

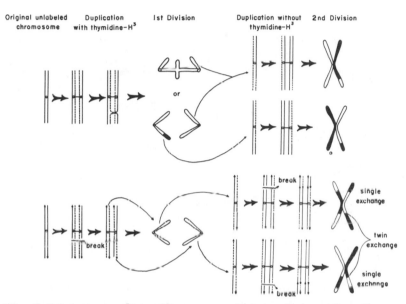

Fig. 5. *Diagram to show the pattern of sister chromatid exchanges predicted if rejoining is restricted by a difference in the two subunits*

The broken lines represent the labeled subunits, but in the sketches of anaphase and metaphase chromosomes the solid black region represents unlabeled material while the region in outline represents labeled material. Exchanges between single subunits in different chromatid as shown at the top did not occur, or were undetectable. Exchanges appear to follow the scheme diagrammed in the lower half of the figure.

Dr. Taylor: Yes, but to explain the frequencies observed we have to assume that exchanges are only between whole chromatids.

Dr. Ris: Is it a double strand?

Dr. Taylor: It is a double strand of something—let's say DNA.

Dr. Auerbach: Does the frequency depend on the label?

Dr. Taylor: It is not changed by the labeling.

Dr. Lindsley: These twins look like they are actually homologous, or am I confused?

Dr. Taylor: These two chromosomes are descended from the original chromatid. Presumably, it replicated once, exchanges occurred, and then it replicated again. The exchanges were revealed at the following metaphase; so these are descendants from one original chromosome. They are not homologous; they are identical. The other

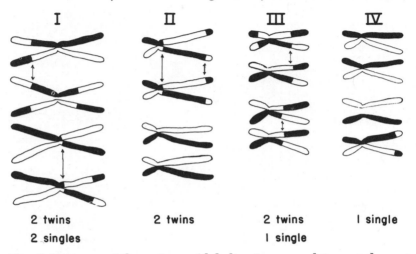

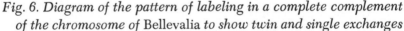

Fig. 6. Diagram of the pattern of labeling in a complete complement of the chromosome of Bellevalia *to show twin and single exchanges*

The 16 chromosomes at the second division are formed by the replication of the diploid set of eight chromosomes labeled with thymidine-H³ during one synthetic cycle.

homologous pair is here. This is a tetraploid cell (Fig. 6). It is not the first division after labeling but the second.

Dr. Gray: I am not sure whether this was Dr. Auerbach's point but can one exclude the possibility, viz., that this was caused by the thymidine label?

Dr. Taylor: It cannot be excluded with certainty. However, for this type of analysis, i.e., to test for a difference between the subunits, it would not matter whether it is caused by the irradiation or not. For other reasons it is an important point and we would like to establish it one way or another.

The twin exchanges are those which occur in the first interphase,

and the single exchanges are those which occur in the second interphase according to this hypothesis. When the treatment of the two
interphases was similar, the frequency of exchanges per chromosome
was the same.

The radiation from the tritium should be two times as great in the
first interphase because both of the chromatids have tritium incorporated, but in the second interphase only one in each chromosome
contains radioisotope. So, if it were the tritium, we would expect
perhaps half as many exchanges in the second interphase as the
first. The number is equal.

Dr. Evans: This argument is reinforced by the fact, if my memory
is correct, that the frequency of true full chromatid aberrations was
very low.

Dr. Taylor: Yes, the frequency of chromatid aberrations between
nonhomologous chromatids was very low. The frequency of sister
chromatid exchanges is between one-half and one per chromosome
per interphase. For interchromosomal exchanges the frequency is
less than 1 per 100 chromosomes. This is very low compared to the
sister chromatid exchanges.

Dr. Wolff: How does that compare with the frequencies that Wim-
ber got for equivalent treatments?

Dr. Taylor: I think that he got higher ones, but I think that he
put more tritium in. You can break the chromosome, of course, if
you put in enough thymidine-H^3.

I apologize, because I have not been able to go through the whole
argument. I am sure it is not entirely clear, but I must move on to
other topics. The conclusion reached is that the chromatid is analogous to the Watson-Crick double helix.

Dr. Ris: If you mention a chromatid, isn't that a half-chromosome?

Dr. Taylor: Yes, a chromatid is analogous to the double helix and
after anaphase it will presumably not have changed. It is still substantially the same structure.

I do not wish to say anything further about morphology because
others will speak of that later, I will say that I certainly agree that a
chromosome at anaphase is in some sense physically double. You
can see that with a light microscope. I will show you a model later
which illustrates what I mean.

One argument against a multistranded chromosome is the difficulty of explaining the appearance of mutation. Perhaps I can illustrate with a diagram the problem that one encounters if you accept the semiconservative model for replication and then assume that the genetic information is redundant, i.e., present in many strands. The lines represent one subunit of a multistranded chromatid. I have only four lines. I want to deal with a simple multistranded model. In the absence of mistakes in the semiconservative scheme, an error in replication of one strand will have no way of ever spreading to the rest of the strands in the chromatid.

Let's admit that the chromosome could occasionally make a mistake in segregation of strands. I don't think there is any evidence that it does, but we can certainly expect chromosomes to make an occasional mistake. Let us suppose that separation of the two subunits occurs in the plane at right angles to the usual cleavage. This could allow both descendants of a mutant strand to go to one chromatid. Let's be generous and say that this mistake could occur one time in ten. If you had four units, one mistake would spread it to two of them; two mistakes would spread it to four of them. Before you could get all of the units changed in a chromatid, there would have to be 100 cycles of division. This seems to me a very good argument against a multistranded chromatid.

Dr. Auerbach: It depends on the cause of mutation.

Dr. Taylor: I am assuming that this is the type of mutation that would affect single DNA double helices. You could have deletions of whole multistranded segments and these would show up immediately.

Now I want to say a word about the mechanism of reunion. As you know, protein synthesis is a requirement for reunion, as shown by Dr. Wolff's experiments. I think that we have some evidence now that DNA replication is also required for reunion. We have been working on this problem for only a few months and the results are not published. [Editorial Note: Since the symposium the data have been published, Taylor *et al.*, 1962.]

We began the study by using FUDR (fluorouracil deoxyriboside), an analog of thymidine, which Cohen *et al.* (1958) have shown to be a specific inhibitor of the enzyme thymidylate synthetase. The enzyme adds a methyl group to deoxyuridylate to form thymidylate. This appears to be the only pathway for the *de novo* synthesis of the thymidylic acid in the cell.

The analog, FUDR, has a fluorine atom at the five position where the methyl should be added. Presumably, it is phosphorylated by the kinase which phosphorylates thymidine. The FUDR monophosphate binds irreversibly with the enzyme, thymidylate synthetase, and completely blocks the synthesis of thymidylic acid. When cells are denied thymidylic acid, DNA replication is stopped.

Dr. Wolff: Would not RNA be blocked also?

Dr. Taylor: For RNA synthesis this methylating enzyme is not required. The FUDR does not interfere with other enzymes as far as we know. However, it is converted to fluorouridylic acid in some types of cells. The fluorouridylic acid is then incorporated into RNA and perhaps other uracil-containing components, but the fluorouracil is not incorporated into DNA.

We first used FUDR with the idea that it would force complete substitution of tritiated thymidine in newly synthesized DNA and produce hot spots in chromosomes. It did not work presumably because the cell has a limited kinase activity for phosphorylating thymidine. A faster rate of incorporation cannot necessarily be induced by blocking the *de novo* pathway. *Vicia* is not very efficient in the utilization of thymidine. For example, it takes at least one-half hour to get in enough tritiated thymidine for autoradiographic studies. Since we did not increase the incorporation much, we have not carried that work any further. We did find interesting effects on the chromosome by the use of this analog, FUDR.

Oh yes, I was about to omit a point that might be considered before we proceed with a discussion of the FUDR effect. I refer to the observation that chromosome reproduction may be asynchronous among chromosomes in a cell as well as among the various regions of a single chromosome. Figure 3 shows the pattern of labeling when thymidine-H³ is available during the last stages of replication of a Chinese hamster cell in culture. One arm of the X chromosome and the whole of the Y chromosome begin replication late and continue for an interval after most other chromosomes are finished.

Dr. Wolff: How much time variation do you have? In other words, how short a treatment does it take before you would pick up partial labeling?

Dr. Taylor: For the hamster cell we use a pulse of 10 minutes, but you will pick it up if you give continuous treatment, because in those cells which are near the end of the replication only those chromosomes which are late in finishing up will get labeled. Since these cells will be the first ones to come to division, you will see the same pattern whether you give continuous treatment or whether you give a pulse type of treatment. But, of course, if you allow continuous labeling, the other cells may get so heavily labeled that their autoradiograms interfere with the analysis of these lightly labeled ones.

Dr. Moses: These are not FUDR-treated cells, are they?

Dr. Taylor: No, these are quite normal, growing cells, labeled with thymidine.

Figure 7 shows a female human complement, 46 chromosomes, and here is one of the X chromosomes that is late. I do not mean that it is completely out of phase with the rest of the complement, but that its replication continues longer than most of the other chromosomes.

In the case of the hamster, these chromosomes, the X and the Y and a few others, continue replication about one-half hour after all of the others are complete.

At the beginning of replication, the Y chromosome, one arm of the X, and almost the whole of some small autosomes wait about three hours before they start, compared with the others; so they are quite strikingly asynchronous.

Dr. Wolff: Is this a rate phenomena? If you took these same slides and let them sit in the icebox to expose for months and months, would you then find faint labeling indicating that there was some DNA synthesis going on?

Dr. Taylor: We have not left them for months and months. However, it seems that there may be parts of the chromosome that can be completely finished before the end of the DNA synthesis phase.

Dr. Auerbach: Where you get differences between autosomes, do the homologs behave similarly?

Dr. Taylor: Similarly, but not necessarily identically.

Dr. Yerganian: With the assistance of L. A. Grodzins, we are attempting to expose classic diploid cultures to tritiated thymidine for 10 seconds only, in an effort to check whether or not similar sites along autosomal homologues replicate synchronously. In general, homologs do follow on course.

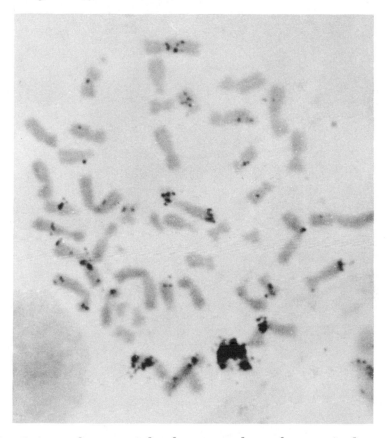

Fig. 7. Autoradiogram of the chromosomal complement of a human leucocyte (female)

One X chromosome is late in replication and is heavily labeled because the cell was given a pulse of thymidine near the end of its DNA replication period.

Dr. Taylor: In connection with this, I should perhaps emphasize that the two homologous X chromosomes of the female are quite different and that the X and the Y are strikingly different.

We come back now to *Vicia* and the effect of the FUDR. This is

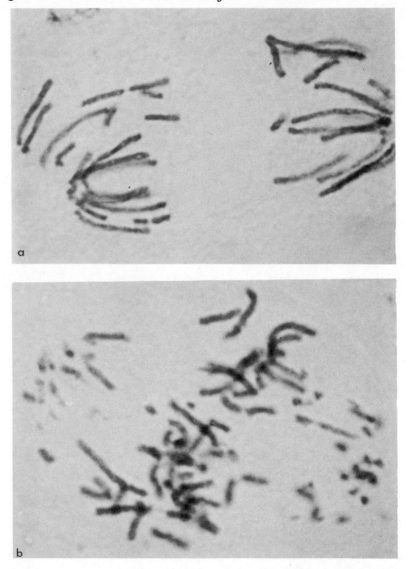

Fig. 8. Vicia *root cells at anaphase after treatment with FUDR*
   (*10⁻⁶ M*)

(a) Gaps and fragments four hours after immersion of root in the inhibitor;
(b) severe fragmentation in a cell arriving at division six hours after beginning
of treatment (from Taylor *et al.*, 1962).

the normal chromosome complement that many of you are familiar with in anaphase. There are four gaps, nucleolus organizer regions (NOR) that are quite normal. We take these into account in scoring gaps.

The first indications of damage from FUDR are gaps which appear within three or four hours after the beginning of the treatment. Figure 8a shows a damaged anaphase with both gaps and fragments. I think that the fragments are completely free. In addition, there is a gap close to the centromere.

Dr. Lindsley: Are the gaps generally in the centromere region?

Dr. Taylor: Not necessarily, they tend to be localized at particular sites and I have a strong feeling that these are the sites of late replication. In fact, they seem to correspond at least to some degree to the hot spots reported by Woodard *et al.* (1961) from labeling with thymidine-H³ late in replication. However, the replication pattern is not so precisely asynchronous as that demonstrated in the Chinese hamster cells.

Breaks do occur very frequently at the NOR region, but we have ignored those because they are so hard to score. In control preparations, one sees displacement of the segment distal to the NOR often enough to make such scoring difficult. All gaps or breaks counted are in excess of these.

Figure 8b shows a really drastically affected cell at anaphase. This cell was fixed six hours after treatment.

Dr. Pollard: This is compared to what patients get when they treat them with it.

Dr. Taylor: Dr. Hsu (personal communication) showed that it does the same thing to mammalian cells in culture. The chromosomes were completely shattered.

I should mention here the length of the G2 period in *Vicia* and its correlation with these events. G2 in *Vicia* was reported by Howard and Pelc (1951) to be approximately eight hours on the basis of P³² labeling. We have repeated the experiments with tritiated thymidine and found it to be between four and six hours. This is perhaps not surprising, because the detection of incorporation of P³² requires a longer contact compared to thymidine-H³. Apparently, synthesis of DNA tapers off gradually, and we can label cells nearer the end of synthesis by means of thymidine-H^3 of high specific activity. The length of $G2$ corresponds almost precisely with the time required for appearance of major damage from FUDR, so we think that the effects that we see occur in those cells that were in the late stages of synthesis and have proceeded on to metaphase or anaphase.

Dr. Swanson: What is the concentration that you use?

Dr. Taylor: To produce the breakage we use 10^{-6} M. This is a good feature of the FUDR effect. You do not have to load up the cell with the chemical to get an effect. A concentration of 10^{-6} M gives us just about the saturation effect on the gaps and breakage. However, few breaks or gaps are produced by a concentration of 10^{-7} M within six hours.

Dr. Evans: I have not understood one point. Are you giving continuous treatment or a pulse treatment?

Dr. Taylor: The roots remain in the solution of FUDR continuously.

Dr. Evans: Then in six hours you start seeing these gross effects, but previous to this you do not get any gross effects?

Dr. Taylor: That is correct. Gaps are the first damage one sees, and then one begins to see breaks at least within four hours with 10^{-6} M.

Dr. Ris: Do you get micronuclei?

Dr. Taylor: We have not followed the cells far enough to study these very much. Some of these cells survive, but I don't think this one with extensive damage would.

Dr. Yerganian: Would you get continuous breakage as in mammalian systems?

Dr. Taylor: Practically all divisions stop within eight hours.

Dr. Evans: Can we discuss that? This is going to be an important point if no further divisions occur after eight hours.

Dr. Taylor: Yes, but let us finish this breakage story. At metaphase we see what appear to be clean chromatid breaks, but I suppose they could be gaps. Some of them, however, are almost certainly isolocus breaks with complete dislocation of fragments.

Dr. Swanson: You get no exchanges?

Dr. Taylor: No exchanges. We do see rather badly shattered late

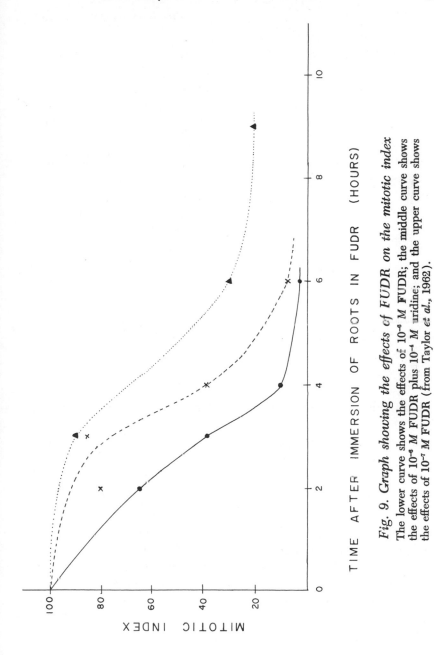

TIME AFTER IMMERSION OF ROOTS IN FUDR (HOURS)

Fig. 9. Graph showing the effects of FUDR on the mitotic index
The lower curve shows the effects of 10^{-6} *M* FUDR; the middle curve shows
the effects of 10^{-6} *M* FUDR plus 10^{-4} *M* uridine; and the upper curve shows
the effects of 10^{-7} *M* FUDR (from Taylor *et al.*, 1962).

prophases, and I assume that these have free fragments. Some of them, of course, are gaps, but no exchanges and no reunions occur in any of these cells. I have looked at thousands of cells and I have never seen any evidence of reunion.

Dr. Swanson: You get isolocus breaks but no sister reunion.

Dr. Taylor: No sister reunion. Figure 9 shows the effect of FUDR on division rate. We found this difficult to establish with precision. *Vicia* fluctuates so much in its mitotic index that this curve may represent only an approximate rate of change. We count all of the anaphases in the last 2 mm of the secondary root to get the mitotic index.

Figure 9 shows the curve for a concentration of 10^{-7} M FUDR. Within three to four hours at this concentration there appears to be little effect on the number of mitoses. The effect shows up between four and eight hours, but there are still divisions up to 10 or 12 hours. With 10^{-6} M FUDR there is an effect within two hours and I assume that this is a side effect, i.e., the secondary effect perhaps from the incorporation of fluorourocil into RNA. With 10^{-6} FUDR plus 10^{-4} uridine to try to compete with this RNA effect we find that the divisions are not affected nearly so fast. Therefore, I think we can partially overcome this side effect.

Dr. Wolff: What is the lower curve?

Dr. Taylor: That represents the change in mitotic index with 10^{-6} M FUDR.

Dr. Evans: Have you made a measure of the timing of $G2$ with tritiated thymidine after you have given FUDR, or are you just extrapolating?

Dr. Taylor: We made the measurement on untreated cells. We have tried to label after FUDR but we cannot get enough label into the cells damaged by FUDR to detect. In the late synthesis when the damage occurs, the rate of labeling is so slow that so far we have not been able to detect it, at least not with our conditions.

Dr. Evans: I asked this because if you start putting the roots into a solution which they do not like for any given reason, then you are quite liable to slow up mitosis and $G2$, and what you are really measuring there is the ratio of cells in mitosis and interphase. It is not permissible to say that if the index falls at six hours you have allowed six hours' worth of cells to go through.

Dr. Taylor: Yes, I admit that. We may be slowing up events. Since my thesis is that the effect which we are seeing is produced at the end of DNA replication, this is an important point, but there is additional evidence besides the timing. Timing is one factor, but I think the strongest evidence that we are interfering with DNA replication comes from another observation—that we can cure these lesions with thymidine in the presence of FUDR. If the effect is on DNA replication, this would be predicted because thymidine is phosphorylated by an enzyme which is not inhibited by FUDR. The thymidylate synthetase system is bypassed and the thymidine triphosphate formed is incorporated into DNA.

Dr. Wolff: Do you mean cure the lesion or prevent its formation?

Dr. Taylor: My contention is that they are cured because you can give FUDR (10^{-6} M) for 2–3 hours, then add thymidine (10^{-4} M) and reverse the effect.

Dr. Wolff: But you do not know that the treatment produced a lesion if you do not see any lesion at the end of two to three hours. What happens if you treat for three and one-half or four hours, get some lesions, and then add thymidine?

Dr. Taylor: If you treat for three hours, you may get an occasional cell that comes through with a lesion, but those arriving an hour later appear to be cured.

Dr. Evans: When do you score these?

Dr. Taylor: At anaphase.

Dr. Evans: And the cells take about two hours?

Dr. Taylor: I have no measure of that, but it should be about the same as with any other culture.

Dr. Evans: Then you give it the treatment and push in your thymidine?

Dr. Taylor: Yes, we give 10^{-4} M thymidine. If we give 10^{-6} M thymidine, the damage is only partially cured; a concentration of 10^{-5} M cures more, and 10^{-4} M cures most of them.

Dr. Evans: If the lesion occurs in S then it is in existence until the end of G2, but if the lesions are not made until the end of G2, and this is possible, then you might be having not repair but prevention. Is this clear?

Dr. Taylor: That is a possibility.

Dr. Revell: The latest time at which you can give thymidine is three hours?

Dr. Taylor: That is the latest time we have used so far.

Dr. Revell: That is just before mitosis, just before prophase?

Dr. Taylor: Yes, if you give thymidine and repair the lesions, there are still no reunions, no bridges, no exchanges produced. Therefore the lesions are repairable and are not breaks in the sense that they can rejoin, if you will grant me that there are lesions, at least I wish to think of the damage in that way.

Dr. Lindsley: Have you cured them with hot thymidine?

Dr. Taylor: I think that we have some slides being exposed, but we have no results. I think that such incorporation will be difficult to detect in *Vicia* because it has a very inefficient system for getting thymidine into the cell.

Dr. Lindsley: Enough is incorporated to cure the lesion, however.

Dr. Taylor: Sufficient to cure it, yes, but even if thymidine of very high specific activity is incorporated, the pieces of DNA may be too small to detect. Pieces of several million molecular weight would be too small to detect by our methods.

Dr. Auerbach: I am getting a bit confused about the timings. What was your answer to Dr. Wolff's question about whether the lesions are cured and not prevented? Is it just the timing?

Dr. Taylor: A concentration of 10^{-6} M produces these drastic lesions within four to six hours. If we give thymidine (10^{-4} M), the lesions are all cured by the time the chromosomes appeared at anaphase.

Dr. Totter: This means that you cannot remove the FUDR for three hours.

Dr. Taylor: We have not done that experiment. I know that there is a lag before the cell recovers from the FUDR, and I would predict that you could take the roots out at three hours and get essentially the same effect as with continuous treatment, but we have not done the experiment.

Dr. Lindsley: Is the FUDR removable?

Dr. Taylor: No, you could not get it out of the cell. It is bound to the enzyme and, according to Cohen, it is irreversibly bound.

Dr. Evans: Have you put roots in the solution and then had a look at the frequency of mitosis at periods of longer than six hours? Does the mitotic index stay very low?

Dr. Taylor: We examined roots at intervals up to 24 hours, and with 10^{-7} M FUDR the mitotic index falls to almost zero within 10 to 14 hours. They may recover slightly, but this could be from the depletion of the FUDR.

Dr. Evans: Harold Smith has some data which you might have seen, he put roots into 5-aminouracil and the mitotic index fell down to zero at about 10 hours. Then he left the roots in this solution, took them out a day later, and found that he got almost synchronous mitotis coming through.

Dr. Taylor: Almost synchronous?

Dr. Evans: Yes, and the indication is that this analog blocks the cells in S. This conclusion is being tested with timing experiments using tritiated thymidine. That is why I asked whether you had measured G2. I suspect that the cells might have been blocked in S.

Dr. Taylor: We have some information on what happens in recovery. There is a partial synchrony because some blocked cells come through after a lag when FUDR is removed, but thymidine speeds up recovery and there are no breaks in cells treated with thymidine. Most of the cells in synthesis are therefore blocked and can wait for a number of hours for thymidylic acid. There is apparently a feedback mechanism that stops them in synthesis. According to my interpretation, the cells in late stages of synthesis either do not have this feedback control or it does not operate fast enough, and they go on with DNA replication incomplete. This implies. that one of the subunits of the chromosome has gaps in it. The healing of the lesions is just the finishing of replication.

Dr. Ris: Did you make any cytophotometric studies on this?

Dr. Taylor: No, we have not. If my interpretation is correct, the lesions contain single-stranded DNA. This would imply that the DNA subunits can separate before they replicate because the two chromatids get completely apart just as they would if they had finished replication.

Let me make one other point, that is, BUDR (bromouracil deoxyriboside) cures the lesions just as well or just about as well as thymidine. This would be predicted because it is incorporated into DNA in the same way that thymidine is.

Hsu has reported that BUDR will cause breaks in the chromosome. I do not doubt this, but we do not see any breaks from BUDR in our material.

Now let's come back to reunion of broken chromosomes.

Dr. Wolff: What about straight uridine?

Dr. Taylor: For what?

Dr. Wolff: I won't use the word cure. Will it prevent the appearance of the lesion?

Dr. Taylor: No, it will not. Perhaps it decreases the number slightly. If we give 10^{-4} uridine with 10^{-6} M FUDR, there are more cells to score but not much reduction in damage per cell.

Dr. Wolff: And uridylic acid?

Dr. Taylor: We have not tried it.

Dr. Swanson: Would you get hot spots with your curing?

Dr. Taylor: Somebody asked me that before, but we do not have the information yet. Now let us return to the effect of FUDR on radiation-induced lesions. Experiments are possible because 10^{-7} M FUDR produces no visible lesions within six hours, and yet it does, as you saw, prevent or slow down cell division at a rate that would indicate that it stops DNA replication. We have not yet performed experiments to check this by independent means. I tried to do the experiment with tritiated deoxyuridine to see if it could be incorporated in the presence of the inhibitor. It should not be because it cannot be converted to thymidylic acid. With the controls I just got enough to detect, so I could not be sure that FUDR was preventing incorporation of deoxyuridine-H^3. We will do the experiment with cytidine-H^3 or some other label.

Dr. Wolff: In Elkind's laboratory, Saltzman found that 10^{-7} M FUDR to mammalian cells knocked out DNA, and also knocked down RNA synthesis to half its rate and affected protein synthesis.

Dr. Taylor: We have not measured RNA synthesis. We did try other inhibitors, for example, 6-azauridine, which is a good inhibitor of the enzyme orotidylic decarboxylase. Since orotidylate is an intermediate in the synthesis of most of all pyrimidines, both RNA and DNA synthesis should be affected.

This inhibitor had no effect that we could observe on *Vicia* roots at a rather high concentration. We tried deoxyuridine to see whether that produced an effect, and it did not.

Dr. Wolff: Do you mean cytological effect?

Dr. Taylor: Yes, and we tried quite a number of other base analogs, but none of them produced an effect like FUDR even when used at 10^{-3} M concentrations.

Dr. Pollard: Did you try the iodine compound?

Dr. Taylor: No, we have not yet. We have it on schedule. It should act like BUDR perhaps with more damage to the cell.

Let's get to the radiation breakage. We can use a concentration of 10^{-3} M FUDR and observe no lesions. This gives us a chance to irradiate in the presence of this concentration and to observe what happens to the rejoining of chromosomes. We are limited in cytological experiments because we have to work in a short period. I do not have any results with split-dose experiments. That can perhaps be done with FUDR, but what we have measured is the reunion of chromatids to produce the typical chromatid bridge and fragment at anaphase. We can see the very clear chromatid bridges with fragments, and they can be scored in the presence of quite a number of fragments and gaps.

We decided to look for this aberration in the presence of the inhibitor after irradiation. After trying various doses, we decided to give 25 r of x radiation and waited four hours to fix with and without the FUDR.

In control material, we got 6.7 percent of the cells with this type of bridge in four hours after 25 r of radiation. With 10^{-7} M FUDR 30 minutes before 25 r and continuous treatment for four hours we got 1.1 percent of the cells with bridges. We had some indications that this was sufficient time to stop most DNA replication. We got a rather striking effect, you see.

We increased the concentration to 10^{-6} M FUDR, but this produced breaks or lesions that cannot be distinguished from the radiation-induced lesions.

Dr. Lindsley: How many do you get in untreated material?

Dr. Taylor: Unirradiated? None.

Dr. Lindsley. What if you put thymidine in?

Dr. Taylor: I will come to that in a minute.

Dr. Auerbach: You have a prevention of bridge formation, but did you have any evidence of breaks or lesions or gaps produced by x rays?

Dr. Taylor: Yes, in the controls and in those treated with 10^{-7} FUDR there are many fragments and gaps.

Dr. Auerbach: What is the difference between 6.7 and 1.1, which in some way causes discernible breaks which were not joined by bridges?

Dr. Taylor: The number of fragments is higher when irradiation follows treatment with 10^{-7} M FUDR, but I doubt that the scoring is accurate enough to correlate the difference with the number of bridges that fail to form. The sensitivity might be changed anyway.

Dr. Wolff: If there is a peak of sensitivity and this chemical is slowing down division as Dr. Evans suggested, it might be that you would be sampling different cells at the end of this four-hour period in each of the cases. It might give results something like that.

Dr. Taylor: That is right. How much change in sensitivity occurs between three and four hours? Is it very great?

Dr. Evans: If your chemical is slowing up phophase, then you can reduce your bridge treatment at four hours quite considerably.

Dr. Taylor: Let me come to the next point which may help clear up this question: What will happen if we give these cells thymidine after irradiation? When we give thymidine after FUDR, there is still a reduction in division rate. There is a recovery of the population of cells which have been inhibited, but we do get about the same number of cells coming through the division within three, four, or five hours, whether or not we give thymidine. We gave FUDR (10^{-7} M) pretreatment for 30 minutes, irradiated with 25 r, and then put the cells in a concentration of 10^{-4} M thymidine. The number of cells with bridges, if I remember correctly, was 5.4 percent. The reversal is perhaps not complete, but it is in the right direction.

Dr. Wolff: Thymidine might be getting rid of the inhibition in cell cycle too.

Dr. Auerbach: What is the evidence for an effect on rejoining?

Dr. Evans: There isn't any as it stands.

Dr. Taylor: We can only say that we get more nearly the usual number of bridges if we give the cell thymidine after irradiation.

Dr. Steffensen: Would it help your case to report the frequency of acentric fragments?

Dr. Taylor: Do you mean the reduction of free fragments by thymidine?

Dr. Steffensen: Are your free fragments the reciprocal of your exchanges?

Dr. Taylor: I doubt that our scoring of free fragments is accurate enough to make the correlation.

Dr. Steffensen: You would need to prove that there is some kind of production effect.

Dr. Taylor: In addition to the obvious free fragments, there are these gaps that are difficult to classify. Some may be free fragments and others may not. There is one more point I wish to make. BUDR (10^{-4} *M*) will have about the same effect as thymidine in restoring the usual number of bridges.

Dr. Wolff: We know that if we irradiate in late G2 we get chromatid aberrations showing rejoining. This, now, should not be subject to the effects of synthesis.

Dr. Taylor: My tentative conclusion at the moment is that DNA replication may be required for rejoining at any time, but it would, of course, have to be tentative. DNA replication can occur even in early prophase or very late interphase to cure the lesions three hours after FUDR treatment.

Dr. Wolff: Then you would expect FUDR to work at periods other than S, and you are trying to make the point that it works only in S.

Dr. Taylor: FUDR produces the lesions only in S. According to my interpretation, the lesions can persist and be cured much later when thymidine is added. It can therefore allow reunion.

We must assume that these lesions produced by FUDR can be repaired because all the cells coming through division for hours after adding thymidine are free of aberrations. Therefore, I think that whatever these lesions are, and I interpret them as gaps in one subunit of a chromatid, they are capable of repair. Therefore, I would extrapolate this concept to cover the similar kinds of lesions produced by irradiation. The radiation-induced gaps are probably breaks in one subunit of the chromatid which can be repaired at some later stage.

Let me give you very quickly a picture of the rejoining of chromatids. Let me call this in Fig. 10 a replicating unit of the chromatid. I don't know how long it is and I don't know whether or not it exists,

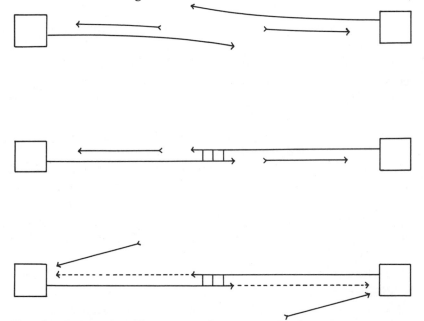

Fig. 10. *Diagram of the proposed steps involved in the reunion of broken chromatids*

Fragments of two units of replication are shown. Each line represents a subunit of a chromatid, presumably a single polynucleotide chain. Dashed lines represent the new polymer required to complete a new unit.

but I want to think of it as a small piece of a chromosome that can replicate without participation of any adjacent unit. On the basis of the studies of synchrony and asynchrony it seems that there must be many of these along some kinds of chromosomes, i.e., many replicating units that are reproducing simultaneously. Another way of stating the hypothesis is that there are many growing points for DNA replication.

Let's say that breakage is an interruption in the DNA chain. We are forgetting for the moment the protein that may also be involved. Since we were using inhibitors that affected DNA synthesis primarily, I should like to restrict our discussion to that component.

Let's say that there are two broken ends at the right distance for interaction. I think that this is a very important point which was brought out in Dr. Atwood's discussion. Let us suppose that the DNA chains do not break at the same site. The two single unpaired chains at the end may make contact by base pairing in a short region (Fig. 10). If the chains end in three OH groups, DNA polymerase can add nucleotides and each chain will grow and copy the antiparallel chain, perhaps to the end of the replicating unit.

Dr. Wolff: This is only true when the primer pieces are very small; when the primer pieces are bigger, I think that it really makes a whole new strand.

Dr. Taylor: Perhaps it is not necessary to assume that the two antiparallel chains copy to the end of a replication unit. However, if copying does occur this way, two short single chains will be cast off at each locus where healing occurs. Figure 10 shows single strands of DNA, but they would represent half-chromatids if we assume that the chromatid is one DNA double helix.

This lesion is completely cured, after the copying has occurred as illustrated. The process would require polymer synthesis.

Dr. Lindsley: How about those illegitimate bases where you have base pairing?

Dr. Taylor: I assume that the contact will only occur if a few base pairs can be formed in the regular way.

Dr. Lindsley: The picture that you have should give slightly different aberrations to the two daughter cells—aberrations whose break points differ in position by a length of chromosome corresponding to the region of illegitimate base-pairing sequence in the replication units involved. If you had good genetic control—

Dr. Evans: Doesn't it demand that you can only join one way, so that if you get a join the other two broken parts are eligible for joining only if they are oriented the right way around? But does it not also mean that you have an equal chance of having the wrong parts together, that is, of not satisfying the correct directional requirements. If there was a wrong base, they wouldn't fit. In other words, there is a one-to-one choice. In addition, there is also a chance that the other two pieces on top of the figure might not join. This would mean that you might expect to find a very high frequency of incomplete aberrations and, in fact, we observe 5 or 10 percent with x rays.

Dr. Taylor: One would expect that nongrowing ends, that is, 5'-phosphates or chains ending in 5'OH groups, would join 50 percent of the time. However, I think that such union could lead to rejoining. The two short ends might copy their complementary strands to the point of union and then lead to an opening of the break again. However, if there are *H*-linkers holding the structure together, the growing ends might by-pass that point, pair with each other, and lead to a reunion as indicated for the longer growing chains.

Dr. Evans: I think that there is an even chance of not getting a join.

Dr. Lindsley: Maybe that would give restitution.

Dr. Atwood: Could you go into further detail as to why it would not join?

Dr. Evans: It will not join if one demands that a directional requirement within the strands be satisfied before joining of the broken strands can occur, and this is a fact which you accept, is it not?

Dr. Atwood: Yes.

Dr. Evans: Then, if the free ends which are in closest association do not satisfy this requirement, they cannot join; the broken strands involved will have to be moved in order to join. I should have thought that the probability of having the directional requirement satisfied between two broken strands which are close together is one-half.

Dr. Atwood: Facts suggest that it is very preferentially for the right orientation.

Dr. Evans: If it is a random affair, one should expect a complete joining in only 50 percent of the cases; in other words, 50 percent incompleteness in the exchanges.

Dr. Pollard: What happens if you get it wrong? It just does nothing?

Dr. Taylor: There are enzymes in the cell and if these chop frayed ends, chains with the correct polarity and a few bases complementary to those on the other end might eventually be produced.

Dr. Lindsley: But you can put pairs of breaks into your system here that cannot undergo exchange.

Dr. Taylor: Perhaps, but the limited reaction of the DNA polymerase studied by Kornberg, or some similar reaction, might heal any break.

Dr. Lindsley: It is possible to have a situation which can only give

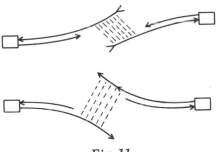

Fig. 11

you restitution, isn't it? The pair of breaks shown in Fig. 11 can give base pairing only in the combinations shown.

Dr. Auerbach: I agree. This might be connected with some noticeable genetical position effect, but, on the other hand, there are many rearrangements that do not give a position effect.

Dr. Taylor: Doesn't this all depend on how the various parts function, whether there are noncoding regions, or whether there are repeat regions?

Dr. Lindsley: I do not think that this rejoining scheme need lead to mutation associated with the rejoin, but it must lead to slightly different aberrations in the two daughter cells, and, if the irradiated cell is a sperm, it leads to a mosaic individual, half of whose cells carry one aberration and the other half of which carry a similar aberration but with slightly displaced break points. In the vast majority of cases, however, the mosaicism should be undetectable.

Dr. Chu: I can think of two alternatives for your curing hypothesis: one is that if you add FUDR of 10^{-7} M it might also alter the segregation of the dicentric. You may fail to see a bridge in anaphase.

The second possibility would be that if you had a little bit more FUDR the bridge would be further broken up. Therefore, if it breaks up, you fail to see it.

Dr. Taylor: Let's take the two points separately. I am quite sure that we could see the other type of aberration if it occurred, that is, the loop type of dicentric.

The second point is a good one. If we give 10^{-6} *M* FUDR, we may produce so many potential breaks that the bridges never show because they break early in anaphase. However, this is unlikely to occur with 10^{-7} *M* FUDR.

Dr. Chu: You don't know. You modify the cell.

Dr. Taylor: Let me say that the number of fragments produced by a combination of 10^{-7} *M* FUDR and 25 r compared to 25 r alone is not very different. If one assumes that each bridge which fails to form would be replaced by two fragments in the FUDR-treated cells, there is very little difference.

Dr. Totter: Would you say a word about the hypothesis of a DNA turnover which you just outlined?

Dr. Taylor: Yes, this would appear to provide a mechanism for DNA turnover if single-chain elimination occurs as a part of the repair mechanism. The hypothesis should be testable by isotope experiments. One would have to find a way to break DNA without destroying the cell's ability to replicate DNA. There are already some experiments that are suggestive. There is the report in which cultured cells were grown in the presence of acid DNase (Baeckeland *et al.*, 1957). DNA accumulated in the cytoplasm in stainable amounts and amounts that could be detected with tritiated thymidine. In addition, Das and Alfert (1961) report that moderate doses of radiation increased DNA replication in certain kinds of cells.

Dr. Lindsley: Do you really feel comfortable about a mechanism which throws away large pieces of chromosome?

Dr. Taylor: These are not so large.

Dr. Lindsley: They are half a chromosome, are they not?

Dr. Taylor: No, I would expect the replicating unit to be a very small part of a chromosome.

Dr. Lindsley: If you do eventually come to the conclusion that you alluded to earlier in the discussion, that the chromosome could be one long DNA structure, then what is discarded becomes a very long piece, does it not?

Dr. Taylor: Then I would have to modify my hypothesis.

Dr. Lindsley: You would not be willing to throw away half a chromosome?

Dr. Taylor: Not at the moment.

Dr. Wolff: In Elkind's laboratory, when they went to as high a concentration of FUDR as 10^{-5} M, they inhibited DNA, RNA, and protein.

Dr. Taylor: It probably would here. FUDR may have many effects on the cell, but I am basing my argument on the very low concentration used and the mechanism of action which Cohen and others have reported. Biochemical studies on *Vicia* have not been made, of course. Such experiments might prove quite difficult, but I suppose that they should be done eventually.

Dr. Conger: It seems to me that these replicating units you are talking about, the ones that get damaged, are just many orders of magnitude smaller than the effects which you postulate come out of damages to these units. Take the gaps, for instance. How big are they in relation to the size of these things?

Dr. Taylor: The gaps that we see? I have no way of knowing how long they are, except cytologically, and that might be one to several microns.

Dr. Conger: Are these replicating units a micron long, in your thinking?

Dr. Taylor: Yes, the replicating units could very easily be that long. If you stop replication, you may interrupt the replication of at least a micron of DNA. That is not very much, a piece of less than two million molecular weight.

Dr. Conger: Then you must lose not only a tiny crack but the whole thing.

Dr. Taylor: The replicating unit might be 3 or 4 μ of DNA which would have a molecular weight of six to eight million.

Dr. Evans: Dr. Conger's point is that it is a micron long at metaphase.

Dr. Taylor: The gap may be seen only after a break has actually occurred, but we could not detect one or several DNA strands stretched across the gap.

Dr. Sparrow: I do not see why these two things are incompatible. I do not see why the ends cannot sometimes pull apart very little or as much as a micron at other times. Radiation-induced fragments are of all sizes, so why can't these be? It does not say that much of the strand was initially involved.

Dr. Conger: I cannot help but think that there is a volume, or length, of chromosome unaccounted for. Taylor proposes that the event commences with a very tiny crack or gap in one strand, say 1/100 (1/1000 ?) of a micron wide. It is a gap, not a deletion which he proposes. Now we know that the observed gap at metaphase is about one micron wide. This means that the gap has expanded by a very large factor, say about 100 times its initial (Taylor) length.

If Taylor is correct, then either: (1) the sister strand should have a segment opposite the gap stretched to 100 times its normal length (i.e., would have a diameter about 1/10 normal); or (2) the ends of the broken strand withdraw back from the gap, increasing it 100 times, which would give them fat ends (roughly four to five times normal diameter), which is illustrated in Fig. 12.

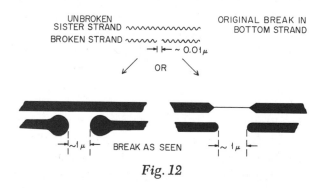

Fig. 12

Dr. Taylor: To make a comparison we would have to have exact measurements on both chromatids, ignoring the gap.

Dr. Conger: I do not think that I need a measurement for the difference between an angstrom and a micron.

Dr. Taylor: But could you have as much DNA packed in this

chromatid as in its sister? If a small region were single-stranded, it might interfere with the coiling or folding and thereby produce a weak spot.

Dr. Neary: Shall we have Dr. Moses' slides now?

Dr. Moses: I will truly be brief. I would like to present about five minutes' worth of electron-microscope evidence, which is relevant now but will probably not be so later on.[*]

There exists an intriguing structure that may reflect a basic pattern of chromosome organization, and I would like to discuss it at this point.

It is now well known that a linear complex can be seen with the electron microscope in the axis of paired meiotic chromosomes of primary spermatocytes and oocytes. This structure has been reported in a sufficiently wide variety of animal and plant species to say that it is probably of regular occurrence in meiosis. Because it appears to be a special concomitant of synaptic chromosomes, it has been termed the "synaptinemal complex" (Moses, 1958). Whether and how it plays a role in the pairing process itself has not been determined.

When the complex lies in the plane of a longitudinal section through the axis of a bivalent chromosome, it is seen to consist of at least one pair of thin, dense, parallel strands (Fig. 13). In some forms a third filament is prominent, lying between the main pair but differing from them somewhat in fine structure; its relationship to the complex is not clear. In transverse section, the two main elements of the complex are seen centered in the bivalent (Fig. 14). Not infrequently, single axial strands of the same size and organization as the main elements are observed in cross and longitudinal sections (Moses, 1960), and from this it has been supposed that these are the axial structures of a single, unpaired chromosome. Thus the paired axial complex of the bivalent would be made up principally of one element contributed by each of the two homologues. In the unpaired state, the individual axial element is linear, and extends along a considerable portion, if not the entirety, of the chromosome's length. Moreover, it is the clearest morphological

[*] The work described was supported by grants from the USPHS (RG–6753) and American Cancer Society (E–213).

manifestation of linearity so far observed that is intermediate in size between the chromosome itself and the 100-Å microfibril that is probably the structural unit of chromatin. On this basis it is reasonable to assume as a working hypothesis that it represents the structural backbone of the chromosome, or at least that it embodies the or-

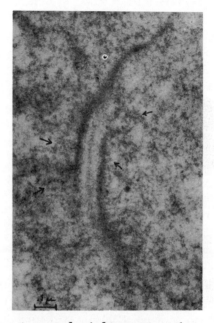

Fig. 13. Electron micrograph of thin section of rat primary spermatocyte

A short segment of the synaptinemal complex is seen in longitudinal section where the axis of a bivalent chromosome lies in the plane of the section. Microfibrils emerge radially from the axial elements (arrows) but are obscured by dense granules often associated with them. Double fixation with formaldehyde and O_8O_4, embedded in araldite unstained ($\times$ 70,000 approx.).

ganizational pattern of which chromosome linearity is a consequence (Moses, 1956). It is argued that the circumstances responsible for the axial structure, being visible, are unique to meiotic pairing (uncoiling, modifications attending synapsis, etc.) and account for the complex being not as easily seen in mitotic chromosomes. Admittedly these are assumptions, but it is nonetheless a fundamental truth that whatever the axis does represent its structure must be compatible with any generalized model of chromosome organization.

If the unit axial element actually does represent the chromosomal backbone and is in a sense the chromonema, then we should expect certain morphological consequences. It should not appear as a single structure as it does in most forms, but should reflect the two chromatids of which the primary meiotic chromosome is composed. There is evidence to indicate that this is indeed the case. In some species the lateral elements of the complex are in fact obviously double most of the time (Moses, 1956, 1960), and in others they are occasionally

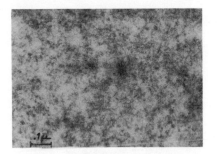

Fig. 14. Electron micrograph of thin section of rat primary spermatocyte

Same preparation as in Fig. 13, axial complex is seen in transverse section ($\times$ 70,000 approx.).

so. Figure 15 shows a cross section of the complex in a bivalent primary spermatocyte chromosome of the rat in a region where the lateral elements are double. Such views are not uncommon and probably represent later stages in the chromosome's development during which the chromatids separate, possibly concomitant with shortening and thickening of the axial elements. In earlier stages of the process chromosomal material is not as condensed about the axis and consequently the axial elements, which are themselves composed of this material, are more attenuated. Presumably, any chromatid segregation that may have occurred at this point is simply not apparent.

The elementary structural component of these chromosomes, as of chromatin in general, is a twisted fibril of the order of 100 Å in diameter. Such microfibrils are almost a universal constituent of Feulgen-positive areas, though various other structural components may also be present. Those in synaptic chromosomes are closer to 70 Å in actual measurement and are frequently associated with granular material of from one to several hundred angstroms in diameter (Moses, 1960). The microfibrils are relatively free of such associated material near the axial elements and tend to be ordered and oriented radially around the axis, emerging perpendicularly to it. In thin section, the element itself is seen to be composed, at least

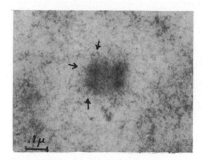

Fig. 15. Electron micrograph of thin section of rat primary spermatocyte

Transverse section of complex presumed to be in later stage by virtue of degree of condensation. Each of the two main elements is double. Arrows point to radiating microfibrils. Double fixation with permanganate and formaldehyde, embedded in methacrylate, unstained (× 77,000 approx.).

in part, of agglomerations of the microfibrils, possibly in association with additional material. The spacing between the microfibrils as they emerge from the axis often appears quite regular and of the order of only a few hundred angstroms. Fibrils often radiate in tufts and together with associated dense granules, etc. probably give the chromosome its fuzzy appearance in the light microscope.

The relationship of the microfibrils to the synaptinemal complex is more apparent in recent studies using double fixation with potassium permanganate and formaldehyde (Kaye and Moses, 1960). Although marked alterations in fine structure have occurred that are undoubtedly artifacts of this fixation, the basic organization is unchanged and is in fact more obvious. The alterations that may extract certain materials (e.g., some lipids) and leave others such as nucleo-proteins in a clotted state are in a sense analogous to those produced by such fixations as the acetic alcohol used regularly by light-microscope cytologists for studying chromosomes. This fixative is

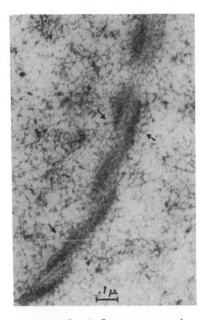

Fig. 16. Electron micrograph of thin section of rat primary sperma-tocyte

Synaptinemal complex twisted presumably as homologues are twisted to form bivalent. At this late stage the lateral elements are formed of a thick tangle of microfibrils which emerge normal to the axis (arrows). Double fixation with formaldehyde and permanganate, embedded in methacrylate, stained with uranyl acetate ($\times$ 68,000 approx.).

favored because of the accentuation and clarification of structure it provides, although the chemical and physical changes that it pro-duces are most severe. Figure 16 shows the twisting axial complex of a bivalent at a late synaptitene stage. The radiating microfibrils are apparent, as are those which are matted together to form the complex itself. In such thin sections it cannot be said whether the microfibrils are free-ending or loops.

I wish to concentrate on Fig. 17, which shows a short length of the axial element of a single homologue. From its dimensions it is assumed to represent an early stage of synaptic development. The bristlelike disposition of microfibrils along the slender axis is strikingly apparent here. The point I wish to stress is that *the axial*

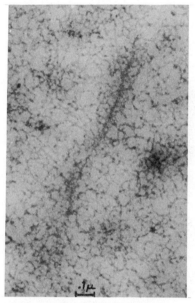

Fig. 17. Electron micrograph of thin section of rat spermatocyte

Single axial element of one chromosome (homologue) which, because of its attenuated appearance is thought to be at an early stage. Note thin axis composed of fine tangle of microfibrils which emanate like kinked bristles along it. Double fixation with permanganate and formaldehyde, embedded in methacrylate, stained with uranyl acetate (× 66,000 approx.).

strand is not more than twice the diameter of a single microfibril. Thus, if the axis is composed of more than two subunits, they must be smaller than the microfibril. It has not been demonstrated unequivocally that either the axial strand or the microfibril contains DNA, but the circumstantial evidence is strong that they do. If it is assumed that the 100-Å fibril is the basic unit structure of the chromosome and that the axial element is essentially a second-order arrangement of the fibrils, then a number of simple models may be used to account for the structures observed and to render them compatible with the requirements of Dr. Taylor's tritiated thymidine replication and segregation experiments.

One model that is perhaps somewhat more attractive for reasons that cannot be discussed in this limited time depicts a homologue (one G2 chromosome consisting of two chromatids) as two end-to-

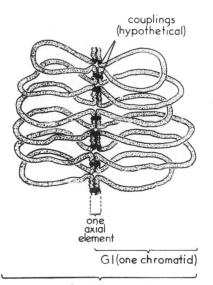

Fig. 18. Schematic representation of one way by which one (G2) chromosome can be composed of two end-to-end chains of microfibrils to produce the kind of structure seen in Fig. 17, assuming that microfibrils are loops

end chains of microfibrils with their couplings aligned in parallel along the axis (Fig. 18). The resulting axial filament with the possible accompaniment of additional material and the condensation of more microfibrils around it, would then become the axial element. Two such homologues would pair to form a bivalent, and the essentially bipartite axial complex would result. The fibril loops thus formed would not be recognized as such in thin sections and only their origins would be seen clearly emerging radially from the axis.

The resemblance to the lampbrush chromosome of urodele oocytes as depicted by Gall (1958) is obvious. The chromosome (chromatid) is thus essentially a single long microfibril in the G1 or unreplicated state, and a pair of fibrils in the G2 or replicated state as shown.

If each fibril represents one molecule (double helix) of DNA, then the model is similar in principle to that proposed by Freese (1958) and favored by Taylor (1960) to explain his results. However, there is an obvious discrepancy between the 70-Å width of the fibril and the 25- to 30-Å width predicted for a nucleohistone molecule (Wilkins, 1959), although conceivably the molecule might be highly coiled and padded out with other than histone protein. Dr. Ris believes that the "100-Å" fibril consists of two subfibrils and that each of these is a double helix of DNA together with histone (Ris, 1961). Accordingly, the G1 chromosome would then be equivalent to two long DNA molecules, and an additional segregation mechanism would have to be invoked to explain Dr. Taylor's results. Modifications of this model can, however, be devised to get around this difficulty, but there is little point in speculating further in the absence of applicable evidence. It is my present opinion that it is more difficult to fit a multistranded model (where "strand" is equivalent to 100-Å microfibril) to our observations than a single-stranded one and I therefore favor the latter. In any case the structure itself is a very real contribution of electron microscopy, and I submit it and its possible significance for your attention during this discussion of chromosome organization.

Dr. Ris: Shadow casting with heavy metal of flattened structures gives only limited information on three-dimensional structure. We have used the critical-point method of Anderson. In the study of nucleic acids, the method of Kleinschmidt and Lang combined with specific heavy-metal staining as used recently by Stoeckenius should be more reliable than metal shadowing.

Dr. Moses: I want to make it clear that there is this inconsistency, but this is what the electron microscope shows. There is no comparable evidence for the protein. There is obviously dense material in the center of the axial structure, but there is no cytochemical evidence yet to indicate whether this is DNA, DNA protein, protein, or possibly something else.

Dr. Wolff: What about your fibrils? Do you think that they are DNA only because of their size?

Dr. Moses: I think that they are DNA because they appear wherever Feulgen-positive material appears.

Undoubtedly, the fibrils must contain protein as well as DNA. Both histone and nonhistone protein have been demonstrated to be associated intimately with DNA.

Dr. Gray: If you had BUDR in large quantities in DNA, wouldn't this show up?

Dr. Moses: If the concentration of incorporated BUDR molecules were sufficiently high, there is a good chance of increasing the density sufficiently to distinguish it.

Dr. Gray: Forty percent of the thymidine would be replaced with BUDR, and bromine is a very heavy atom.

Dr. Sparrow: I would like to ask Dr. Moses how his model would account for differences in chromosomes of different sizes, for instance, the very large chromosomes like *Trillium* and many other Liliaceous plants? You don't visualize any number in the central strands or DNA do you?

Dr. Moses: The only evidence I have is that concerning the axial complexes in decapods, such as crayfish which have very many tiny chromosomes. Basically, the organization of the complexes in these different chromosomes is similar. As a matter of fact, the smaller chromosomes are more complex than the large ones.

Dr. Yerganian: I would like to add that we are in the process of isolating single-cell-derived clones which have differential spiralization, or lack the development of major coils in distinct regions of certain chromosomes. Once their propagation is standardized, I believe the absence of major coils will serve well for electron microscopy and will alleviate some of the factors that presently hinder an interpretation, as Dr. Moses has indicated.

Dr. Sparrow: I would like to present very briefly one bit of evidence in support of Dr. Moses' conclusions.

During the past winter, when Dr. Evans was in our laboratory, we irradiated several species of plant at the extremes of the range of chromosome size and, as far as we can tell, the efficiency of breakage in these very large chromosomes and in these very small chromosomes is constant. If the very large chromosomes were multistranded compared to the small ones, it would be more difficult to visualize why they had the same breakability as the very small ones. This might be indirect support for what Dr. Moses just said, i.e., that he does not visualize and difference in strand number between the big chromosomes and the little ones.

References

Freese, E. 1958. Cold Spring Harbor Symposia Quant. Biol. 23: 13.

Gall, J. G. 1958. *In* The Chemical Basis of Development, W. D. McElroy and B. Glass, eds., 103. Baltimore: The Johns Hopkins Press.

Kaye, G., and M. J. Moses. 1960. Anat. Record 136: 222.

Moses, J. M. 1956. J. Biophys. Biochem. Cytol. 2: 215.

—— 1958. J. Biophys. Biochem. Cytol. 4: 633.

—— 1960. *In* Proceedings of the Fourth International Congress on Electron Microscopy, W. Bargmann, ed., 199. Berlin: Springer-Verlag.

Ris, H. 1961. Can. J. Genet. Cytol. 3: 95.

Taylor, J. H. 1957. Am. Naturalist 91: 209.

—— 1960. *In* The Cell Physiology of Neoplasia, 547. Austin, Texas: University of Texas Press.

Taylor, J. H., W. F. Haut, and J. Tung. 1962. Proc. Natl. Acad. Sci. U.S. 48: 190.

Wilkins, M. H. F., Zubay, G., and Wilson, H. R. 1959. J. Mol. Biol. 1: 179.

Part 3

Biophysical Studies of

Chromosome Aberrations

Chromosome Aberrations and

Free Radicals

*Dr. A. D. Conger:** I think it is interesting that in a session considering biological molecules and structures which are the most conservative I should be talking about radicals, but I shall. It has been difficult for me to think of the things that I know in this area at the present time which really add a great deal to ideas or notions about chromosome breakage or rejoining or other phenomena which we are considering. But there may be some points that do touch on the subject and perhaps add a little bit.

There are problems associated with the study of free radicals, especially in irradiated biological materials, that make the observations or experiments fall into two fairly clear groups; the separation can be made in the way the radicals respond or in the kinetics that are involved. I will list these now, and although I will not deal with them strictly in order at least we can keep them separate in our minds. I think that the divisions which one would make are as follows.

First, for radiation-induced radicals and radical reactions, a fairly clear distinction can be made between things that are happening immediately and radical reactions that are happening over some appreciable lengths of time after irradiation.

Experiments of the kind we would be interested in are ones that correlate radicals and chromosomal effects occurring during irradiation. The sad thing that I have to say is that there is very little information on immediate radical reactions. Most of what is known comes from general radiation chemistry. I will come back to that.

* This work was supported in part by a research grant from the U.S. Atomic Energy Commission [Contract AT–(40–1)–2579].

Another way of subdividing is to make a distinction between reactions which occur in wet materials and those in dry ones. This is in practice similar to the first method of subdivision. Reactions which are happening in wet materials, that is, normal, wet, metabolizing cells, are those which happen immediately, and are therefore the ones that we really know the least about experimentally.

On the other hand, in dry materials—solid materials is the way I prefer to think of them—reactions are happening over a time that is appreciable enough so that some experiments can be done and some things can be found out about them.

A third sort of division that one could make is between effects which have been studied in pure compounds, about which there is quite a bit of information, and effects which have been studied in complex biological cruds, as whole tissues. There is a great deal of information in all of these things, but connecting this with chromosomes and chromosomal effects is fairly difficult, especially at the present time.

Studies pertinent to what I shall be talking about come from different areas and different interests. Some deal with free radicals in pure compounds, some in complex biological objects, such as spores and seeds (as well as biological damage in the same objects), and some come from primarily radiobiological effects rather than radical studies.

Free radicals induced by radiation in pure compounds, particularly biological molecules, have been studied extensively by Gordy and his collaborators at Duke (Gordy and Shields, 1958, 1960, and earlier papers; Kurita and Gordy, 1961*a,b*); by Zimmer (1957, 1959, and others); the Ehrenbergs (1958, 1960); Kirby-Smith and Randolph (1959); and Randolph (1961). Radicals in irradiated whole biological objects and correlations of radical and biological effects in the same object have been reported on by Powers, Webb, Ehret, and Smaller at Argonne (Ehret *et al.*, 1960; Powers *et al.*, 1960, 1961; Powers, 1961) for bacterial spores, and in seeds by the Ehrenbergs (1958, 1960); by Zimmer and the Ehrenbergs (1957) and Zimmer (1959, and earlier); and by Conger and Randolph (1959) and Conger (1961). The extensive literature on radiobiological experiments in seeds has been most recently reviewed by Konzak *et al.*

(1961), Nilan (1960), and Caldecott (1960). In these general references I have selected only the more recent, or review, papers of the persons or groups most active in the field; references to the earlier publications will be found in the ones cited here.

Let me refer briefly to the first group, namely, reactions that happen immediately at the time of irradiation; there is very little information on this. As a matter of fact, I think that if we consider immediate reactions, in wet systems, modern studies by electron spin resonance methods on the detection of free radicals have added almost nothing to the knowledge that exists with respect to radiochemistry of water or aqueous systems. On this subject, I think Dr. Hart could go through the futures of the production of free radicals in irradiated water or aqueous systems to far more profit than I could. I know of only a few attempts which have been made to detect free-radical production in irradiated aqueous solutions or in plain water. I know of a number of unsuccessful ones in which great efforts have been expended to achieve this. The successful work with which I am familiar is by Boag in L. H. Gray's laboratory. He has been able to detect radicals almost simultaneously with a burst from their pulsed electron generator (about 2-μsec pulses); radicals are detected, but what these are is not really resolved, and Dr. Gray can probably correct this or add to it.

In the wet biological systems, which is really almost the same thing as immediate reactions, the same comments apply. I am excluding experiments analyzing radical reactions in enzyme studies or radicals induced by light. This has been done successfully. Commoner (1958 and others) is perhaps the one who has done most in this, but I do not see how his work applies in any way directly, or readily, to the thing that we are most interested in at this symposium—chromosomes and things that do happen to them.

Let me now go to the other class of studies, namely, those in materials in which radicals have been looked for during postirradiation, and this means we are mostly speaking about dry or solid systems. This takes us immediately out of the areas we have considered thus far in this symposium, where we have been mostly talking about reactions in wet metabolizing cells.

What are some of the general findings of these studies on radicals produced by ionizing radiations and detected postirradiation in biological stuff? The facts are that the yield of radicals which persist to be detected following radiation is greatest when the material is dry, when oxygen is present, when low-ion-density radiation is used, and when the material is at low temperature (or at least not hot). In general, any environmental circumstance that makes the material behave as a highly viscous or solid material or generates ionizations remotely from one another maximizes radical yield.

Conditions which minimize the yield of radicals seen following irradiation, or prevent any persisting after irradiation are, in general, the opposite of these. In general, the wet condition, anoxia, and high-ion-density irradiation give a far lower yield, as does heat. The yield is less at high than at low temperatures, in general, but for most dry biological materials the heat required to eliminate radicals is greater than 100°.

The presence of radical scavengers and the presence of hydrogen donors will reduce yield.

Another fact is that in most of the materials that have been studied, particularly the mixed biological materials but also many of the pure compounds, what is seen is a complex radical signal, undoubtedly the product of a very complex population of free radicals existing in the organic material. However, there have been studies with pure compounds in which the specific radical that has been induced by the irradiation has been identified (as by Gordy and collaborators, in Gordy and Shields, 1960, Kurita and Gordy, 1961, and in earlier papers).

Now let me mention a few things that have been done with pure compounds.

Dr. Pollard: Are you going to mention quantitative numbers? I would like to know whether when you take, say, a protein molecule and inactivate this with, say, one ion pair or something similar, there is an equivalent yield in radicals which corresponds to that. In other words, are we just looking at a physical trick which is quite unrelated, or is it quite related?

Dr. Conger: At the present time, I think you have to have faith.

Dr. Gray: I would agree.

Dr. Conger: Dr. Gray can give some exact numbers for this, but I will say that the doses required to produce appreciable numbers of free radicals which can be detected in dry materials are in the same dose range used for biological experiments in the same material. For instance, in dry seeds we can detect radicals with doses as low as 5 kr, where 10 to 80 kr is the biological range.

Dr. Pollard: Biological crud in your terms?

Dr. Conger: That is why I used the term, that is what it is.

Dr. Pollard: Ordinary chemicals that you can get in a bottle. How many does it take to produce one?

Dr. Kirby-Smith: In the case of one of the amino acids, one gets almost the same number of radicals formed as the number of primary ionizations.

Dr. Conger: There have been cases of one radical produced and detected per one ion pair.

Dr. Pollard: It seems to me that it is very important to establish this. You used the word faith—forget about faith. We have obtained a lot of very good measurements on what it takes to inactivate proteins that are quite well characterized biologically. We know what they do and we know the effect of temperature and other variables. It seems to me that we can also measure the radicals produced in this same amount of radiation by assaying that the two should be equal or not even approximately equal; then we have a clear case that one is the same thing to the other. This I have not seen done.

I want to know if that is the number observed in a particular protein or a particular enzyme. I would like to know this so that I can relate it to a biological effect.

Dr. Conger: Quantitative data on the number of ionizations required to produce one radical have been reported for a number of amino acids and dipeptides. These were irradiated dry, with x or gamma rays. Values range from one to approximately 30 ionizations per radical, but most are between one and four. Randolph (1061) gives a compilation of these values. Such data for proteins is very sparse; values between about 150 and 2×10^3 ionizations per radical are reported for dry proteins (freeze-dried and native). Heat denaturation before irradiation increased yield 100 to 500 times.

Dr. Gray: You have to consider that many radicals may be lost in the time interval between irradiation and observation. You can only observe radicals that remain.

Dr. Kirby-Smith: These are the ones that everybody wants to look at and yet it is difficult to see these very quickly.

Dr. Conger: The immediate ones, yes.

Dr. Gray: That is what everyone is trying to do.

Dr. Conger: But you agree that it has not been done yet?

Dr. Gray: Yes, I do agree that it has not been done.

Dr. Hart: Low temperatures are required before you can hold the radicals from irradiated ice in place, for if you irradiate ice above nitrogen temperatures you have reaction not only of the radicals with themselves but also with the products that are formed in the radiation spurs. This phenomenon has been well established in liquid water.

Dr. Sparrow: How far do you have to go?

Dr. Hart: The OH radical appears to be held at liquid-nitrogen temperature and at liquid-helium temperatures, I believe that the hydrogen atom is held as well.

Dr. Kirby-Smith: But the protein is still held.

Dr. Hart: I think the evidence is that this does happen, but the smaller radicals require lower temperatures.

Dr. Sparrow: Is it a gradual phenomenon?

Dr. Hart: Yes, free-radical reactions occur in ice. Hydrogen and hydrogen peroxide dissolved in ice combine quite rapidly at temperatures substantially below the freezing point of water.

Dr. Caldecott: This is not consistent with the biological damage that takes place at very low temperatures. One can hold the biological damage that would take place at normal temperatures by storing at the temperature of dry ice or below. Above the temperature of dry ice, biological damage takes place.

Dr. Hart: This is true. Reactions take place in ice but the yield is lower by a factor of about three compared to liquid water where the radicals can diffuse and react.

Dr. Conger: I think that what you are mentioning is a little different, Dr. Caldecott. So far as I know, in all of the biological materials, if you store them at these low temperatures, the damage will not develop at the time they are so stabilized.

Dr. Caldecott: So one would assume that these radicals are not moving around at temperatures considerably above that of liquid nitrogen.

Dr. Conger: You are talking about radicals which are radicals of large organic molecules and embedded in a matrix of large molecules, and Dr. Hart is talking about water.

Dr. Hart: The OH radical appears to be released from its location at temperatures of about −130 to −150, and as you raise the temperature to −120 thermal luminescence occurs.

Dr. Conger: You show something identical in the water system. What you do, in substance, is change the viscosity or the rigidity of the water system by freezing it, not by changing the molecular size. But in polymers or in monomers one can change radical lifetime not only by temperature but also by the concentration, by the degree of cross-linking, or by the degree of linking; as the molecule is made more concentrated in its solvent, or bigger and bigger or more cross-linked, the lifetime of the radicals gets longer and longer, until finally they are stable even at room temperature or higher. I think that this is true of the biological materials, especially big molecules as being distinct from the small molecules or radicals.

Dr. Pollard: One theory of inactivating a biological entity is that nothing occurs until water gets in. This would be a very simple theory to accept, because it would only be the radicals which stay there that do it. I am not saying that this is a good theory. The point is that a correlation would ease the experiments.

Dr. Conger: We do know that in very dry biological materials, extremely dry in the ordinary biological sense, damage will develop without any water being added.

Dr. Atwood: You cannot test the system without adding water at some time.

Dr. Conger: That is true.

Dr. Pollard: Appleyard found that if you irradiate hemoglobin dry there is no change whatever in its absorption spectrum, but the moment water hits it, it is completely changed.

Dr. Atwood: I think that is very plausible.

Dr. Conger: There has been no evidence that this damage develops during the time it is stored dry and does not happen at the moment that it gets wet that I know of. I think that it is a little simpler to think of it as developing during the time it is stored dry, but I know of nothing to prove it.

Dr. Gray: What about Dr. Powers' story? If you store dry for a long period of time before the spore comes in contact with water, the radiation damage may be modified by various agents during this interval. The extent to which you can modify the damage with oxygen after a period of dry storage changes with time. This is an example of modification which is testable and which has gone on dry.

Dr. Conger: There are a number of other cases like this where you can impose a modification during the storage, but I still think that you could wiggle out of it and say that it has induced a change which expresses itself when it gets wet.

Dr. Gray: Yes, it reacts differently to an agent while it is still dry, but you test it wet.

Dr. Conger: Now I want to talk a little bit about some of the things which have been done with pure compounds, and I wish to stick mostly to pure compounds of the kinds that we think are important in the chromosome, namely, proteins and nucleic acids, and I will speak a little bit about amino acids. First, what has been found out about the radicals which can be detected during postirradiation in irradiated dry DNA? Let me stipulate the conditions. This is with ionizing radiation, the DNA is irradiated dry in air at normal temperature. When this is done, the postirradiation yield of radicals is extremely low. As a matter of fact, in order to produce a number of radicals which can be detected by the instruments at their highest sensitivity, you require doses on the order of millions of rads. Contrariwise, proteins so treated show a quite high yield of radicals during postirradiation, so that in this respect there is a very striking difference between the two compounds DNA and protein.

Dr. Lindsley: What happens to DNA under those conditions? What would be the effect of such a treatment on transforming activity, for instance?

Dr. Pollard: It would be completely destroyed.

Dr. Gray: By those doses.

Dr. Steffensen: One question: Could the signal that you get from DNA be ascribable to the protein contamination?

Dr. Conger: Yes, it could. In the first studies of irradiated DNA, postirradiation free-radical signals were reported. It appears now that most of the signal which was detected was due to the protein contamination associated with the DNA, and I believe that this is fairly firm now.

Dr. Kirby-Smith: This might be the time to put in one more comment about DNA. Recently, you know, there were reports of very broad resonances in purportedly pure DNA which were hundreds of gauss wide. These have now been explained as being due to paramagnetic impurities, so we don't have to worry about them.

Dr. Gray: There is the Blumenthal story, too, reporting very broad resonances in DNA.

Dr. Wolff: Yet you did get signals when you used nucleic acids.

Dr. Conger: Yes, indeed. In some experiments we used a very highly purified DNA sample kindly given me by Dr. E. Volkin. When we compared results from this very pure DNA with results from the usual DNA preparation, we could attribute quantitatively most of the radical signal in the ordinary DNA to the proportion of protein in the material, and I think that this is fairly good information now.

Results from high-ion-density radiation conform to the generalization I gave earlier. You get a lower yield both in DNA and in proteins than with x rays.

Let me mention what happens with uv irradiation of these two compounds. You get a high yield in DNA and low yield in the proteins. It is exactly opposite from ionizing radiations. Dr. Kirby-Smith who did this uv work has made a hypothesis or suggestion from this that with ionizing radiation what is broken in the chromosome is the protein, and with uv irradiation what is damaged in the chromosomes is the DNA (Kirby-Smith and Randolph, 1959, and paper in this symposium).

Dr. Gray: Is this on the basis of equal ergs per gram of absorbed uv energy in DNA and protein?

Dr. Kirby-Smith: Yes, for equal amounts of absorbed uv energy, more radicals are produced in DNA than in proteins.

Dr. Conger: If we accept this idea—and it does not seem any more ridiculous than some I have had—it would mean that the continuity of the chromosome is alternating DNA and protein, or at least that it is born by them. I do not want to argue about this. As a matter of fact, I don't think Dr. Kirby-Smith would either.

Dr. Atwood: Genetic damage is completely explicable without thinking about the protein.

Dr. Conger: I was applying it to the chromosome to be broken.

Dr. Wolff: But there could also be an energy transfer from the nucleic acid which absorbs the energy to the protein. The experiments that Chu mentioned having performed showed that when he irradiated with the wavelength that damaged nucleic acids he didn't get shattering. But if he put in a protein-synthesis inhibitor like chloramphenicol he got shattering. Of course, it might be that he affected other enzymes rather than the protein of the chromosomes. But he has a system in which he could sort this out.

Dr. Auerbach: Can you break plant chromosomes with uv? I suspect you can. Then, if your theory is right, double treatments with x ray and uv should not be synergistic in producing rearrangements, but rather additive because breaks in protein would rejoin with breaks in protein and breaks in DNA with other breaks in DNA. I think that this could be used to test your theory.

Dr. Kirby-Smith: We will speak of these things later on. I am going to speak on this very subject.

Dr. Conger: Although we are roommates at this meeting, we do not talk to each other, at least on this subject.

The radiation of pure compounds, especially amino acids, peptides, and proteins, has been studied very extensively by Gordy and his co-workers. I did want to make a special point of this. They showed that the radical signal found after irradiation of protein is not the summation of the signals that would be produced by the amino acids of which it is made. Most of the radicals induced in proteins became concentrated at particular sites. In sulphur-bearing proteins, for example, they became concentrated in a particular amino acid, cysteine, on the sulphur. Here it was quite clear that energy absorbed at random along the protein molecule was being concentrated in specific sites, namely, at the sulphur bonds of the cysteine amino acid in the protein.

Radicals will also concentrate themselves in a double bond. This has been found in a number of other pure compounds. I believe that there is not much question any more but that the energy absorbed randomly along the molecule or along a long chain can be transferred to particular sites and will reside there; and this is where the radical derived from these initial events will come to reside.

Now let me move to some of the things which are known about free-radical induction in biological cruds, and some of the relationships of this information to biological effects in the same things. Biological damages which develop following irradiation can be compared with radicals which are detected after irradiation and which decay at greater or lesser rates.

This means that most of the information is going to come from the two biological materials which have been used extensively for this kind of work, the dry spores of *Bacillus megatherium,* which have been used by Dr. Powers and his people at Argonne National Laboratory to such great profit, and also barley seeds, which are a radiobiological instrument that has been used for a long time and whose long-time exponent we have here, Dr. Caldecott.

The biological information from the bacterial spores is derived solely from the analysis of spore inactivation. For the other material, barley seeds, about 90 percent of the information is derived from measurements of growth that seedlings will make when they are wet and grown in a Petri dish after the irradiation. So, in spore experiments we measure killing, and in seed experiments we measure damage to seedling growth.

That there is a correlation between genetic damage and cell inactivation, and between damage to seedling growth and the chromosomes, we all know. I do not wish to amplify this here. But I do wish to say that as a result of the work that we and other people have been doing, and the things that we have been finding out about biological aftereffect and the factors that can modify it, I have come to believe that the connection between, say, damage to seedling growth and damage to chromosomes becomes less and less obvious the more we find out.

The chromosomal work which has been done in relation to biological effect and free radicals in the seeds is quite small, and it mostly comes from analyses of interchanges detected at the first metaphase of meiosis in the plants grown from the irradiated seeds. This, you see, makes the chromosomal detection quite remote from the event that induced it.

Dr. Caldecott: There has been a lot done which parallels the meiotic work precisely.

Dr. Conger: There is a small amount of information which is a little closer to home, i.e., measurement of aberrations in the root or shoot tip grown from irradiated seeds; the cells we are looking at are in their first division following irradiation.

Dr. Caldecott: It has been done mostly in shoots, rather than in roots.

Dr. Conger: We do have some information from root chromosomal analysis which we can correlate with the biological aftereffect. The results are very similar to the damage to seedling height. Dryness, presence of oxygen, low ion density, and normal room temperature all maximize postradiation chromosomal damage; wetness, high ion density, anoxia, and low temperatures all minimize or prevent it.

The presence of radical scavengers, such as nitric oxide administered during postirradiation, wipes out the radicals and also prevents the development of biological damage which would otherwise develop during postirradiation, as was first shown by Sparrmann and the Ehrenbergs (1959) and also has been shown for spores (Ehret *et al.*, 1960; Powers *et al.*, 1960) and barley seeds (Conger, 1961).

Hydrogen donors, as L. Powers first showed in his spores with H_2S, will do the same thing, and we have shown that H_2S will also do it in seeds (Powers and Kaleta, 1960; Conger, 1961).

In general, from the observations which have been made on barley seeds where we analyze both biological damage and free radicals, it seems as though the amount of biological damage which will develop during postirradiation is a function of the number of radicals that survive to the end of the irradiation, and then the number of these which decay. There seem to be two ways, in a biological sense, in which radicals can disappear—they cause more damage or they don't—and some of the factors which cause biologically harmless disappearance of radicals are the addition of water, nitric oxide, or hydrogen sulphide. These make good sense. I believe that the addition of water, by allowing recombination, prevents further radical-molecule reactions which could involve a critical molecule; the nitric oxide, being itself a free radical, combines with the organic radicals preventing further reactions; and the H_2S, by donating a hydrogen, restores the organic radical to its original condition.

The cases in which radical decay causes the production of more damage are decay in the dry state and decay with oxygen present. If the material is stored in the anoxic stage and you interpose treatments which can eliminate the radicals in the absence of oxygen, such as NO or H_2S, then any damage which might have developed by the addition of oxygen is prevented.

Dr. Wolff: Does the system have to be wet for this oxygen damage to occur?

Dr. Conger: No, the oxygen damage occurs in the dry state.

Dr. Wolff: Didn't you find that your radicals decayed when they were kept dry in powdered seeds?

Dr. Conger: Yes, they do decay. I postulate that no damage can develop if the radicals do not decay and in general—

Dr. Gray: This implies that there is an inverse correlation with the radicals that persist?

Dr. Conger: Yes, no damage develops unless the radicals decay. If you freeze the seeds to liquid-nitrogen temperature, then the radicals do not decay, and no damage develops, either. It depends on irradiation under a circumstance so that radicals persist during postirradiation, and then on circumstances which permit them to decay.

There are radicals which exist during postirradiation that do not cause the development of any more postirradiation damage.

Dr. Sparrow: They do if you irradiate at low temperatures, and it simply stops their disappearance.

Dr. Conger: Low temperature does not prevent their formation, just their disappearance; it doesn't in water either.

Dr. Caldecott: They appear in nitrogen and, if you maintain the seed in nitrogen at 18°C–30°C for 12 to 24 hours, it is no longer possible to get any additional effect by putting them in oxygen, so that the latent site is dissipated, and in nitrogen.

Dr. Conger: We have some experiments that do not agree with this; if we store anoxically and then later admit oxygen, some more damage does develop.

Dr. Caldecott: This is a temperature-dependent phenomenon. If you keep them at 27° or 85°, you get completely different results. If you keep them at 85°, you eliminate the effect of the oxygen medium certainly within 15 minutes. So there is a great temperature variation.

Dr. Conger: Now to some specific subjects which have occurred to me, for which the free-radical information may throw some light, or have some bearing, on chromosome-breakage problems.

In our radical studies in dry objects, we found fewer radicals immediately during postirradiation anoxically (in N_2) than with O_2 (air) present. Either fewer radicals are being made anoxically, or they decay more rapidly. Since we found that postirradiation radical decay is more rapid in air than anoxically, probably fewer radicals are being made for the same dose under anoxic than under oxygenated conditions, and radiation chemistry studies agree with this conclusion. In the past, we did some experiments on the influence of oxygen on radiosensitivity, the oxygen effect, or perhaps I should say the "immediate" (during irradiation) oxygen effect to distinguish it from the postirradiation effect of oxygen which I have been talking about this morning.

The experiments were on chromosomal aberration production in *Tradescantia* by high-intensity x rays under anoxic and oxygenated (air) conditions (Conger, unpublished). We found fewer aberrations for the same dose in N_2, as usual, but in particular found that the yield of chromosome exchanges was almost perfectly dose-squared (i.e., almost perfectly two-hit) with N_2, but less than dose-squared, about $dose^{1.6}$, with air (therefore, an appreciable fraction of the air exchanges are one-hit, i.e., one-particle exchanges). Similarly, for isochromatid aberrations, the ratio of isochromatid to chromatid deletions was greater in air than in N_2, and the isochromatid yield versus dose was more curved (i.e., more were two-hit) in

N_2 than in air. The air-nitrogen differences for the three observations were compatible. We concluded from these experiments that although the ion density was identical in air and in N_2 (the same x rays were used for both), the radical density—and the radicals are what cause the aberrations—is greater in air than in N_2, and this is what explains the results.

Regarding Dr. Revell's delayed exchange-induction hypothesis which we have discussed at length, I can see no support for, or against, it from the free-radical information. He is dealing with wet cells, of course, and in these radicals are extremely short-lived, which may be evidence against his hypothesis, though I personally feel that this is probably not pertinent at all. It is a shame that we have at present almost no information on "immediate" radicals.

Dr. Wolff (1956) and Dr. Sax have shown in the past that there are "fast" and "slow" rejoining chromosome breaks. The evidence came from x-rayed *Tradescantia*, and showed that for the same dose given over progressively longer times (lower intensity) the yield of exchange aberrations declined with dose time, very rapidly at first and then more slowly. Similarly, a number of radical studies have shown "fast" and "slow" decaying radicals induced by irradiation. For example, Lawton, Balwit, and Powell (1960) found that irradiated polyethylene had in it a number of identifiably different radical species which differed not only in their radical signal fine-structure and relative numbers, but particularly in their rate of decay. Some decayed much more rapidly than others; furthermore, some decayed so rapidly at room temperature that none survived to be detected during postirradiation (but did survive when irradiated at liquid-nitrogen temperature). This phenomenon, of a number of different radicals induced by radiation of materials, even of pure compounds, having very different reaction rates, is well documented by now. It may be, for the fast- and slow-exchange aberrations I have just mentioned, that the interpretation of fast and slow induction, rather than *rejoining*, would be acceptable.

One last thing: It has been shown that in some dry objects, pollen and seeds, chromosomal aberrations are induced by pure oxygen, at oxygen concentrations greater than that of air, in the absence of any radiation whatsoever (Conger and Fairchild, 1952). At the time the work was done it was suggested that the aberrations were produced by free radicals, just as with radiation, except that with oxygen the radicals were generated by enzymatic oxidation reactions, rather than by ionizations. Actually, flavoprotein respiration in the nucleus was suspected as being the agent. Since then, free-radical production by enzymatic respiration has been demonstrated, as well as generation of radicals in dry cells by high oxygen concentrations.

Dr. Giles: I would like to call on Dr. Hart to make some remarks about radiation in water in connection with Dr. Conger's earlier discussion.

Dr. Hart: I thought that perhaps at this point it might be worthwhile to bring to your attention a few facts about the radiation chemistry of water. Radiation chemists have studied water for some time, and you may be able to draw certain parallels between what happens in the radiolysis in a simple molecule like water and what happens in your chromosomes.

Our present idea is that in the case of light-particle radiations, such as x rays and gamma rays, there are spurs in which an appreciable amount of energy is deposited, and in the case of gamma rays these are several thousand angstrom units apart.

What you are concerned with, and what the radiation chemists have been concerned with, is what happens within these spurs. Within a spur—and we believe now that we know the approximate size of these spurs or "hot spots"—is the place where ionization occurs. The reaction is

$$H_2O = H_2O^+ + e^-.$$

Then, within a sphere of about 30-Å diameter, there are about five water molecules dissociated. When I say dissociated, I mean water molecules that have either been dissociated by ionization or by excitation. So, within this volume, we have about five dissociated water molecules yielding H and OH free radicals. These species have unpaired electrons and they are very reactive.

In water these free radicals react to give us hydrogen and hydrogen peroxide, and the cross reaction forms water:

$$H + H = H_2$$
$$OH + OH = H_2O_2$$
$$H + OH = H_2O.$$

Radiation chemists have spent a great deal of time in elaborating the picture that you see here in connection with the effects on materials that are added to the water. Only the H atoms and the hydroxyl radicals escaping the above reactions are effective in promoting chemical changes. Clearly, the H atoms forming hydrogen molecules and the hydroxyl radicals forming hydrogen peroxide, and the H and OH radicals combining to form water, are ineffective (except for the possible subsequent reaction of hydrogen peroxide) in promoting chemical changes. Yields in radiation chemistry are expressed in terms of molecules or radicals liberated per 100 ev of absorbed energy expressed in this way: hydrogen atoms escaping the spur have a yield $g(H)$ of three and the hydroxyl radical yield $g(OH)$ is about the same. So, for every 100 ev of energy, we have approximately three hydrogen atoms and three hydroxyl radicals that diffuse from the spur and react with other materials.

What can these species do in the water? The hydrogen atom is a very powerful reducing agent, and the hydroxyl radical is a very powerful oxidizing species. Consequently, they react with all known organic substances present in the water, and, of course, they react with oxidizable and reducible inorganic ions. For example, a simple electron-transfer reaction takes place between the hydroxyl radical and the chloride ion as follows:

$$Cl^- + OH = Cl + OH^-.$$

And, in the case of a simple molecule, like dissolved deuterium, either the OH radical or the hydrogen atom will react:

$$OH + D_2 = HOD + D$$
$$H + D_2 = HD + D.$$

Since the HH bond is a strong one, it is clear that the hydrogen atom will break weaker bonds, such as CH, SH, SS, etc. And, in the case of many molecules, both of these free radicals are reactive. In general, however, the reactive species in irradiated water may induce either reducing or oxidizing reactions.

Complex biological systems have not been studied as extensively by radiation chemists as have many of the simple inorganic and organic systems. However, studies of these simple systems show that the radicals react with amine groups, carboxy groups, alcohol groups,

etc., and in each case the primary product of such a reaction is a
free radical, whether the reaction occurs through a hydrogen atom
or through the hydroxyl group. In the case of the reaction

$$OH + RH = R\cdot + H_2O,$$

where RH is a hydrogen-containing organic molecule, water is usually a reaction product. The resulting free radical $R\cdot$ has varying
degrees of reactivity. In general, it has lower reactivity than the
hydroxyl group, and its fate may be reaction with another inert
organic radical to form a dimer

$$R\cdot + R^1 = R{-}R^1,$$

or it may react with dissolved oxygen to form a peroxy radical. The
trend in all these reactions is to produce free radicals of lower and
lower reactivity.

Now what does this mean in your biological system? You reduce
the reactivity of the radical and you increase its life, so the more
complex these radicals are, the longer they live. In the special case
of oxygen, peroxy radicals result, leading to complex products that
are effective in promoting oxidative chemical changes over very long
periods of time. And so the reactive OH radicals, initially produced
in the water, eventually lead to rather inert radicals or compounds
capable of promoting chemical changes.

It now appears that the phenomena in irradiated water cannot be
satisfactorily explained by the simple free-radical reaction. Within
the past few years there has been an impressive group of studies
requiring a second reducing species to account for the reactions. It
is believed that the secondary electron (the normal source of the
hydrogen atom) may react with solute molecules before the hydrogen atom is produced. Radiation chemists have found that this species, which may be a hydrated electron, or one just prior to hydration,
has a rate constant of reaction with molecules such as oxygen and
hydrogen peroxide which is very different from that of the hydrogen
atom. This reducing species is particularly effective in neutral solutions, possibly because it is converted to a hydrogen atom in acid
solutions by the reaction

$$e_{aq}^- + H^+ = H.$$

Hydrogen atom reactions are therefore favored in strong acids, and the solvated electron reactions are favored in neutral or basic solutions. In many cases the reactions of these two species are indistinguishable from one another. For example, in the case of hydrogen peroxide, the reactions are

$$H + H_2O_2 = H_2O + OH$$

$$e_{aq}^- + H_2O_2 = OH^- + OH,$$

but since the hydrated electron reactions are of the order of 100 to 1000 times faster than hydrogen atom reactions, significant differences in product yields are found in simple chemical systems. Doubtless, differences will appear in complex organic systems as well. It may be of help in an interpretation of biological phenomena to think of relatively faster reactions of organic groups present with these hydrated electrons, rather than the much slower reactions of hydrogen atoms with these groups. I would imagine that since the cell is in an essentially neutral environment the hydrated electron reactions are the expected ones. However, much still needs to be learned about the radiation chemistry of aqueous solutions in the neutral and alkaline ranges before extensive speculation on reactions of this type is justified.

Dr. Wolff: Isn't the OH reactive, too?

Dr. Conger: And the upper reaction on your diagram is at least 50 times as fast?

Dr. Hart: That is the minimum. This is also true in the case of oxygen. The theory is as discussed above, i.e., this hydrated electron reacts with a hydrogen ion to form the hydrogen atom. So, in strong acid solutions, we find that the species generated during irradiation are less reactive with oxygen than the species generated in neutral solution. As I pointed out, the hydrated electron is also more reactive with hydrogen peroxide than is the hydrogen atom.

This hydrated electron can also react with other molecules in the same way that it does with hydrogen peroxide and oxygen. For example, with formic acid, there is a possibility that the following reactions occur:

$$e_{aq}^- + HCOOH = HCO + OH^-$$

$$H + HCOOH = H_2 + COOH.$$

In water we have these very reactive zones that have initial diameters of the order of 30 Å, and there is reason to think that similar zones form in biological material. After all, the electron densities in these media are quite similar.

These reactive zones are, in the case of electron radiation, about 5000 Å apart. Diffusion of the reactive species out from this zone should not be very different in biological systems and in water. A knowledge of the reactions occurring in water should help in the interpretation of the biological reactions.

Dr. Wolff: Do reactions of water interacting with organic compounds lead to unreactive organic radicals?

Dr. Hart: No, they could be reactive, and since they have unpaired electrons they will all react.

Dr. Wolff: How frequently would you suspect this to occur in comparison, say, to the radicals that we know, from work done on dry systems, can be induced directly in organic compounds? Would this be much more important than, say, radicals reacting with radiation-induced radicals in proteins?

Dr. Hart: You might end up with the same radical since transfer of radicals from one molecule to another is quite an important process, particularly in polymerization. The reaction is

$$R \cdot + R'SH \rightarrow RH + R'S \cdot.$$

I think there are certain mercaptans that have done this. In polymerization, dodecylmercaptan is a very important transfer chemical. It functions by shortening the polymer chain.

Dr. Conger: We have exactly the same, and we already know the RSH does it.

Dr. Hart: The analogy is the same in radiation chemistry. Depending on the system, stable radicals develop from the reactive ones. I think that this is one of the important concepts that can be carried over to biological systems.

Dr. Conger: I want to ask a specific question: How fast is the production of H_2O_2 in water with low-ion-density radiation and oxygen present? It is not limiting in these things you are talking about, is it?

Dr. Hart: Hydrogen peroxide?

Dr. Conger: Yes, production by irradiation with low-ion-density radiation, x, or gamma rays, with oxygen present. The peroxide is going to exist instantaneously and react in these two reactions you have below, one of which is going to be 50 times more rapid than the other.

Dr. Hart: That is right. If you plot the hydrogen peroxide as a function of dose in neutral solution, the curves are always concave downwards. The reason for this is that the hydrogen peroxide initially formed reacts with the electron or the hydrogen atom that is produced in the water.

Dr. Atwood: What kind of radical would react with water?

Dr. Hart: Neither the H nor the OH radicals react with water. We have worked with the hydrogen atom and the deuterium atom in aqueous solutions, and the deuterium atom will not exchange with the H atoms of water at room temperature. Dr. R. F. Firestone found a vapor-phase thermal exchange to give a hydrogen atom plus HDO. This reaction takes place beginning at about 150°C, but at room temperature a deuterium atom is unreactive in water.

As far as I know there is no positive proof that OH will react with water. These are the two most reactive species in water, and it is to be expected that organic radicals generated from H and OH radicals will not react with water either.

Dr. Conger: May I ask another question? It is really the one Dr. Atwood asked, and I want to confirm it.

We have the idea that the radicals which are present in the organic biological materials are of the sort you are talking about here. We know they disappear when water is added; we know this experimentally for radicals and we know also that with wetting no further biological damage results. Radiation chemists have told me that the water is not making the radicals disappear by reaction with the water, so my conclusion has been that the organic radicals of the kinds you showed (and we have in our dry seeds) disappear by being allowed to move now that they are hydrated, and they meet each other and recombine. Do you agree that this is right?

Dr. Hart: You are perfectly right. The viscosity of the medium is lowered by the water; now the radicals can diffuse and combine.

Dr. Conger: I am simply delighted.

Dr. Hart: You were talking the other day about radical formation in water. There has been some recent work by Dorfman at Argonne who has irradiated dissolved benzene in water with 0.4- to 5-μsec electron beams. The primary reaction of the hydroxyl radical with benzene is the transient hydroxycyclohexadienyl radical OHC_6H_6.

Dr. Conger: Of very short life?

Dr. Hart: This radical has a lifetime that depends upon its concentration. The absorption spectrum of the hydroxycyclohexadienyl radical has been photographed and its disappearance studied as a function of time. This reaction occurs over the course of microseconds. Unstable dimers are the resulting products giving diphenyl by slow postirradiation reactions.

Dr. Atwood: There is a concentration dependence involved, and if you extrapolate to zero concentration you get the maximal lifetime of the radical. Is that the case?

Dr. Hart: That is the case. However, at the relatively high concentration of radicals within the spur, this reaction is all over in 10^{-8} seconds. At the relatively low concentrations of radicals emerging from the spur, the lifetime is in the range of 10^{-6} to 10^{-3} seconds if the dose rate is low enough. At the dose rates available with pulsed electron beams, free-radical concentrations generated are about 10^{-5} to 10^{-3} M. At these concentrations an entirely new technique is made available for studying the interaction of the H and OH radicals.

Dr. Conger: This is 10^{-4} per what?

Dr. Hart: These are moles per liter of free radicals present in the entire irradiated volume. Under cobalt-60 irradiation the steady-state concentration of free radicals is as low as 10^{-9} M.

Dr. Pollard: We have been measuring the viscosity of bacterial cell juice, and it runs about 10,000 times that of water. Would you conclude that this means many more stable radicals?

Dr. Hart: Yes.

Dr. Giles: I think we should, unfortunately, conclude this discussion by Dr. Hart since we do have a number of other things to cover.

I will now call on Dr. Caldecott to discuss some of the work mentioned earlier by Dr. Conger.

Dr. Caldecott: Before I present the data I need to know the manner in which the seedling-height data and the chromosome-aberration data were obtained by Dr. Conger. Can you give me a rundown on this? Can you tell me how you sampled the population?

Dr. Conger: I don't think I did tell that because I did not get to talk about the chromosomal-aberration analysis that we did make, but I will tell one as an example. It is the phenomenon that Dr. Caldecott found, and that we found too. For seeds which received a given dose and were then stored dry with oxygen present, we noticed a bimodal distribution in seedling height when they were allowed to grow. Most of the seeds were very appreciably damaged, so they grew only about 1 cm high. But a small fraction of the population grew as much as if they had received no radiation at all, about 14 cm high. We then performed a similar experiment, but planted the seeds out on a grid in Petri dishes which allowed us to keep track of every seed. We snipped a root off all these seeds 24 hours after germination for chromosomal preparations, and then allowed them to grow for seedling-height measurements.

The seeds that grew tall had very few chromosomal aberrations in their root tips at the first division, but seeds which grew only a little bit, the heavily damaged ones, had a high chromosome-aberration frequency.

Dr. Caldecott: What sort of populations did you work with and how did you sample the populations? You recognize that in a control population you get some that run the spectrum in seedling height.

Dr. Conger: The distribution of the control population is normal, not at all like the bimodal irradiated one.

Dr. Caldecott: How many seeds and how many cells were analyzed per seed?

Dr. Conger: In this experiment we had 100 irradiated seeds, more in the controls. We got the distribution-in-height for all the seeds. We kept track of every individual seed.

Dr. Caldecott: I want to know the conclusion drawn from these studies. Is it that there is no relationship between seedling height and chromosomal damage?

Dr. Conger: No, here the conclusion is that there is a relationship.

Dr. Wolff: This afternoon you said there wasn't.

Dr. Conger: No, I didn't, I said that the connection gets difficult.

Dr. Caldecott: There are a couple of points that need to be brought out here. A really important factor when one subjects a dry seed to hydration after it has been irradiated is whether or not there is oxygen present in the water. If the water is anaerobic, a different effect is obtained than if it is aerobic. So, in order to obtain consistent reproducible results, one must hydrate under specific conditions. We have not discussed this point here, and yet it is basic.

Dr. Conger: I didn't mention it, but we usually hydrate anoxically.

Dr. Caldecott: I would like to show you the point that Dr. Conger

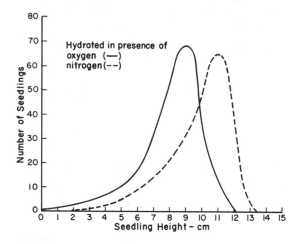

Fig. 1. *Distribution of seedling heights at seven days, from seeds given 5000 r of x rays and then immediately hydrated in the presence of either oxygen or nitrogen*

has been talking about with reference to distributions of seedling heights in irradiated populations. Figure 1 shows the distribution of heights from a population of seeds that were very dry, 4 percent water in the embryo or below, at the time they were irradiated. The seeds were hydrated, immediately after x irradiation, in the presence of either nitrogen or oxygen. Note the difference between those hydrated in oxygen and those in nitrogen. It is an absolutely reproducible result. It never fails, it occurs at all doses of irradiation from the smallest with which one can measure a biological effect to those which are lethal to the population.

This (Fig. 2) is the type of bimodality in seedling-height distribution that we have been noticing for a number of years and which occurs when a population of seeds, instead of being germinated immediately after irradiation, is stored; in this instance, for eight days. If storage is for as little as four hours, the effect is pronounced.

The type of distribution is not altered by postirradiation storage in oxygen, nitrogen, or helium, although the extent of the injury that takes place is greater in the oxygen atmosphere.

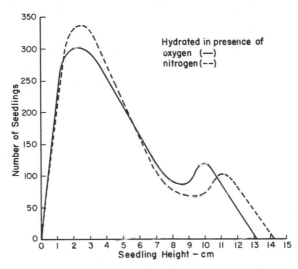

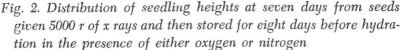

Fig. 2. Distribution of seedling heights at seven days from seeds given 5000 r of x rays and then stored for eight days before hydration in the presence of either oxygen or nitrogen

One point that is important to drive home is the relationship between seedling height and genetic damage. These data (Figs. 3 and 4) demonstrate that increased injury, as it is manifest in reduction in seedling height, is closely correlated with genetic damage both in terms of mutations and chromosomal aberrations.

Dr. Lindsley: Related to seedling height?

Dr. Caldecott: The shorter the seedling, the greater the aberration frequency. I want to drive this point home. I think it is very basic. It is one we have gone round and round on for quite a long time. If one handles barley seeds properly, both root and shoot data can be obtained for length, and aberrations can be determined at the first cycle of divisions after irradiation. We have done this and found a good correlation between root and shoot length. The frequencies of anaphase bridges and fragments were also parallel. If the frequency was high in the shoot it was also high in the terminal root.

Dr. Wolff: Why is it higher where your curves switch over? Your nitrogen curve there is higher yet, and your interchanges are lower in that particular case (Fig. 3).

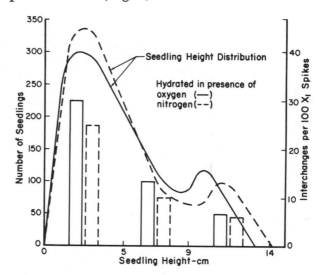

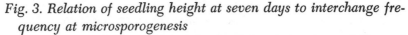

Fig. 3. Relation of seedling height at seven days to interchange frequency at microsporogenesis

Plants grown from dormant barley seeds subjected to 5000 r of x rays and stored for eight days before hydration in the presence of either oxygen or nitrogen.

Dr. Caldecott: This is one of the problems that one encounters. When one has a normal distribution of heights, one has a number of individuals in the population that would have been short, without being subjected to irradiation. If they incur very little radiation damage, they will still fall in the medium classes that are represented on the graph. As a result, there is always a point where, without very large populations, the error will be large. This explains the inconsistency on this point and emphasizes the need for using very large populations in this type of study.

There are two other points I want to make, because there is one kind of damage that can be made to persist for days after one irradiates very dry seeds, that is, the sensitivity of the seeds to the presence of oxygen in the water in which they are steeped. The method for maintaining this type of effect, which results from eliminating the storage phenomenon, is to simply preheat the seeds for 15 minutes or more at a temperature of 75° C; that is, subject them to heat be-

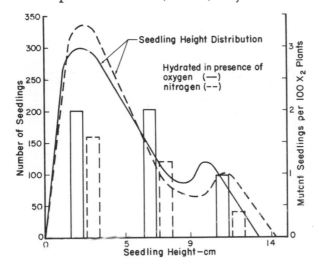

Fig. 4. Relation of X_1 seedling height at seven days to X_2 seedling mutation frequency

X_1 plants grown from dormant barley seeds subjected to 5000 r of x rays and stored for eight days before hydration in the presence of either oxygen or nitrogen.

fore x-raying them. When this is done the seeds incur some protection from the irradiation, the storage phenomenon is eliminated; bimodality is eliminated, with the result that there is a normal distribution of heights about the mean (Figs. 5, 6).

If there are radicals in the system that are sitting around waiting to decay, they will not do so if the system has had a high-temperature treatment before it has been subjected to x irradiation. It is unlikely that a radical could be maintained indefinitely in these seeds when they are maintained at room temperature. We believe that the postirradiation effect is due to some sort of a sensitive site, a lesion, if you will, that only becomes manifest in the form of injury when hydration takes place in the presence of oxygen or when oxygen is present in the seed. Possibly the heat treatment drives oxygen from the seed, even in an oxygen atmosphere, it does not rediffuse to sensitive sites in the seed for considerable periods of time.

Dr. Wolff: Does this temperature shock get rid of the chromosomal damage too?

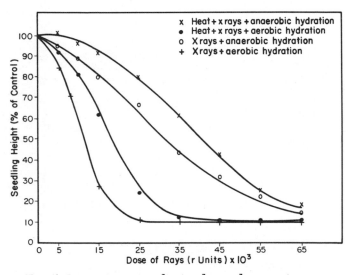

Fig. 5. Protection x irradiation by preheat treatment

Dr. Caldecott: Yes, in every case we have looked at.

Dr. Giles: Are there any specific questions for Dr. Caldecott?

Dr. Conger: If I gave the impression that there is no difference between seedling height and chromosomal damage, I am sorry; I did not intend to. What I did say was that the connection between the two gets more and more tenuous, to me at least, as we find out more and more things about them, including particular facts which disagree. I don't know the explanation for the disagreements yet, but, in general, my feeling, as well as that of other people, is that they are related.

Dr. Caldecott: What facts disagree? That is what I would like to know.

Dr. Conger: A fair number of them disagree. For instance, the addition of pure oxygen causes no increase in postirradiation damage or decay of radicals over that in air, but it does increase aberrations. I think that this may be due to induction of aberrations by oxygen, but there is a synergism that we have not yet analyzed. This is just one disagreement.

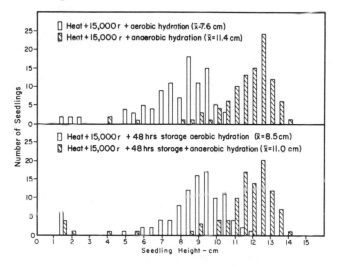

Fig. 6. Elimination of sensitivity to storage but not to oxygen resulting from a preirradiation temperature treatment at 75°C

I see that Dr. Caldecott and I disagree on particulars, but in general we are not in disagreement. I must say that when Dr. Caldecott tells us that he has found this curious bimodal distribution of seedling height for eight years or so, I am distressed to learn it, because we had to find it out the hard way, by experiment. He has never treated his data on mean seedling height in a way which led me to suspect that it was not derived from normal distributions.

Dr. Caldecott: I too am distressed, Dr. Conger, but for the opposite reason. If you had followed the Swedish work and my work you would recognize why. The basis for our explanation of the difference in ion density, as being the best explanation of the differences between thermal and fast neutrons on the one hand and x rays on the other hand, was frequency distribution of seedling heights (Caldecott, Folik, and Morris, 1952). If this wasn't clear from the data presented, it should have been from the pictorial display in the two other papers (Caldecott, 1954, 1955).

It should be borne in mind that if seeds with an embryo water content below about 8 percent are merely placed on moist blotters, after irradiation, which was the procedure until about 1955, they undergo storage while hydration is taking place and this causes a skewed distribution of heights. Drs. Fluke and Forro and I discussed this many times in the early 1950s and the reason we returned to looking at preirradiation and postirradiation effects along the lines done in the 1940s (see the review in Caldecott, 1952) was to try and resolve the problem.

Dr. Conger: I guess a number of people stumbled onto this phenomenon by accident.

I would like to say something that is pertinent to the point Dr. Caldecott made about the considerable importance of the presence of oxygen during the time of hydration. This means the time at which you throw the little seeds in water to wet them up so that they will start growing. This is important for the aftereffect. I would like to give a few relative numbers because I think the oxygen-at-hydration phenomenon, in relation to other postirradiation modifiers, is considerably less important.

For example, by storage after irradiation, we can enhance damage by as much as 10 to 20 times, but conservatively by five times. But by hydrating with oxygen present (rather than absent), damage is increased only 20 to 50 percent, say up to a factor of two. Would you agree, Dr. Caldecott?

Dr. Caldecott: First, let me emphasize that I use the word "hydration" because it is descriptive. The presence of oxygen in the water increases radiosensitivity by a factor of from two to five when one looks at aberration frequency and mutation frequency. It depends on the water content of the seed at the time of irradiation. Bear in mind, however, that seedling height dose curves are sigmoidal; hence the difference, using this criteria, is relative, and its magnitude depends on the point at which one chooses to make and estimate (Fig. 5).

Dr. Gray: Can you give the ratio horizontally?

Dr. Caldecott: Yes, if you take the total area under the curves, this is one way of doing it, but you have to remember that you are looking at a sigmoidal relationship, not a linear relationship, so that this varies with dose.

Dr. Conger: I conclude that what I was going to say is fruitless. The point I was going to make is that the difference caused by the presence or absence of oxygen at the time of hydration is much less than the difference that is caused by storage under different conditions. This may be challenged.

I had gone along on the general idea that if a radical, an organic radical in my case ($R\cdot$)—and this agrees with what Dr. Hart was saying—is permitted to see oxygen in the dry state, it forms an organic peroxyl radical ($ROO\cdot$) and this event, or something it inevitably leads to, is what causes damage. Powers has shown the same thing for his spores. Anyway, the formation of the peroxyl radical is the thing that causes damage to be fixed. It is irretrievable at this point.

If we interpose $NO\cdot$ before the organic radical ($R\cdot$) sees oxygen, radicals disappear and we think it goes to RON, and now the organic radical is prevented from reacting with the oxygen.

Returning to the point that Dr. Caldecott was making, that the effectiveness of oxygen at hydration is something that persists for a very long period of time, I wish to add this. We studied gas diffusion and water diffusion into dry seeds, and into separated seed embryos and endosperm. Now we found that gas diffusion was more rapid than water diffusion. For example, oxygen diffusion was saturated at about 10 minutes as I remember, whereas water diffusion was considerably slower initially and was not saturated for greater than 15 minutes (actually, for biological effect, I find the oxygen effect is saturated by a minute or less exposure to oxygen).

Dr. Caldecott: Is that the whole seed or the embryo?

Dr. Conger: I am talking here about separated embryos, but when seeds are hydrated with oxygen present, what I think we really have done is allowed these seeds or embryos to see oxygen for an appreciable length of time before they see water. This would be a reasonable interpretation using the general notions we have about what is happening in these seeds as a result of the radicals that are present in them during postirradiation.

Dr. Caldecott: Are you saying that the embryo and the endosperm hydrate at the same rate?

Dr. Conger: No, the embryo hydrates more rapidly than the endosperm or the whole seed. That is why I did it separately.

Dr. Caldecott: The embryo in our material hydrates to 45 percent water within 15 minutes after steeping is initiated. It takes the endosperm more than 24 hours to approach this level.

Dr. Conger: The endosperm is of no moment here.

Dr. Caldecott: The embryo hydrates very, very rapidly. Within minutes it is at water-content levels which would be normal, i.e., 10 to 15 percent.

The reason I labor these points is that these types of experiments are virtually 100 percent reproducible. I would like to take you into the storage phenomenon as a function of temperature and the effect of hydration after they are irradiated as a function of time (Fig. 7a).

If one takes dry seeds (look at the 20°C lines) and stores them after irradiation for 40 to 48 hours, injury increases in the way indicated. It will continue to increase for a matter of months at 20°C. The lines are given showing hydration in the presence of oxygen and nitrogen. Note that they come together between 42 and 78 hours. If one raises the temperature 7°, they come together between 8 and 12 hours.

The other point is that if one takes these same seeds and stores them at 85°C, it will actually work at any temperature above 70°C for the same period of time, the sensitivity to the hydration in the presence of oxygen and nitrogen is eliminated within 15 minutes. The two lines stay parallel and after about 24 hours recovery sets in. This thermal recovery equals about half the difference between the damage initially induced when the seeds are hydrated in the presence of oxygen or nitrogen.

The other point I wanted to bring up is with reference to postirradiation storage at dry-ice temperature. Note that the data indicate that the low temperature held reactive sites in a labile state (Fig. 7b).

Dr. Pollard: It might be a very good thing to study heat alone.

Dr. Caldecott: We have done this very extensively.

Dr. Pollard: You should note what is happening, its effects on DNA, etc.

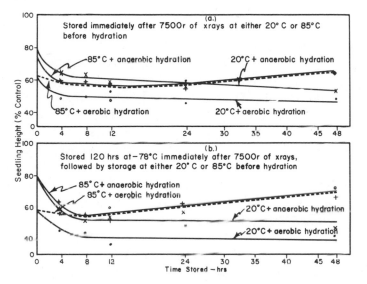

Fig. 7. The effect of postirradiation temperature on x-ray-induced storage injury and the suppression of injury progression by low temperature

Dr. Caldecott: It gives no increase of any kind of the damage that we can detect.

Dr. Pollard: Give them some more.

Dr. Caldecott: We have given them 112°C and this kills them.

Dr. Pollard: Come on down; it is cooking at 89°.

Dr. Caldecott: You could hold them for one hour at 112°C and have them survive. The only temperatures I really used are 75°, 85°, and 112°.

Dr. Pollard: You get the melting of DNA within a few degrees. You don't want to do it dry.

Dr. Caldecott: It has to be dry. If you heat seeds with an embryo water content of 12 percent, they will be killed by a temperature of 60°C.

Dr. Pollard: It has nothing to do with DNA. It can only be protein.

Dr. Giles: One final remark, Dr. Conger.

Dr. Conger: Again, I think that Dr. Caldecott and I are not disagreeing on results, but we may disagree a little bit in interpretation, as for these heating experiments where he preheated to 85°C before irradiation and found a difference from seeds not preheated. I agree with the difference all right, but I disagree in the interpretation. I have said that we found that the water content of the seeds is a very important variable in these aftereffect-damage experiments, and I wondered if the water content had been changed by this 85° heat pretreatment, and it had, even in previously dried (evacuated over P_2O_5) but unheated seeds. Now we have found that both the number of postirradiation radicals and the amount of postirradiation damage which will develop are profoundly influenced by the water content of the seeds. Both are nil in the region of greater than about 12 percent water content, increase very steeply and to a great extent in the region of about 12 to 14 percent water, with a maximum at about 3 to 4 percent, and then actually decline (to about 50 percent the maximum value at 3 to 4 percent water) to 1 percent water, the lowest we have been able to go. Knowing this, and also finding that 85° heat pretreatment dried the seeds (they lost weight), we interpret the effect of heat treatment as being due to drying, not to heat per se. We could cause the same effect by drying with other means, such as extended evacuation. I would not wish to extend this to other heat treatments, say a postirradiation treatment, since our heat experiments have been the most troublesome of any we have done. But this case, at least, seemed clear.

Dr. Caldecott: The water content after heating for 15 minutes and 24 hours was quite different. The biological result was, however, very similar. I believe the heat treatment resulted in all of the seeds being equal in radiosensitivity; possibly due to equilibrating them, in critical sites, with reference to oxygen and amount of bound water.

Dr. Giles: I think the Chairman at this point has the power to turn on the heat to get to the next speaker. I would like to pass on to the next topic, the effect of combined radiations, and call on Dr. Kirby-Smith who will talk about x rays plus ultraviolet.

References

Caldecott, R. 1952. Genetics 37: 136.

—— 1954. Science 120: 809.

—— 1955. Radiation Research 2: 339.

—— 1961. *In* Symposium on the Effects of Ionizing Radiation on Seeds, Karlsruhe, Germany, August 8–12, 1960, 3. Vienna: International Atomic Energy Agency.

Caldecott, R. S., E. F. Frolik, and R. A. Morris. Proc. Natl. Acad. Sci. U.S. 38: 804.

Commoner, B., B. B. Lippincott, and J. V. Passoneau. 1958. Proc. Natl. Acad. Sci. U.S. 44: 1099.

Conger, A. D. 1961. J. Cellular Comp. Physiol. 58, Suppl. 1: 27.

Conger, A. D., and L. M. Fairchild. 1952. Proc. Natl. Acad. Sci. U.S. 38: 289.

Conger, A. D., and M. L. Randolph. 1959. Radiation Research 11: 54.

Ehrenberg, A., and L. Ehrenberg. 1958. Arkiv Fysik 14: 133.

Ehrenberg, L. 1960. Genet. agrar. 12: 364.

Ehret, C. F., B. Smaller, F. L. Powers, and R. B. Webb. 1960. Science 132: 1768.

Faberge, A. C. 1951. Genetics 36: 549.

Gordy, W., and H. Shields. 1958. Radiation Research 9: 611.

—— 1960. Proc. Natl. Acad. Sci. U.S. 46: 1124.

Kirby-Smith, J. S., and M. L. Randolph. 1959. Intern. J. Radiation Biol. Suppl.: 11.

Konzak, C. F., R. A. Nilan, J. R. Harle, and R. E. Heiner. 1961. Brookhaven Symposia in Biol., No. 14: 128.

Kurita, Y., and W. Gordy. 1961a. J. Chem. Phys. 34: 1285.

—— 1961b. J. Chem. Phys. 34: 282.

Lawton, E. J., J. S. Balwit, and R. S. Powell. 1960. J. Chem. Phys. 33: 395.

Nilan, R. A. 1960. Genet. agrar. 12: 283.

Powers, E. L. 1961. J. Cellular Comp. Physiol. 58, Suppl. 1: 13.

Powers, E. L., C. F. Ehret, and B. Smaller. 1961. *In* Free Radicals in Biological Systems, H. S. Blois, Jr., *et al.*, eds., 351. New York: Academic Press.

Powers, E. L., and B. F. Kaleta. 1960. Science 132: 959.

Powers, E. L., R. B. Webb, and C. F. Ehret. 1960. Radiation Research, Suppl. 2: 94.

Randolph, M. L. 1961. *In* Free Radicals in Biological Systems, M. S. Blois, Jr., *et al.*, eds., New York: Academic Press.

Sparrman, B., L. Ehrenberg, and A. Ehrenberg. 1959. Acta Chem. Scand. 13: 199.

Swanson, C. P. 1940. Proc. Natl. Acad. Sci. U.S. 26: 366.

Wolff, S., and H. E. Luippold. 1956. Proc. Natl. Acad. Sci. U.S. 42: 510.

Zimmer, K. G. 1959. Radiation Research, Suppl. 1: 519.

Zimmer, K. G., L. Ehrenberg, and A. Ehrenberg. 1957. Strahlentherapie 103: 3.

Effects of Combined UV and X Radiations on Chromosome Breakage in Tradescantia Pollen

Dr. J. S. Kirby-Smith: I would like to present in a very brief manner some results dealing with the induction of chromosome aberrations in *Tradescantia* pollen by combined treatment with ultraviolet and ionizing radiations. In addition to this work, which has been done in collaboration with Dr. Benedetto Nicoletti and Mrs. M. G. Miller, I will also briefly mention some recent results obtained in our laboratory by Dr. Harvey Cromroy dealing with factors modifying the ultraviolet sensitivity of pollen which have some bearing on the problems of present interest. In all instances our experimental material has been *Tradescantia paludosa* pollen, irradiated in the dry state and cultured on a lactose agar medium after the method of Bishop as modified by Conger. Chromosome aberrations were then examined at metaphase of the pollen-tube mitosis in Feulgen-stained preparations.

Before speaking of the results of the combined treatments, I would like to review a few of the similarities and contrasts in the action of ultraviolet and ionizing radiation on chromosome breakage in this material. I believe that this approach will be of value in the interpretation of our results to be presented later.

First, it is well established that exposure of dry pollen to ultraviolet radiation results in chromosomal aberrations (Swanson, 1944; Kirby-Smith and Craig, 1957) in the dry pollen grain. Furthermore, all the types of aberrations, except for the very infrequent, exotic, complex ones which we sometimes see with ionizing radiation, are observed in the material treated with ultraviolet. Although ultraviolet thus leads to the same general qualitative types of aberrations as those produced by ionizing radiations, there is one considerable difference in the results produced by these radiations, namely, that the relative frequencies of the various types of aberrations are drastically different in the two cases. In our hands, for example, in the x-ray-treated dry pollen grains, we observe very few chromatid deletions, in contrast to the very high frequency of gaps reported earlier in this meeting for other materials. For x-ray-induced aberrations, the ratio of chromatid to isochromatids is 1:3; in ultraviolet-treated material this ratio is more like 2:1 (Kirby-Smith and Craig, 1957). However, in more recent work, this ratio for ultraviolet-induced aberrations, at very low doses and using a more rigorous definition for a chromatid deletion, seems to be closer to the ratio for x rays. Exchanges are very rare for ultraviolet-treated material when compared with the frequencies observed in x-rayed pollen.

A second and more striking contrast in the results of these different radiations is a drastic difference in the numbers of incomplete isochromatid aberrations observed for the two cases. Specifically for x rays, only a few percent of isochromatids are of the incomplete class; for ultraviolet, approximately 45 percent of isochromatids are incomplete for pollen irradiated in air and 65 percent for irradiations carried out in nitrogen.

The third major difference or the third point which I want to make has already been mentioned by Dr. Chu, namely, the tremendous fragmentation that is observed in the chromosomes after ultraviolet treatment. Miss Lovelace first observed this in pollen irradiated in the dry state, and then cultured and examined in the pollen-tube mitosis. She found entire chromatid arms or, in some cases, the whole complement of chromosomes completely fragmented into a series of dots and small fragments.

Dr. Wolff: Was this with the protein-absorbing wavelengths as in Chu's case?

Dr. Kirby-Smith: Miss Lovelace made no detailed quantitative measurements of the wavelength dependence of this phenomenon. Miss Craig and I in later work (1954) observed fragmentation in the region from 3020 to 2350 Å. Contrary to Dr. Chu's report yesterday for mammalian cells, 2650 Å was the wavelength of maximum effectiveness in pollen, although we did find some fragmentation at 2804 Å. Whether these differences reflect fundamental differences in wet and dry material, I don't know. I am reluctant to believe that this discrepancy between our results and those of Dr. Chu is a reflection of bad dosimetry, since we carried out the dose measurements for both experiments.

Bearing in mind these general facts concerning ultraviolet-induced aberrations alone, I would now like to speak of the combined effects of ultraviolet and ionizing radiations. It is an attractive approach at least in principle to look at combined effects, particularly when we reach an impasse in the interpretation of the effects of these agents, when applied alone, and one wishfully thinks that by compounding difficulties one may help solve the unequal problems.

Swanson, to give a little historical background, was the first to use this method, at least in *Tradescantia,* and looked at the effects of pretreatment and posttreatment with uv- or x-ray-induced chromosomal damage in growing pollen-tube cultures. Swanson observed a decrease in the aberrations which one would expect from a simple additive relation.

Miss Lovelace (1952) looked not at the growing pollen tube but at the dry pollen grain and obtained somewhat ambiguous results. In some cases simple additivity was observed, but more often a very large synergism or increase over the simple additive effects of ultraviolet and x rays or gamma rays was found for isochromatid aberrations; however, an opposite effect is the case for exchanges. Owing to this lack of reproducibility, the work was never brought beyond the exploratory stage.

Several years ago in studies of x-ray-induced free radicals in *Tradescantia* pollen using the electron spin resonance technique, we observed (Kirby-Smith and Randolph, 1960) that posttreatment with ultraviolet radiation markedly reduced the x-ray-induced magnetic resonances. This result prompted us to look again at the effect of combined x-ray and uv radiations at the chromosomal level, since one might expect that a physical posttreatment which removed free radicals produced by ionizing radiation should result in less chromosome breakage. The results of the first experiments are shown in Table 1 and indicate a definite synergistic effect on the action of these agents, regardless of whether the uv is delivered as a pretreatment or a posttreatment; a simple and attractive explanation of the

Table 1. Effect of Ultraviolet and X Radiations on the Production of Chromatid Aberrations

		Aberrations (in percent)		
Treatment	*Cells scored*	*Chromatid*	*Isochromatid*	*Exchange*
Control	212	0.00	0.47	0.47
x ray[a]	291	1.72	12.7	2.40
uv[b]	400	0.00	1.75	0.25
uv-x ray	292	8.22	57.0	23.0
x ray-uv	250	5.60	70.0	16.0

[a] Dose: 150 rad.
[b] Dose: 0.2×10^6 ergs/cm².

phenomenon can be achieved by assuming that x rays produce a number of chromosomal lesions which will result in primary breakage only if additional energy in the form of uv quanta are delivered to these sites. In other words, the action of uv, according to this hypothesis, is to uncover potential x-ray chromosomal damage. Unfortunately, since uv pretreatment also acts synergistically, such a simple and naïve theory must be rejected unless one makes additional assumptions involving long-lived uv-induced lesions capable of interacting with subsequent ionizing events. Accordingly, I believe we must abandon explanations of this type, and at the moment we strongly favor the hypothesis that uv results in the inactivation or inhibition of chromosome-rejoining mechanisms, in accordance with the ideas proposed by Wolff.

We will return to this point after examining some of the other observed features of this synergism. One of the most striking aspects of the phenomenon, noted also by Miss Lovelace, is its wide variability in magnitude. This is indicated in Table 2 which shows a three-

Table 2. Synergistic Effect of Ultraviolet and X Radiation

Treatment	*Dose*	*Cells scored*	*Isochromatid* (in percent)
x ray	50 rad	250	4.40
uv	0.1×10^6 ergs/cm²	300	2.00
x ray-uv		300	18.0
x ray	50 rad	200	4.50
uv	0.1×10^6 ergs/cm²	115	5.00
x ray-uv		146	112

to fourfold increase in the synergism in two similar experiments performed some weeks apart. In controlled experiments to determine the sensitivity of the phenomenon, we have found that (1) pretreatment or exposure of pollen grains to high humidity prior to uv exposure results in a decrease in its magnitude and (2) exposure to large amounts of solar radiation in the greenhouse prior to further treatments increases the magnitude of the synergism. This is indicated in the results in Table 2; Experiment 1 was performed on pollen gathered on a damp, dark morning and Experiment 2 on material which had received larger amounts of solar radiation on a dry, relatively bright morning.

The dependence of the magnitude of the synergistic action on the interval between the treatments is indicated in Table 3. These data

Table 3. Effect of Various Time Intervals on the Synergistic Action of X Rays and Ultraviolet Radiation

		Isochromatid aberrations	
Treatment	*Cells scored*	*Number*	*Percent*
A. $\text{x} \xrightarrow{\text{10 min.}} \text{uv} \xrightarrow{\text{10, 30, 60 min.}} \text{sowed}$			
Control	250	5	2
x ray	300	6	2
uv	250	5	2
x-uv_{10}	201	26	13
x-uv_{30}	150	27	18
x-uv_{60}	100	13	13
B. $\text{x} \xrightarrow{\text{15, 60, 90 min.}} \text{uv} \xrightarrow{\text{10 min.}} \text{sowed}$			
Control	150	0	0.0
x ray	250	1	0.4
uv	250	4	1.6
$\text{x}_{15}\text{-uv}$	200	95	48
$\text{x}_{60}\text{-uv}$	200	100	50
$\text{x}_{90}\text{-uv}$	200	81	41
C. $\text{uv} \xrightarrow{\text{15, 60, 120 min.}} \text{x} \xrightarrow{\text{10 min.}} \text{sowed}$			
Control	250	2	0.8
uv	300	7	2.3
x ray	300	3	1.0
$\text{uv}_{15}\text{-x}$	300	16	5.3
$\text{uv}_{60}\text{-x}$	300	82	27.0
$\text{uv}_{120}\text{-x}$	300	23	7.7

also indicate the extreme sensitivity or magnitude of the synergism as observed in pollen subjected to midsummer conditions in the greenhouse, or to low humidity and radiation from artificial sources (fluorescent and incandescent lamp) in the laboratory. Under these conditions, it is of interest to note that as little as 1 rad of x rays, combined with 0.01×10^6 ergs/cm^2 of uv, results in a very significant increase in aberration frequency over that expected from a simple additive effect. These results have been repeatedly observed, and there is no question as to their validity.

If we expose pollen to x rays, followed closely (within 5 or 10 minutes) by uv treatment, and vary the interval between these treatments and sowing, the aberration frequencies rise to a maximum at a 30-minute interval and then decrease as indicated in Table 3A. If the material is first exposed to x rays, and the interval between subsequent uv treatment varied, the data in Table 3B are obtained showing a decline in aberration frequency with time. This latter behavior is, I believe, an indication that primary breaks remain open in pollen up to several hours in the dry condition. If, on the other hand, we give uv and vary the interval between it and x-ray exposure (Table 3C), the results are qualitatively similar to these for the x-uv case, where the interval between final treatment and sowing of the pollen is varied. These time-interval experiments all appear compatible with the hypothesis that the action of ultraviolet radiation is on a rejoining mechanism.

Added support for this belief also comes from some preliminary studies of the dependence of the synergism on uv dose, as indicated in Fig. 1. The fact that, keeping x-ray-dose constant, the magnitude of the synergistic effect appears to saturate as the uv exposure is increased, supports the idea that above some critical uv dose level the rejoining mechanism is rendered inactive. If this were not the case, we would expect a steadily increasing aberration frequency rather than the approach to a plateau or saturation. At this saturation level, we would thus expect ideally that all primary x-ray breaks remain open and result in aberrations.

Dr. Wolff: Have you tried to put these into the formula that Atwood put on the board the other day?

Dr. Kirby-Smith: No, we usually run into the shattering phenomenon in this region, and the scoring is too difficult for very quantitative treatment. We may, with more care in scoring, perhaps be able to do this.

Dr. Lindsley: What happens when you pull your x-ray dose down?

Dr. Kirby-Smith: There is some indication, at least in one experiment, that reducing the x-ray dose tends to reduce the level at which saturation occurs.

Dr. Conger: What is the uv aberration frequency, above?

Dr. Kirby-Smith: It is very slight.

Dr. Atwood: Do you have a region in the plateau where there is no shattering?

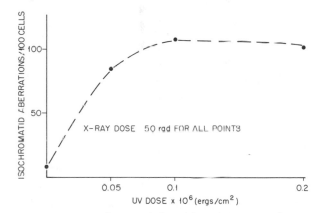

Fig. 1. Dependence of the synergism on uv dose

Dr. Kirby-Smith: Fragmentation usually occurs before the plateau is reached.

Dr. Atwood: The point of this is that it would be another method of getting primary break frequency.

Dr. Conger: Is this dose, or exposure?

Dr. Kirby-Smith: It is exposure, and at only one wavelength, 2650 Å.

Dr. Chu: With regard to Dr. Atwood's comment, for mammalian cells we give only 1/10 or 1/20 of the total uv exposure given to pollen grains. Since shattering is produced with fairly small amounts of uv, we are now trying to see if we can induce chromosome aberrations with much less uv, i.e., before shattering occurs.

Dr. Conger: Do you get chromosome shattering in these mammalian cells in tissue culture with uv?

Dr. Chu: We do at a wavelength of 2804 Å, but have not yet obtained an action spectrum.

Dr. Kirby-Smith: I would like to point out that for action spectrum measurements Dr. Chu's material is much superior to the *Tradescantia* pollen grain. These mammalian cells lie flat against the quartz support with minimal cytoplasm shielding the nucleus.

Dr. Atwood: I am not clear as to what you meant about 27 percent with 1 rad when you knocked out the rejoining. Is this 27 percent of the cells?

Dr. Kirby-Smith: In this case we mean 27 isochromatid aberrations per 100 cells examined.

Dr. Atwood: Is the stage G1 equivalent, or G2?

Dr. Kirby-Smith: It would be G2.

Dr. Evans: I think that the rejoining idea seems very feasible, but a question which we ought to consider is whether or not we can get rejoining in this sort of dehydrated system. For instance, I think there is evidence that in the irradiation of dry seeds the yield of chromosome damage is independent of dose rate but is simply a function of dose, with the complication of the storage phenomenon.

Dr. Kirby-Smith: I do not know of the actual water content. However, all our experiments are carried out at 50 percent relative humidity; under these conditions the cells are by no means completely dehydrated.

Dr. Moses: How do you take into account the very high uv absorption of the cell wall?

Dr. Kirby-Smith: When Miss Craig and I were determining the qualitative action spectrum for uv breakage, we used the data of Uber (1939) for absorption in maize pollen. Similar data for *Tradescantia* pollen would admittedly be desirable, but I don't believe that the general shape of the curves would be drastically changed. Our curve showed conclusively that the peak for ultraviolet-induced aberrations was at 2650 Å and not in the protein maximum.

Dr. Atwood: When you say that a certain one is an iso, does it have to be at the same level or can it be just in the same arm but at a different place?

Dr. Kirby-Smith: Are you speaking of the incomplete isos?

Dr. Atwood: Are the incomplete isos always homologous, Dr. Kirby-Smith?

Dr. Kirby-Smith: Yes.

Dr. Auerbach: You said that uv inhibits rejoining, but that you get more exchanges. Do you mean inhibition of rejoining in the old order, that is, inhibition of restitution?

Dr. Kirby-Smith: That is right.

Dr. Gray: Why does it affect one type of joining and not the other?

Dr. Auerbach: With a general inhibitor of rejoining, you should get more unjoined breaks. Could it be that you produce some kind of movement of the chromosomes?

Dr. Kirby-Smith: It might be. I admit that this is certainly difficult.

Dr. Conger: Dr. Kirby-Smith said that rejoining was reduced when you gave the uv with the x rays, but he did have more exchanges, just as Dr. Auerbach said.

Dr. Auerbach: It is just the opposite from what Swanson found and how he interpreted it.

Dr. Kirby-Smith: Swanson's material was in the growing pollen.

Dr. Auerbach: He thought that uv kept the broken ends together, but now it seems they are made to move apart.

Dr. Swanson: I have not picked up any isos or exchanges. All I ever found were single chromatid deletions.

Dr. Kirby-Smith: Even for ultraviolet alone you found only deletions in the growing pollen tubes.

Dr. Swanson: But this is a rapidly growing metabolizing pollen tube, in contrast to a dehydrated pollen grain.

Dr. Auerbach: Dr. Kirby-Smith seems to imply a distinction in kind between reunion in the old order and reunion in a new order. I always thought this depended on movement.

Dr. Wolff: In regard to this question of Dr. Auerbach's about the exchanges that Dr. Kirby-Smith got, I should think that if rejoining were knocked out by 90 percent, so that you got many more breaks in the system, when they rejoin later you would get an increase in exchanges as well as an increase in single breaks.

Dr. Auerbach: My comment was that I always imagined that there was nothing essentially different between restitution and formation of aberrations, and that inhibiting the one would also inhibit the other.

Dr. Wolff: The point is that if you had very many more breaks in the system because you had inhibited restitution, when rejoining takes place later there will be a greater chance for reunion to occur because of the concurrent presence of a greater number of breaks. I think you will, therefore, observe more exchanges.

Dr. Gray: Have you any idea what this dose of radiation would be doing to DNA, protein, and the cell metabolism? I think that the effect looks so dramatic partly because the efficiency of uv alone in causing the aberrations is awfully low, and the dose of uv you are giving in terms of rads (i.e., ergs per gram) in the protein is very high. It might be equivalent to giving the cell 100,000 rad of energy in the form of uv, which I suspect has introduced all sorts of defects into many different systems of the cell, and it would be nice to know the effects of the uv on all forms of metabolism, and particularly DNA metabolism, because this would have an important bearing on the x-ray damage.

Dr. Kirby-Smith: We do not know what this dose of uv is doing to cell metabolism. I agree that there should be some effects on these processes, for as you say the uv dose in terms of rads is quite high. For example, using the absorption coefficients for maize pollen walls and cytoplasm as determined by Uber (1939), and assuming that the absorption coefficient for *Tradescantia* pollen cytoplasm is approximately equivalent, a surface exposure of 10^6 erg/cm^2 results in an energy absorption roughly 5×10^7 erg/cm or 5×10^5 rad.

An uv exposure of 0.1×10^6 erg (that used in some of the synergistic studies) is thus equivalent to 50,000 rad, a figure quite in line with your estimate of 100,000 rad.

Before closing, I would like to discuss some more recent experimental results which may have considerable bearing on this synergism. You will remember that exposure of pollen to solar radiation in the greenhouse appears to potentiate the synergism, and an obvious approach to the problem would be to pretreat pollen with various radiation bands in the solar spectrum. Although we ultimately expect to carry out such experiments in connection with combined x-ray and uv irradiations, we have at present restricted our efforts in this connection to some exploratory studies of the effects of pretreatment with visible and near-visible radiation on sensitivity of pollen to uv alone. This work has been carried out by Dr. Harvey Cromroy in our laboratory and covers the wavelength region from 4000 to 7800 Å. The results of this work show a marked dependence of uv-induced chromosomal-aberration frequency on the wavelength regions used in pretreatment. It is clearly evident that far-red radiation (7800 Å) initially increases the observed uv aberration rate, and that red radiation (6000 Å) decreases this aberration rate. In these experiments a standard uv dose (exposure) of 1×10^6 erg/cm² has been used in connection with an equal exposure to the radiation used in pretreatment. This red-far red behavior of *Tradescantia* pollen is very reminiscent of effects of red and far-red radiation on such phenomena as germination of lettuce seed, floral initiation, and many other photobiological processes studied and reported on by Borthwick and Hendricks and other investigators. Experiments are now in progress to determine whether the effect of red and far red in *Tradescantia* pollen is reversible in the same manner found for these other systems. It also remains to be determined whether or not red and far-red radiation act in the same way in sensitizing *Tradescantia* pollen to the synergistic action of uv and x rays.

Dr. Swanson: If one exposes barley or maize embryos to x ray and red-far red and then, after 10 days of growth, measures either root or shoot length, we find that red tends to counteract the effects of x rays, while far red enhances them.

Dr. Klein: Is this on root length? I would like to comment that there is very little information concerning the effect of light on root development and growth. As far as most people have been able to determine by running relatively numerous experiments, there is no effect of either red, far red, or any light on root elongation, so this is something that makes me wonder. It seems to affect the growth after radiation. How do you account for this?

Dr. Swanson: I am not explaining it. I am merely saying that this is what we get. It is not an absolutely consistent thing, but rather a general picture that we have come up with.

Dr. Totter: A moment ago someone asked whether this far-red effect was confined to plants. I cannot answer that exactly, but I would like to tell about an experiment that Williams and Hamner have done at the University of Georgia. They have been working with animal sperm and they have found that if it is collected in total darkness and handled in total darkness it does not respire. Exposure to a very small amount of light sets up respiration. They do not have an action spectrum yet, but the indications are that the induction by light of respiration may be a red light trigger mechanism.

Dr. Wolff: Gordon and Surry have found that if they irradiate rat mitochondria they get a red-far red effect on the amount of phosphorylation that occurs, the amount of ATP formed is affected.

Dr. Klein: Wasn't there actually some tumor work done on live rats or mice with implantations and far-red and x radiations?

Dr. Wolff: I don't know. Was this by Gordon?

Dr. Swanson: He has done it on an ascites tumor cell, using ana-phase bridge frequencies as a criterion of effect. He gets a far-red potentiation. I believe that this is correct, so the phenomenon is not confined to plants.

Dr. Giles: Are there any more specific questions for Dr. Kirby-Smith? If not, I think we should pass on to the next paper since time is passing along rapidly. We will now turn to the next topic, aberrations in human chromosomes and their medical implications. The first topic concerns dose relations in the induction of human chromosome aberrations, to be discussed here by Dr. Chu.

References

Borthwick, H. A., S. B. Hendricks, E. H. Toole, and V. K. Toole. 1952. Proc. Natl. Acad. Sci. U.S. 38: 662.

Kirby-Smith, J. S., and Doris L. Craig. 1957. Genetics 42: 176.

Kirby-Smith, J. S., and M. L. Randolph. 1960. J. Cellular Comp. Physiol. Suppl. 58: 1.

Lovelace, Roberta. 1952. Genetics 37: 602.

Swanson, C. P. 1944. Genetics 29: 61.

Uber, F. M. 1939. Am. J. Botany 26: 799.

Part 4

Aberrations of Human Chromosomes and

Their Medical Implications

Dose Relations in the Induction of
Human Chromosome Aberrations

Dr. E. H. Y. Chu: There is evidence, both direct and indirect, for chromosome damage *in vivo* in human tissues at relatively modest doses of radiation. However, planned, precise quantitative studies in man are so obviously impossible that a number of investigators have turned to tissue culture material for a better measurement of chromosomal sensitivity to radiation. The approach has been to apply doses of radiation to tissue culture cells and then to score for visible chromosome abnormalities of a variety of types at intervals thereafter.

The first quantitative data on the chromosome changes in human cells under tissue culture conditions were obtained in 1957 by Bender. Puck and associates (1958) have determined x-ray survival curves for populations of single human cells and have attempted to correlate the mean lethal dose required to produce chromosome abnormalities with that for colony formation in plating experiments. Further data on spontaneous and induced human chromosome aberrations have been obtained in several laboratories.

More recently, thanks to the development of short-term cultures of leucocytes from human peripheral blood, chromosome-aberration analyses have been made on persons exposed to accidental or therapeutical radiations. Bender and Gooch (1962a) have recently analyzed leucocytes which were irradiated *in vitro*.

The available data on human chromosome aberrations do not appear in good agreement, and different interpretations of these results have been given by various investigators. It seems worth-while to re-examine and evaluate these experimental results and to attempt to draw certain conclusions regarding dose-effect relationships. Using our own work (Chu, Giles, and Passano, 1961) as a framework and citing other studies, I shall try to consider the types of aberrations, the spontaneous and induced rates, the radiosensitivity of human chromosomes, and other related problems.

Types of aberrations

Both metaphase and postmetaphase aberrations have been scored by different investigators as an indication of damage to chromosomes by ionizing radiations.

Qualitatively, our studies indicated clearly that the types of metaphase aberrations induced by irradiation of human somatic chromosomes are the same as those found in comparable experiments, for example, the classical studies employing *Tradescantia* microspores. Both chromatid and chromosome aberrations occur, and essentially all expected types in both categories have been found.

Achromatic lesions are nonstained or faintly stained regions distributed randomly along the chromosome, and are present both spontaneously and in treated cells. They are not kinetochores or secondary constrictions. The size of the lesion may vary; a faint connecting threadlike material may often be visible. Achromatic lesions were scored but were not included in the calculation of aberration frequency.

The temporal distribution of the two major categories (chromatid and chromosome aberrations) corresponds in general to the pattern anticipated from previous studies. Chromatid aberrations are found during the first 25 hours after irradiation. There is mixture of chromatid and chromosome types at 30 hours. Chromosome type becomes predominant when the cells are fixed at 42 hours or later postirradiation periods. This shift of types is also evident in Bender's data (1960) on tissue culture cells.

In human leucocyte cultures, Bender and Gooch (1962a) found that first mitoses occur between 42 and 48 hours after the initiation of culture. Between 66 and 72 hours, mitotic activity reaches a maximum, but all of the divisions are still first mitoses. This is taken to indicate that the blood cells capable of division under these conditions are in the pre-DNA-synthesis (G1) phase in the peripheral circulation. This observation confirms an independent autoradiographic study by Bender and Prescott (1962). Thus, when the blood sample was irradiated immediately after withdrawal from the body and before *in vitro* culture, only chromosomal types of aberrations were found. On the other hand, if the culture cells were irradiated at 42 hours and fixed at 48 hours, induced chromatid aberrations were observed (Bender, personal communication).

Analyses at anaphase and telophase stages are not as precise as scoring metaphase chromosomes following colchicine treatment (Wolff and Luippold, 1957; Conger, 1958), but the scoring can be done much more rapidly. The types of aberrations found were dot and rod deletions, either single or in pairs, and bridges, with or without acentric fragments. The acentric rod and dot deletions are presumably chromatid deletions, involving one or both sister chromatids, while the chromatid bridges may be the results of at least two events: (1) isochromatid deletions followed by fusion of the broken ends of the centric chromatids, and (2) asymmetrical chromatid exchanges. Chromosome dicentrics and ring chromosomes also occasionally form bridges at anaphase and telophase.

Spontaneous aberrations

A surprisingly high frequency of spontaneous aberrations has been observed in the control material *in vitro* (Table 1). This is probably attributable to the tissue culture conditions which, in turn, are variable in different laboratories. Despite the conscientious efforts of the investigator to match the *in vitro* environment to that of the *in vivo*, the two situations cannot be said, in a strict sense, to be the same. It is well known that a variety of factors or agents are responsible for cellular alterations and chromosomal abnormalities in cells grown in culture (cf. Chu, 1962). Sax and Passano (1961) have shown, in a diploid human fibroblast cell line, that the spontaneous aberration frequency is directly proportional to the length of *in vitro* cultivation. Bender (1957, 1960) has used for experiments human kidney epithelioid cells shortly after the cells were put in culture (during the second to the fourth passage), and the low spontaneous rate he observed probably remained unchanged during the early

E. H. Y. *Chu*

Table 1. *Spontaneous Human Chromosome Aberration Frequencies*[a]

Cell type	Cell stage	Frequency	Tissue origin and other remarks	Investigator
E	M	0.01 breaks/cell 0.012 breaks/cell	Kidney H3 line Kidney H16 line	Bender (1957, 1960)
F	M	0.234 aberrations/cell	Skin from 4 individuals; aberrations include 1 achromatic lesion and 1 cell with sticky chromosome	Puck (1958)
F + E	A + T	0.006–0.009 aberrations/cell 0.015–0.030 aberrations/cell	Embryonic lung Embryonic brain	Lindsten (1959); Fraccaro (1960)
F	A + T	0.0142 ± 0.0017 chromosome rearrangements/cell	1.5–2-month total embryos	Dubinin *et al.* (1960a,b)
F	A + T	0.036 aberrations/cell 0.201 aberrations/cell	Skin culture for 1.5 months Skin culture for 6 months	Sax and Passano (1961)
F + E	M	0.10 aberrations/cell	Skin, kidney, and total embryos	Chu *et al.* (1961)
L	M	0 chromosome breaks/cell 0.024 chromatid breaks/cell	5 individuals	Bender and Gooch (1962b)
L	M	0.0023 chromosome breaks/cell 0.0139 chromatid breaks/cell	4 individuals	Bender and Gooch (1962a)

[a] E, epithelioid cells; F, fibroblastlike cells; L, leucocytes; M, metaphase; A, anaphase; T, telophase.

passages. Most of our experiments were performed within a few weeks after initial biopsy on cultures of human skin or embryonic fibroblasts and kidney epithelioid cells. The findings from these two studies are still quite different (Table 1).

The observed aberration frequency is further influenced by cell type, cell stage, and the observer (cf. discussions in Bender, 1960; Chu *et al.*, 1961; and the following sections under "induced aberrations"). In any event, however, the spontaneous frequency observed in human cells *in vitro* is probably much higher than those actually occurring *in vivo*. It would be difficult to assume, as these findings would suggest, that a highly mosaic chromosomal constitution exists in the human body. Spontaneous chromosomal abnormalities (due to mitotic errors and chromosome breakage and reunions) do occur very sporadically *in vivo*, but they probably are eliminated because selection normally would favor the normal karyotype. This view is supported by Bender's (Bender, 1960; Bender and Gooch, 1962*a,b*) observations of a much lower spontaneous aberration frequency in human circulating blood (first *in vitro* mitoses examined within a few days in culture) and in the bone marrow of the *Ateles* monkey and the Chinese hamster. It should be added that not only chromosome aberrations but also abnormal chromosome numbers (aneuploidy) have been found in human cell cultures.

The spontaneous chromosome aberrations observed in tissue culture cells can, of course, serve as the control values for the treated series under the identical experimental conditions. Furthermore, almost all the spontaneous aberrations are of the chromatid type, a fact particularly useful in calculating the induced rate when only the chromosome type of aberration is induced (the chromosomes are effectively single when irradiated).

Aberrations *induced* in vivo

Fliedner *et al.* (1959), using squash preparations of bone marrow, noted evidence of chromosome "stickiness," i.e., clumping of chromosomes, and anaphase-bridge formation in a number of persons accidentally exposed to a mixed neutron-gamma-ray beam. Tough *et al.* (1960) studied the chromosome damage in two patients given x-ray treatment for ankylosing spondylitis. Their patients received surface doses of 250 and 1500 rad, respectively, to the spinal regions. Blood was drawn periodically and cultured *in vitro*. Chromosome aberrations in leucocytes were demonstrated.

There are several other brief reports (Boyd *et al.*, 1961; Stewart and Sanderson, 1961; Conen, 1961; Herschberg, 1961) concerning aberrations in the somatic chromosomes of irradiated humans who had been given diagnostic x rays or radioactive iodine. These reports are mostly preliminary. Moreover, since only the surface or administered dose was known or estimated, aberration analysis cannot give quantitative dose-effect information.

Bender and Gooch (1962*b*) found persistent chromosome aberrations in eight men who accidentally had received total-body doses during a nuclear excursion. The chromosomes were not examined until 29 months after exposure, and thus it was not possible to measure dose-effect relationships. However, it is remarkable that chromosome aberrations persisted for such a long time. Either certain abnormal karyotypes have become favorable and coexisted with the normal ones, or the affected stem cells have only come to mitosis during the brief *in vitro* cultivation. It would be interesting to re-examine the karyotypes of these individuals at certain later intervals.

Aberrations induced in vitro

The radiation-induced human chromosome aberration frequencies, arrived at in different laboratories from a variety of tissues and using different experimental and scoring procedures, are summarized in Table 2. At first glance one immediately gains an impression of disagreement and confusion. It seems that not only is a precise comparison of the results of different series difficult, but extreme caution is also necessary in extrapolations to the intact organism. However, if one examines these results more closely, one begins to realize the possible reasons which may account for the differences. In the following paragraphs, various results of human chromosome aberrations will be compared, with particular reference to the kind of aberrations scored, stage sensitivity, and dose relations.

Scoring procedure. The scoring of metaphase chromosome aber-

Table 2. Radiation-Induced Human Chromosome Aberrations[a]

Cell type	Radiation	Aberration type	Aberration frequency	Investigator
E	x rays	Chromatid	0.0027–0.0062 breaks/cell/r	Bender (1957, 1960)
F	x rays	Chromatid + chromosome	0.027 hits/mitosis/r	Puck (1958)
F + E	x rays	Chromatid	0.019–0.043 breaks/cell/r	Chu et al. (1961)
F + E	x rays	Chromosome	0.010–0.015 breaks/cell/r	Chu et al. (1961)
F + E	Co^{60}	Fragment + bridge	0.008–4.5 hits/cell/rad	Lindsten (1959)
F	x rays	Fragment + bridge	0.0024 chromosome rearrangements/ cell/r	Dubinin et al. (1960a,b)
L	x rays	Chromosome	0.0024–0.0039 breaks/cell/r	Bender and Gooch (1962a)

[a] See footnote, Table 1.

rations in human mitotic cells is admittedly tedious since the human chromosomes are small in size and large in number. In Bender's, as well as in our own experiments, attempts have been made in each analysis to identify certain specific chromosomes of the normal complement and to interpret every aberration configuration. Thus, when the metaphase aberration types were scored, the total cell number was not as large as the plant data. The small sampling size is true for all similar works cited.

The scorings of chromosome aberrations (bridges and fragments) in anaphase and telophase cells are relatively rapid, although the interpretation of configurations is less certain at times. Since aberrant chromosomes may move normally to the poles and remain undetected, and bridges may break, the postmetaphase aberration frequency is expected to be much lower than that observed in metaphase. This should be taken into consideration when metaphase and postmetaphase data are compared.

Stage sensitivity. We have concluded that there exists a marked variation in the radiosensitivity of human chromosomes during the mitotic cycle on the basis of observed variations in the frequencies of induced aberrations. Bender (1960) also observed a significant diminution of aberration frequency when the "early" first postirradiation divisions were compared with "late" divisions.

This difference in radiosensitivity before and after chromosome duplication is well known for plant materials. Wolff (1961) explained this difference by presenting evidence that the largest increase of the chromatid class actually comes from isochromatid aberrations. In any case, since the frequencies of detectable aberrations vary significantly in different postirradiation periods, pooling samples of cells which were fixed at different times after irradiation, as has been done in Puck's (1958) calculations, would yield a lower estimation of the aberration rate.

Dose relations. Bender's (1957) early data have demonstrated clearly (1) the feasibility of using human somatic cells *in vitro* for radiation experiments, and (2) the proportional increase of aberration frequency with dose. This and his later results (1960) were expressed in terms of breaks per cell per r, assuming that the observed breakage is a linear function of dose. Bender and Gooch

(1962*a*) pointed out, however, that total breakage actually rises as something greater than the first power of dose, because certain aberrations, such as a portion of isochromatid deletions, actually are the result of two-hit events. This deviation from linearity is evident in Bender's (1960) graphic plot of the total breaks against dose. The deviation of the dose curve from a straight line is probably insignificant when low doses are employed.

Puck's (1958) calculation of 0.027 chromosome hits per mitosis per r was the average of three dose series, each consisting of small samples (40–50 r, 20 cells, 0.045 chromosome hits/mitosis/r; 75 r, 101 cells, 0.020; 150 r, 26 cells, 0.015). According to Puck, "single-hit aberrations are chromosomal defects caused by a single ionizing event and include a complete break in one chromatid only; a break in both chromatids at the same point, presumably reflecting a break in the chromosome before it has doubled. . . . Each of the single-hit aberrations was scored as one, and each of the multi-hit complexes was scored as two." It should be noted that isochromatid aberrations occur after chromosome duplication, although terminal chromosome deletion, a type similar to "non union proximal distal," may result from a break before chromosome duplication. The exact kind of each multihit complex is not stated in Puck's result, although dicentrics and rings have been included in this category.

We have fixed cells at various intervals after irradiation, scored and plotted different types of aberrations separately. The results seem to indicate that for both chromatid and chromosome aberrations two major kinds of dose-effect relationships exist. Terminal deletions increase linearly with dose, isochromatid breaks increase somewhat more than the first power of dose, whereas exchanges increase markedly with some higher power of dose. These relationships are well known for classical materials such as *Tradescantia*.

Lindsten (1959) has published preliminary data of postmetaphase aberrations in human embryonic cells *in vitro* induced by a 100-curie Cobalt-60 source. Fraccaro (1960) also discussed these same experiments which he, Lindsten and Böök performed at Uppsala. Attempts have been made to separate aberrations into two classes: single fragments and double fragments and bridges. Fraccaro carefully stated that "this is a very approximate procedure and should be taken with caution. The first curve has a linear tendency while the other curve looks exponential." The average number of chromosome hits per mitosis per rad in one experiment is shown (Lindsten, 1959) as between 0.008 and 0.14. Other experiments showed unexplained inconsistent values of 0.03 and 1.5 to 4.5.

Dubinin and his co-workers (1960a,b) have accumulated a large amount of data on radiation-induced postmetaphase aberrations. They have used human cells in culture derived by trypsin dissociation from 1.5- to 2-month-old, whole aborted embryos. Low radiation doses (5, 7, 10, 25, and 50 r) were delivered from a 60-kv x-ray machine (4.5 ma, 0.5 mm Al). Most of the cells were fixed at six hours; a small portion within 42 hours. They observed no significant difference when cells were fixed at different postirradiation periods —a finding different from other studies.

They have calculated the aberration frequency in terms of the number of chromosome rearrangements (not breaks) per cell per r, as shown in Table 3. They correctly pointed out that at small dose

Table 3. Induced Chromosome Aberration Frequency in Human Embryonic Fibroblasts In Vitro[a]

| Dose (in r) | Total number of cells | Observed aberration frequency[b] | Induced rate (per r)[c] | |
			Method 1	Method 2
0	3577	0.0142 ± 0.0017	—	—
5	2130	0.0148 ± 0.0026	0.0017	0.00012
7	2893	0.0192 ± 0.0014	0.0021	0.00049
10	3335	0.0296 ± 0.0030	0.0026	0.00154
25	693	0.0720 ± 0.0082	0.0028	0.00231
50	780	0.1130 ± 0.0121	0.0026	0.00238
			$m = 0.0024$	$m = 0.00214$

[a] Adapted from Dubinin et al. (1960b).
[b] The frequency per cell of anaphase and telophase with chromosome rearrangements.
[c] For methods of calculation, see text.

levels the calculations of breaks and rearrangements indicate a basically single-hit mechanism. But, in calculating the induced chromosome aberration frequency, they have used the formula

$$A = (B^2 - C^2)^{1/2},$$

where $A =$ induced aberrations, $B =$ total aberrations, and $C =$

spontaneous aberrations (Table 3, Method 1). Calculated this way, the average induced rate is 0.0024 chromosome rearrangements per cell per r. The formula, however, has no theoretical basis.

It has been shown earlier, in other similar studies, that almost all spontaneous aberrations are of chromatid type and that the majority of them are terminal deletions. A certain proportion of acentric fragments seen at anaphase or telophase should come from the terminal-deletion class. Even certain bridges may be the result of one-hit events, e.g., the opening out of a "proximal sister union"; other bridges may be the result of asymmetrical chromatid exchanges or chromosome dicentrics and rings. Since the observed aberrations, especially the induced, are a mixture of one- and multiple-hit types, this formula cannot be accurately applied to calculate the induced rate.

Another method which is commonly used, but not a perfect one, is to subtract the spontaneous rate, presumably a constant term, from each dose series and to calculate for each dose the induced rate on a per roentgen basis (Table 3, Method 2). The average aberrations (not breaks) per cell per r is 0.00214. Although this average value is similar to that calculated according to Method 1, there exists a greater disparity among different dose series when calculated by Method 2.

More recently, Bender and Gooch (1962a) studied chromosome aberrations induced in human peripheral leucocytes when freshly drawn blood is irradiated *in vitro* before culturing. This procedure is practically the closest possible method for a quantitative estimation of the induced rate *in vivo,* assuming that leucocytes have the same radiosensitivity as other somatic cells. Furthermore, it was found that the induced aberrations were invariably of the chromosome type, thus removing much of the complication by spontaneous aberrations, which are mostly of the chromatid kind and which must have occurred during the *in vitro* cultivation.

They found a very low spontaneous aberration frequency (0.0023 break/cell) of the chromosome type. In fact, this is derived from a single terminal chromosome deletion found in 430 control cells (from four individuals) examined. Since terminal chromosome deletion is indistinguishable from nonunion isochromatid aberration, the spontaneous rate may even be much lower. In their earlier data (Bender and Gooch, 1962b) no chromosome-type aberration was observed in 458 control cells derived from five individuals, although the spontaneous chromatid aberration frequency was 0.024/cell.

The induced rate is 0.0039 break per cell per r when the material was scored at 54 hours. It is 0.0024 when scored at 72 hours. With identical criteria of scoring, these values appear to be remarkably close to, but not lower than, Bender's earlier data on chromatid aberration frequencies in kidney epithelioid cells *in vitro*.

The data for total breakage was fitted by the least-squares method to the expression

$$Y = a + bD + 2cD^2,$$

where $Y = $ the yield of the breaks, $a = $ the control breakage frequency, $D = $ the x-ray dose, and b and $c = $ the coefficients of production for one- and two-break aberrations, respectively. Small terminal deletions on occasion are difficult to distinguish from interstitial deletions, whereas rings and dicentrics are easier to score and the data are more reliable. The data for rings plus dicentrics were fitted by the least-squares method to the expression $Y = bD^2$. The value b $(0.52 \pm 0.07) \times 10^{-5}$ per cell per r^2, serves as a useful "calibration" for use in dose estimation in irradiated humans with x or gamma rays. The dose can be calculated from the following formula:

$$D = [Y/(0.52 \times 10^{-5})]^{1/2}.$$

Relative radiosensitivity and "doubling dose"

The measure of aberration frequency in terms of hits or breaks per cell is not accurate because it presupposes a knowledge of the relation between primary radiation effects on chromosomes and the final appearance of visible aberrations. The coefficient of aberration production for each separate kind of aberration represents a more accurate measure of radiation damage. Such calculations for human chromosomes have been performed by several authors and are shown in Table 4. Bender and Wolff's (1961) calculations, based on Bender's earlier data on kidney epithelioid cells, are actually lower than those for *Tradescantia*. Similar calculations from our results indicate

Table 4. Coefficients of X-Ray-Induced Aberrations in Human Somatic Cells In Vitro *and in* Tradescantia *Microspores*

CHROMATID TYPES

Cells	Chromatid breaks per cell per r ($\times 10^{-2}$)	Isochromatid breaks per cell per r ($\times 10^{-2}$)	Chromatid exchanges per cell per r^2 ($\times 10^{-5}$)
Tradescantia microspores[a]	0.725 ± 0.08	0.271 ± 0.02	$1.81 \ \pm 0.21$
Human somatic cells *in vitro*[b]	0.066 ± 0.10	0.246 ± 0.16	$0.55 \ \pm 0.35$
	0.601 ± 0.067	0.316 ± 0.186	2.157 ± 0.496

CHROMOSOME TYPES

Cells	Chromosome deletions per cell per r ($\times 10^{-2}$)	Asymmetrical exchanges[d] per cell per r^2 ($\times 10^{-5}$)
Tradescantia microspores[a]	0.06 ± 0.01	0.52 ± 0.08
Human leucocytes *in vitro*[c]	0.11 ± 0.012	0.45 ± 0.07

[a] Calculated by D. E. Lea, *Action of Radiations on Living Cells* (Cambridge, Cambridge University Press, 1955, 2d ed.).

[b] The first line calculated from data of Bender (1957, 1960) by Bender and Wolff (1961); the second line from data of Chu *et al.* (1961).

[c] Bender and Gooch (1962a).

[d] Lea (1955, p. 241) used the term "asymmetrical exchanges," which apparently includes both chromosomal asymmetrical intrachanges (rings) and asymmetrical interchanges (dicentrics), as defined and depicted earlier (pp. 137, 194, 195) in his book. Under this heading, he cited the calculations by Lea and Catcheside (*J. Genetics* 44: 216, 1942) of the original data by Thoday (*J. Genetics* 43: 189, 1942). Although Thoday listed separately the chromosome rings and chromosome interchanges, Lea and Catcheside (1942, pp. 217–18) defined "chromosome interchanges" to include both rings and dicentrics. For human leucocytes, the value 0.45 ± 0.07 is the coefficient of dicentric production alone; the coefficient of rings and dicentric production is 0.52 ± 0.07 and is almost identical to that for *Tradescantia*.

that the coefficients of chromatid-aberration production in human and plant cells do not differ significantly. The recent calculations based on the leucocyte result by Bender and Gooch (1962a) also show a remarkable agreement with the plant data. The value for deletions in the last instance is higher because it includes both the terminal and interstitial types.

These results suggest that human mitotic chromosomes do not differ significantly from plant chromosomes in the manner by which chromosome aberrations are induced by x rays. The low x-ray-induced chromosome aberration frequency in human somatic cells cannot, however, be taken to mean that radiosensitivity of human cells—in terms of genetic damage and cell killing—is necessarily the same in plant and human cells (Bender and Wolff, 1961).

Additionally, I would like to discuss the "doubling dose" for human chromosome aberrations, because the term can easily be misunderstood and misquoted. The values obtained for human chromosome aberrations are 3.3 r (Bender, 1957) and 6 r (Dubinin *et al.*, 1960*a,b*). From the leucocyte data, Bender and Gooch (1962*a*) concluded that the value is 0.87 r and may be lower.

These values must be used with extreme caution, because, by definition, they refer only to the dose necessary to double the spontaneous rate of human somatic chromosome breakage in one cell generation. In tissue culture cells in particular, the control value may have derived from several generations of cells, whereas the induced aberrations must come from one generation. "Doubling dose" is not a good measure of chromosomal sensitivity to radiations, because it is limited to the low dose levels which produce mostly "one-hit" type of aberrations similar to those occurring spontaneously. A better measure for all aberration types by the coefficients of aberration production has already been discussed. Furthermore, these values are clearly not the same as the human "doubling dose" for mutation-induction during a 30-year reproductive generation time or other similar terms specifically defined.

Interpretations for discrepancies of data

So far, I have briefly summarized the experimental studies to date on radiation-induced human chromosome breakages. The data appear to encompass a wide range, but upon reexamination a number of interacting factors seem to be responsible, at least in part, for such differences. To recapitulate, the first factor may be the small sampling size (as compared to similar studies with plant materials), owing primarily to the inherent difficulties of the human material. Second, the variable culture conditions, including the type of medium, temperature, etc., conceivably affect the cell generation time as well as other physiological states of the cell. The age of culture has been shown to change the spontaneous aberration rate. Third, the type and quality of radiations and dosimetry certainly should influence the quantitative results somewhat. Fourth, the cell type and tissue of origin may account, in part, for some differences in aberration frequencies. The size and shape of nuclei in the epithelioid versus fibroblastlike cells may change the number and location of active sites (Wolff, 1959; Atwood, this conference) for chromosome breakage and reunion, thus leading to differences in final aberration production. Moreover, there is no reason to assume that human somatic cells of different tissue origin have the same chromosome aberration rate when they are compared with each other or, particularly, to germ-line cells. Fifth, the cell stage at which the cell is irradiated has been shown to have considerable differences in radiosensitivity.

Finally, the method of scoring should be considered as an important factor. Cytologists are, in general, biased in selecting the best cells for scoring, though the bias is in the same direction for both the control and treated materials. The observed chromosome aberrations are already much less than the total chromosomal damage, since a great majority of primary breaks or damages are rejoined or repaired. Also, many aberrations are not detectable, or are not scored (e.g., inversions and translocations). But the data should be comparable with those obtained from classical materials, if the same scoring criteria are adopted. In Puck's data, abnormalities like achromatic lesions (gaps) and sticky chromosomes have been included. He has also overestimated the spontaneous frequency by including questionable anomalies, because "if any subjective element were involved, it could only distort in the direction of minimizing the number of chromosome aberrations attributable to the radiation." In our data, largely gathered in 1958–59, our criterion for a terminal chromatid deletion was a clear discontinuity (without connecting thread) of the chromatid. This may have included certain "gaps" and not true breaks, as have been discussed by Revell in 1959 and during this conference. Bender's criterion for the terminal chromatid deletion is strictly the situation where the fragment is either rotated or displaced. By preference, we have used a lower concentration of colchicine and have selected cells in which sister chromatid pairing is tight and complete. This has helped us in the diagnosis of many aberration types, particularly in detecting more precisely the symmetrical chromatid interchanges. A stronger colchicine concentration tends to separate such pairing and disrupt the configuration of the aberration.

With these considerations, the data for spontaneous and induced chromosome aberration frequency in human chromosomes (Tables 1 and 2) cannot be said to be in as wide disagreement as they first appeared to be. Many fundamental principles of induction of chromosome aberration in human somatic cells are essentially the same as in classical materials. With the increase of our knowledge and improvements of techniques, particularly the leucocyte techniques employed by Bender and others, accurate quantitation from large samples of human materials appears to be possible.

Dr. Giles: Thank you, Dr. Chu. This paper is now open for discussion. I am sorry that Dr. Bender is not here since he has contributed so much of the recent data.

One of the questions I would like to raise with those familiar with the work he has done at Oak Ridge, in connection with the individuals who were exposed to ionizing radiation, is the question of the persistence of such things as dicentrics and rings. I have not myself had an opportunity to talk with him about this, but I wondered whether Dr. Wolff or Dr. Chu have either seen these slides or have an idea as to how one could get persistent dicentrics for such a considerable period of time after exposures.

Dr. Wolff: I can say one thing, though not about Bender's data, years ago Darlington had observed persistent dicentrics in plant material. They were passed on from generation to generation. Also, Davidson has recently irradiated *Vicia faba* growing roots and let them grow for several days. He got dicentrics that had lost any associated fragments and micronuclei. After several days, he would look again and find several cells that had the same dicentric in them. They can persist. He has used this in an attempt to find out a minimum number of cell cycles that have gone on in that period of time. If he saw seven cells with the same dicentric, he would say that at least three cell divisions occurred.

Dr. Swanson: There is a report by Sears and Camara on a dicentric in wheat, but there is a difference in the fact that the centromeres are not of equal strength. One, therefore, dominates over the other, and leads in anaphase movement.

Dr. Giles: It is certainly not impossible where one gets regular disjunctions, but it would seem unusual to have this persistence unless one had a particular type in the human material.

Dr. Gray: Dr. Court-Brown told me recently of a patient of his who had received radiation treatment for ankylosing spondilitis 13 years previously and was showing a high frequency of certain types of chromosomal aberration. I am afraid I can't tell you what kind of aberrations were observed. The blood culture method was used. I think it would be desirable to know whether these aberrations are seen in marrow, for instance, taken direct, because there does seem to be a possibility that the cells that survive irradiation contain injuries which could become manifest when the cells are transferred to culture, in other words, to eliminate the possibility that the aberrations appear as a result of culturing the irradiated cells, and to make sure that they are present under normal conditions.

Dr. Hollaender: If you sample bone marrow, you may get part of the bone marrow which does not have aberrations. When you take the leucocytes, however, you average out what is produced in the bone marrow. That is, you get a sample representative of the cells produced by the total marrow.

I should also mention that an attempt has been made to follow up the people who survived the Hiroshima bomb explosion. After 15 years, no aberrations have yet been found in these people.

Dr. Gray: I agree, but if you are getting some—I think it was 15 or 20 percent of the cells—showing aberrations, then it would not require the examination of very big amounts of bone marrow to find them. A lot of the bone marrow must be contributing if you get such a large frequency of aberrant cells.

Dr. Hollaender: Bone marrow was not tested because it is so much easier to get leucocytes.

Dr. Gray: One should do a few checks to see that the aberrations are actually present.

Dr. Wolff: These are first division after the blood is drawn.

Dr. Gray: It is the effects of transfer to culture conditions which I think should be controlled.

Dr. Evans: A possibility which cannot be overruled until one looked at cells in the bone marrow itself is that the cells which show these aberrations, when they divide in culture, are cells which would not have undergone division at that time in the bone marrow. What you might be seeing are the first divisions of these cells since their exposure to irradiation, culture conditions being the initiator of the divisions. If this were the case, of course, the aberration frequency in the bone marrow itself would be extremely low.

Dr. Hollaender: It should be checked, of course.

Dr. Gray: Yes, I think it should be checked.

Dr. Atwood: I was not looking at the slide closely enough, but did you actually get dicentrics in these three-year radiations?

Dr. Chu: Yes, they were found.

Dr. Atwood: You could have persistent centric rings.

Dr. Auerbach: What are the dicentrics? Are they bridges due to stickiness or a breakage-fusion cycle?

Dr. Chu: This study was made 29 months after exposure and it is now six months hence. Yes, dicentrics were found at the time of the study.

Dr. Atwood: Is this proportion of dicentrics relatively less than it was on the *in vitro* radiated quadrant?

Dr. Chu: I think so.

Dr. Atwood: There is one possibility; it seems a little remote, but it is an explanation. Maybe you have mitotic crossing over and inversions, and this gives you a constant source of dicentrics at every division, but this still looks like much too high a frequency for such a thing.

Dr. Yerganian: On several occasions, the survival capacity of spontaneous dicentrics has been well observed, especially when they overrun the parent culture and literally take over as the stem cell.

Dr. Lindsley: Do they always, usually, or never give bridges in anaphase?

Dr. Yerganian: They undergo nondisjunction and the typical break-bridge-fusion cycle which, in turn, leads to varying lengths of the interstitial regions.

Dr. Wolff: Do you know whether Bender has done experiments along this line with hamsters?

Dr. Chu: He has compared x-ray-induced chromosome aberration frequency both in the *Ateles* monkeys and the Chinese hamsters, *in vitro* and *in vivo*. I do not recall how this particular point is compared as to the proportion of dicentrics.

Dr. Wolff: I am asking whether it is really a radiation effect. Does he pick this up in an animal experiment, too?

Dr. Chu: Yes, but the frequencies are very, very low, as a matter of fact.

Dr. Atwood: When you look at the spontaneous aberrations in leucocyte cultures, do you see anything peculiar about the distribution? Even though they are very rare, do you have cells with two more often than you should?

Dr. Chu: Very few chromosomal types occur spontaneously.

Dr. Lindsley: Can these leucocytes be cloned now?

Dr. Chu: I think his further data should clarify this point of the clonal-selection hypothesis. This study was done six months ago, and he recently has reexamined the same eight people to see whether the kinds or the relative frequencis have changed.

Dr. Lindsley: Will he be able to follow these *in vitro?*

Dr. Chu: No.

Dr. Yerganian: The bone marrow could be used to start primary cultures.

Dr. Swanson: What is the circulating life of a leucocyte?

Dr. Chu: Is there a hematologist here?

Dr. Revell: It depends on what sort of leucocyte it is.

Dr. Chu: Another thing, I want to say that "leucocyte" is a presumed term. We just don't know what kind of cells, because the hematologists do not agree on the type of cells that undergo active mitosis *in vitro*.

Dr. Yerganian: It should be noted that in this system of culturing leucocytes several divisions can occur over a period of 10 days.

References

Atwood, K. C. 1963. Paper in this volume.

Bender, M. A 1957. Science 126: 974.

—— 1960. Intern. J. Radiation Biol. Suppl., Immediate Low Level Effects Ionizing Radiations, Proc. Symposium, Venice 1959: 103.

Bender, M. A, and P. C. Gooch. 1962a. Proc. Natl. Acad. Sci. U.S. 48: 522.

—— 1962b. Radiation Research 16: 44.

Bender, M. A., and D. M. Prescott. 1962. Exptl. Cell Research 27: 221.

Bender, M. A, and S. Wolff. 1961. Am. Naturalist 95: 39.

Boyd, E., W. W. Buchanan, and B. Lennox. 1961. Lancet 1: 977.

Chu, E. H. Y. 1962. Natl. Cancer Inst. Monograph No. 7 (Symposium, Analytic Cell Culture): 55.

Chu, E. H. Y., N. H. Giles, and K. Passano. 1961. Proc. Natl. Acad. Sci. U.S. 47: 830.

Conen, P. E. 1961. Lancet 2: 47.

Conger, A. D. 1958. Proc. Intern. Congr. Genet. 10th Congr. Montreal 2: 57.

Dubinin, N. P., Yu. Ya. Kerkis, and L. I. Lebedieva. 1960a. Akad. Nauk S.S.S.R. (Moskva).

—— 1960b. Akad. Nauk S.S.S.R. (Moskva). (Translated into English by the U.S. Atomic Energy Commission, Office of Technical Information; available from the Office of Technical Services, Department of Commerce, Washington 25, D.C.)

Fliedner, T. M., E. P. Cronkite, V. P. Bond, J. R. Rubini, and G. Andrew. 1959. Acta Haematol. 22: 65.

Fraccaro, M. 1960. Intern. J. Radiation Biol. Suppl., Immediate Low Level Effects Ionizing Radiations, Proc. Symposium, Venice 1959: 117.

Herschberg, S. N. Lancet 2: 104.

Lindsten, J. 1959. Uppsala LäkFören. Förh. 64: 8.

Puck, T. T. 1958. Proc. Natl. Acad. Sci. U.S. 44: 772.

Revell, S. H. 1959. Proc. Roy. Soc. London 150(B): 563.

Sax, H. J., and K. N. Passano. 1961. Am. Naturalist 95: 97.

Stewart, J. S. S., and A. Sanderson. 1961. Lancet 1: 978.

Tough, I. M., K. E. Buckton, A. G. Baikie, and W. M. Court-Brown. 1960. Lancet 2: 849.

Wolff, S. 1959. Radiation Research, Suppl. 1: 453.

—— 1961. J. Cellular Comp. Physiol. 58, Suppl. 1: 151.

Wolff, S., and H. E. Luippold. 1957. Nature 179: 208.

Chromosome Cytology of Medical Anomalies

Dr. G. Yerganian: The topic assigned to me is one that is rapidly becoming difficult to keep up with even though the cytological phase of development is less than three years old. In an effort to conserve time and limit discussion to cytological problems, I wish to refer the reader to two basic and more recent publications (Sohval, 1961; Hirschhorn and Cooper, 1961). A large number of similar review articles continue to appear in a wide variety of journals too numerous to list on this occasion. Nevertheless, I heartily recommend Sohval's (1961) article as a starting point, for it lies in nomenclature, classical cytology, and clinical findings most effectively.

To describe a similar cytological anomaly in relation to sex chromosome and sex chromatin patterns, in addition to clinical features, would readily surpass the space allotted to me. Therefore, I will only take a moment to relate the Barr sex chromatin pattern with the number of sex chromosomes present in metaphase (Barr and Carr, 1960). As you know, the sex chromatin element described by Barr is a crescentlike heteropyknotic body, located peripherally along the nuclear membrane of the metabolic or resting nucleus of normal females (XX) and certain cases of pseudohermaphrodites (XXY, $XXXY$, and $XXXXY$). The present consideration that the sex chromatin body arises from the heterochromatic portion of one of the X chromosomes and the presence of two kinds of X' chromosomes (X_1X_2) is rapidly gaining popularity (Ohno and Makino, 1961; Yerganian *et al.*, 1960; Grumbach and Morishima, 1962). The normal male (XY) and Turner's syndrome (XO) are sex-chromatin-negative. The number of X chromosomes in various multi-X syndromes may be ascertained by simply adding a count of one to the number of sex chromatin (SC) bodies observed. Thus, $SC + 1 =$ number of X chromosomes and, conversely, the number of metaphase X

chromosomes $- 1 =$ number of SC. This relationship has held up surprisingly well, even though the metaphase X chromosome is most difficult to identify from among several pairs of similar appearing medium-sized metacentrics.

Deviation from this expected relationship is certain to indicate mosaicism, i.e., instances where nondisjunction involves the X chromosomes (XO/XX, XO/XY, XX/XXX, $XO/XX/XXX$, etc.). It is noteworthy that in multiple-X syndromes, such as $XXXY$ and $XXXXY$, the extra X's fail to intensify the clinical picture otherwise noted in the typical Klinefelter's syndrome having an XXY sex mechanism and a single sex chromatin body. Thus, extra "lengths" of X-heterochromatin fail to be expressed additively or to overcome the degree of maleness attributed to the presence of a single (small) Y chromosome.

Several individuals having an XO sex mechanism and a positive sex chromatin have been noted (references in Sohval, 1961; Hirschhorn and Cooper, 1961; Grumbach and Morishima, 1962). Repeated diagnoses revealed these instances to be mosaics or XO/XX, XO/XY, and $XO/XX/XXX$, indicating nondisjunction of an X chromosome to have occurred early during embryologic development. Although there is a strong correlation between the number of sex chromatin bodies and expected X chromosomes, the size relationships of the two entities are unequivocal. The smaller-sized sex chromatin body may be a product derived from a portion of comparatively longer sex heterochromatin.

Presence of a single sex chromatin body in cells possessing a single X chromosome is amply demonstrated in the chicken (Koisin and Ishizaki, 1959). In this instance, the female is XO and sex-chromatin-positive, whereas the male is XX and sex-chromatin-negative. In many instances, femaleness is accompanied by sex-chromatin-positiveness, regardless of phylogenetic alteration in sex-determining mechanisms. This biological fact requires further clarification because the great majority (if not all) of the human XO's are sex-chromatin-negative, in the absence of mosaicism.

How may one approach this problem, using simple techniques? Single-cell clonal isolates from human mosaics are an excellent starting point. The added feature that human karyotypes are quite stable *in vitro* will result in the retention of sporadic, clonally isolated non-disjunctions involving sex chromosomes.

Dr. Auerbach: Has anyone tried to see what happens to the Barr bodies in a sex-reversed fowl?

Dr. Yerganian: With respect to the sex chromatin body, I do not know of such studies. Newcomer has interpreted his recent findings (1959) to support a genetic premise (X/autosomal balance) for sex determination. In another report (Newcomer and Donnelly, 1960) he noted sex reversal of a genetic female who experienced an increase in gonadal autosomes as a result of an ovarian tumor.

Dr. Auerbach: It would be interesting to see whether a hen which is physiologically transformed into a cock loses the sex chromatin.

Dr. Yerganian: There is evidence in humans that antibiotics will affect sex chromatin size (Sohval and Casselman, manuscript in preparation). Some British reports claim smaller sex chromatin bodies to accompany reductions in the size of X chromosomes (Jacobs *et al.*, 1960). The elements involved in these instances can also be regarded as trisomics of normally small autosomal types.

Dr. Pavan: Are you also including the drumsticks in your sex chromatin?

Dr. Yerganian: No, not in all cases. The drumstick analysis appears less prominently in the literature because it is not always conducted by chromosome cytologists. It also involves additional steps to prepare, in comparison with the now conventional buccal smear. I would like to leave the human syndromes per se at this point, primarily because it is too extensive a topic. This can be substantiated by the more than 250 publications that have appeared on this subject during the past two years. The many facets pertaining to this subject have been amply considered by Sohval (1961).

There are a number of interesting cytological phenomena now being considered as inherent features that may encourage the formation of the more prevalent types of syndromes. Excellent progress is being made to describe the association of satellites of particular chromosomes (Ohno *et al.*, 1961; Ferguson-Smith and Handmaker, 1961; Lehmann and Forssman, 1962). One or more members of chromosome types 13, 14, 15, 21, and 22 share in the formation of several nucleoli. The satellited portions of the short arms are presumably heterochromatic and any malfunction may be reflected in an over- or underproduction of nucleolar products. These chromosomes resemble one another and an exact identification is not yet feasible, particularly when comparing results from different laboratories.

In the event that satellited chromosomes undergo differential maturation with respect to the coordinated steps in nucleolar formation, delays in metaphase plate orientation may lead to nondisjunction. Spontaneous breaks involving two or more nucleolar-associated chromosomes may give rise to functional translocations, as seen in several familial patterns of Down's syndrome (references in Lehmann and Forssman, 1962). Loss of the acentric fragment(s), composed of the satellite short arms, is apparently nonlethal.

This brings up the question of differential survival capacity of heterochromatic and euchromatic lesions in mammalian systems. I am certain that the literature will show that lesions involving heterochromatic segments fail to be expressed as dominant lethals immediately, and that cell lineage will continue for some time.

Dr. Lindsley: Would you say a little more about that.

Dr. Yerganian: I turn to the Drosophila workers in the audience for their experiences. I am considering large involvements in the form of dicentrics and the like rather than minute alterations.

Dr. Auerbach: Fairly large deficiencies in *Drosophila* are viable in heterozygotes. One also has to consider that a deficiency which is small in relation to a *Drosophila* chromosome would appear longer in man in relation to human chromosomes because the genome is so much more subdivided.

In *Drosophila* I think that a deficiency comprising 1 percent of the whole genome may be viable in heterozygous condition, and if such a deficiency occurs in one of the smaller human chromosomes it would appear a very sizable one.

Dr. Lindsley: One-tenth or one-eighth of the euchromatic length of one of the large chromosomes of *Drosophila* certainly may not be removed and survive as a heterozygote. However, 2 percent of the genome can be removed by removing chromosome 4.

Dr. Auerbach: This is an abnormality, but it is not lethal.

Dr. Yerganian: My premise is that gross anomalies, other than those found presently in certain familial situations involving particular chromosome types, may be lethal, since the numbers of individuals having translocations involving the larger autosomes are too few.

Dr. Lindsley: This is reasonable. I didn't understand what you were saying about heterochromatin.

Dr. Yerganian: It is most difficult, at this time, to define "heterochromatin" in mammalian systems. Therefore, I generally place the term in quotations, to acknowledge the fact that there are certain segments and whole arms of chromosomes that exhibit a differential pattern of DNA synthesis or replication in comparison to the remainder of the complement which may be regarded as "euchromatic" in function. Consequently, these distinct variations are considered to reflect differences in genetic potential. Therefore, loss of a "euchromatic" segment of an autosome will have far greater consequences than loss of a similar-sized portion or an entire sex element, particularly the X_2 and Y counterparts in the human (Yerganian *et al.*, 1960; Grumbach and Morishima, 1962). Although one can detect a number of sex anomalies, especially those monosomic for the X chromosomes, syndromes due to monosomaty of autosomes are either quite rare, or nonviable.

Dr. Giles: Is any case established as a monosomic for an autosome?

Dr. Yerganian: Not as yet.

Dr. Chu: This may survive in tissue culture. Small autosomal deficiencies in tissue culture have survived.

Dr. Yerganian: I will now continue and discuss a few topics of new interests and approaches. Patau and his collaborators (1961) have been exploring the use of partial and complete trisomics, in an effort to provide linkage maps of the various defects featured in the syndrome.

Ultimately, the identification of minute deletions or additions will become one of the greater challenges. Wherever possible, pachytene analyses must be considered hereafter on individuals who do not have a gross metaphase chromosomal anomaly and yet exhibit abnormal development.

The possibility that the single X chromosome in Turner's syndrome (*XO*) may, at times, give rise to sex-chromatin-positive cells in nonmosaic individuals is another aspect that requires further investigation, utilizing tritiated thymidine uptake patterns (Morishima *et al.*, in press). Another case is the male Turner syndrome, having an XO sex mechanism. The status of the X chromosome in certain pseudohermaphroditic states, notably the testicular feminization syndrome (XY), is most perplexing, particularly when occurring among related individuals. The possibility that the X chromosome in the testicular feminization syndrome is only partially completed (judged in the future by tritiated thymidine uptake) in differentiating from the $X_2 \rightarrow X_1$ status, i.e., $X_{1\text{-}2}$, may be regarded as a far more challenging working hypothesis than limiting further investigations by assuming the syndrome to be caused by a single sex-linked recessive or dominant gene.

Another area that requires attention is the screening of solid human malignancies for chromosomal anomalies. With the collaboration of Mr. Rei Kato, I have been viewing a number of children's malignancies *in vitro*. For this occasion, I wish to present several unpublished idiograms of near-diploid malignancies. In general, it can be stated that chromosome anomalies in children's tumors involve the same autosomal types that are known to give rise to the present array of syndromes in man. The high spontaneous breakage rate of certain autosomal types is also recorded in children's tumors.

Dr. Wolff: Is there a distinction between tumors in children and tumors in adults?

Dr. Yerganian: Chromosome numbers in children's tumors are surprisingly restricted to near-diploid modalities, in sharp contrast to malignancies from adults, which are generally near-polyploid (Makino *et al.*, 1959). The tumors which I will discuss have only 45 and 47 chromosomes.

Dr. Wolff: So there is a difference between children and adults?

Dr. Yerganian: Yes, particularly in the early phases of culture following surgery.

Dr. Revell: Do these include teratomas?

Dr. Yerganian: No, although the more interesting malignancies to look forward to studying are those arising in true hermaphrodites in which the rudimentary reproductive organs of both sexes are suspected of having the sex mechanism of only one sex.

Dr. Chu: Before you go on, may I stress one point with which I think everybody is familiar. There is a difference between insects and mammals concerning their hormones. In mammals genetic determination of sex by sex chromosomes can be further modified by hormones during sex differentiation. So we should bear in mind that sex determination by the genetic mechanisms and sex differentiation are probably two separate processes. For example, the testicular feminization type of male pseudohermaphrodite has X and Y sex chromosomes, testes, but a female phenotype. The female phenotype depends on the hormone excretion of the testes.

Dr. Yerganian: This is one of the problems which I mentioned above as needing additional studies. True hermaphrodites and some instances of patients having atypical ovarian or testicular dysgenesis require social and psychological readjustments which may include changes in the habits of dress and corrective surgery (Wilkins, 1960). The rearing of pseudohermaphrodites is a subject which I do not feel qualified to comment upon.

In addition to the influence of imbalanced hormonal secretions mentioned by Dr. Chu in the rarer cases of gonadal dysgenesis, the complex of disturbances under the heading of adrenal hyperplasia or adrenogenital syndromes also require individual care in rearing and treatment. The latter condition is unrelated to karyotypic changes, but genetic lesions or impairment of "heterochromatin" to function normally still remain to be fully evaluated.

The time is not too far away when the approaches of Atwood and Wolff, in estimating sensitivity sites to radiation breakage, and that of others relating chromosome structure, rates, and patterns of DNA synthesis, and a deeper insight in ultrastructural changes, will be applied in reviewing alterations in human physiology. As a step in this direction, Dr. Arlene Longwell and I have been attempting to detect the finer variations in the structural appearance of chromosomes by interferometric measurements. For this purpose, we have employed the Chinese hamster with its low diploid number of 22 clearly defined chromosomes, following procedures outlined by Dr. Longwell (1961).

I can recall the status of mammalian cytology a decade ago, when only a few investigators were attempting to clarify the almost impossible human karyotype without the aid of pretreatments. Today, a large number of researchers claim that the recent advances in human cytogenetics have come about following the "rediscovery" that man possesses 46 instead of 48 chromosomes. I beg to disagree, and say that if man had twice the present number, progress in this direction would still continue so long as helpful techniques, the identification of sex chromatin, and the now classic monosomic and trisomic conditions were known. The large number of reports on chromosomes of mouse and rat ascites tumor cells accrued over the past decade virtually lacked a single statement concerning the fate of sex elements.

The few and more recent findings on both species of hamsters have, comparatively speaking, provided more information on the identification and role of sex elements in normal and malignant rodent cell type (Awa *et al.*, 1959; Yerganian *et al.*, 1960; Ohno and Weiler, 1961; Ishihara *et al.*, in press). As we come closer to considering specific losses and/or gains of chromatin segments and their DNA sequence, we will be encouraged to select the finest of cytological markers which our eyes and microscopes will allow. This approach is certain to reflect in a better understanding of human cytogenetics.

To illustrate the potential of the human karyotype *in vivo* and *in vitro*, I have compiled the various features noted in the more popular experimental species in Table 1. With respect to sensitivity to colchicine, all species respond favorably at dosages of 1.0 mg/kg *in vivo*, or 1 μg/ml of *in vitro* media. The Syrian or golden hamster requires a 100-fold increase in colchicine to arrest metaphases. The present use of Vincaleukoblastine for purposes of arresting mitoses is also timely, particularly for the colchicine-resistant Syrian hamster.

Retention of the initial karyotype, whether it be normal (classic diploid) or that involving an anomaly, for periods up to one year, is thus far limited to Chinese hamster and human tissues. The mouse has been repeatedly found to undergo profound karyotypic alterations and limited proliferation by the third subculture *in vitro*. The rat and Syrian hamster have not been fully studied with respect to chromosome stability during continuous cultivation.

The Barr body or sex chromatin is primarily noted in human rest-

Table 1. *Cellular and Chromosomal Features of Current Experimental Tissues*

Mitotic details	Mouse	Rat	Syrian hamster	Chinese hamster	Human
Sensitivity to colchicine	+	+	±	+	+
Stability during continuous proliferation		?	?	+	+
Visualization of sex chromatin of Barr					+
Readily recognized normal X chromosomes		±	+	+	
Readily recognized normal Y chromosome	±	±	+	+	±
Readily recognized aberrant X chromosomes			±	+	
Readily recognized aberrant Y chromosome	±	±	±	+	±
Readily detected aberrant autosomal types				±	±
Localization of secondary constrictions and/or nucleolar sites				+	+
Nullisomaty, including sex elements			±	±	±
Monosomaty, including sex elements				+	⊥
Trisomaty, including sex elements				±	±
Sex mechanism, other than $XX : XY$				X_1X_2Y	

ing or metabolic cells, regardless of whether the tissue is taken as a buccal smear, skin biopsy, or maintained *in vitro*. Larger and more diffuse chromocentral masses are readily seen as counterparts in female rodent tissues, but little effort has been made to pursue this point. Ohno and his collaborators (references in Ohno and Makino, 1961) have utilized the so-called precocious condensation of heterochromatin witnessed during prophase as being indicative of the single X chromosome giving rise to the sex chromatin body. However, the size relationship is such that only a small portion of heterochromatin would be implicated in forming the sex chromatin during the resting stage. Thus, to dramatize the clarity or visualization of sex chromatin, I have limited the presence of this body to the human female cell type.

In metaphase, the X chromosome has yet to be reported in the mouse karyotype. Similarly, in the rat, one cannot readily select the normal X chromosome in female tissues. Fortunately, the X chromosome in the Syrian hamster is the largest of the complement and one can readily select it from among other large autosomes (Awa *et al.*,

1959; Ohno and Weiler, 1961; Ishihara *et al.*, in press). In polyploid malignancies of the Syrian hamster, the X chromosome becomes most difficult to identify in the presence of new "marker" chromosomes (Ishihara *et al.*, in press). The most easily recognized metaphase X chromosome is that of the Chinese hamster. One can select the sex elements from among the autosomes at magnifications as low as 120×. The human X chromosome presents the most frustrating situation because it resembles several autosomal metacentrics. It is for this reason that caution must be taken in designating specific metacentrics as the X chromosome, even though an excellent correlation is provided by the number of sex chromatin bodies.

The Y chromosomes of most species are readily seen in normal cells. The plus or minus relationship noted in Table 1 indicates the relative ease with which one may visualize it in a given number of cells.

Without sex chromatin analyses in the human, aberrations of the X chromosome would be most difficult to assess. Equally so would be the selection of structural alterations of the X chromosomes in the mouse and rat in the absence of linkage studies. An aberrant form of the X chromosome in the Syrian hamster could be distinguished, provided staining and hypotonic pretreatments were altered slightly to accent the lighter appearance of the long heterochromatic arms. Extensions and deletions of either arm of the two types of X chromosomes in the Chinese hamster usually enhance their heterochromatic nature and serve as appropriate markers.

Exact identification of altered autosomal types are feasible only in the Chinese hamster and human complements. Localization of secondary constrictions and/or nucleolar sites is also restricted to the latter two species at this time.

Since the hamster species and man possess varied forms of chromosomes, monosomaty can be favorably detected, if and when it occurs. In experimental tissues (cultures or transplantable tumors), opportunities to witness monosomaty and nullisomaty involving autosomes may arise following long periods of propagation. More frequently, however, nullisomy involves sex elements of experimental tissues (Yerganian *et al.*, 1960). In the Chinese hamster, the two "homologues" of the X chromosome pair (X_1 and X_2) are distinctly different morphologically and, therefore, a missing member (always the X_2) leads to nullisomy. Extension of the *Triheterosomic* scheme for sex determination, as seen in the Chinese hamster, to other rodents and man (Yerganian *et al.*, 1960) is now being reviewed by a number of independent laboratories (Grumbach and Morishima, 1962; Miles, 1962).

On what basis does one challenge the correctness in assigning the *XX:XY* sex mechanism (so amply demonstrated in *Drosophila*) to man? The *XX:XY* sex mechanism in *Drosophila* is considered to be the most primitive form in the genus. Other species of *Drosophila* have far more complex mechanisms than one usually associates with this genus. Many of the current laboratory rodents having 40 or more chromosomes are routinely considered to have the classical *XX:XY* scheme (Table 2). In sharp contrast, low chromosome species, such

Table 2. Present Status of Sex Chromosome Morphology and Types among More Popular Experimental Tissues (as of February, 1961)

	Chromosome numbers	Sex chromosome relationship	
Species		*Female*	*Male*
Homo sapiens	46	XX[a]	XY[a]
Cricetus auratus	44	XX	XY
Rattus norvegicus	42	XX[a]	XY[a]
Mus musculus	40	XX	XY
Tcherkia nestor[b]	30	XX	XY
Sorex araneus	23	?	XY_1Y_2
Cricetulus griseus[c]	22	X_1X_2[a]	X_1Y[a]
Cricetulus migratorius[b]	20	XX	XY
Ellobius lutescens[b]	17	$\widehat{XX}$?	$\widehat{XY}$
Microtus oregoni[b]	17	$\widehat{XX}$?	$\widehat{XY}$

[a] Allocycly evident (sex chromosome and/or sex chromatin).
[b] Insufficient study.
[c] Evidence other than morphology alone.

as *Cricetulus griseus, Sorex araneus, Ellobius lutescens,* and *Microtus oregoni* possess multiple and attached sex elements (Matthey, 1958; Yerganian, 1961). Even though these species are relatively new in the laboratory, their patterns of sex determination are strongly dependent upon the total number (and clarity) of chromosomes in the complement. In addition, they have not been utilized in genetic research to the same extent as species having 40 or more chromosomes.

Were it not for the recent studies by Russell (1961), the mouse would still be regarded as having the classic mechanism.

The use of tritiated thymidine as a means of identifying difficult or nondescript forms of sex chromosomes has been proposed and demonstrated by Yerganian (1960, 1961) and Morishima, *et al.* (in press), respectively.

Having reviewed the comparatively excellent qualities of the human karyotype, I will now discuss the role of quasidiploidy in relation to the origin of some human syndromes and malignancies. The term quasidiploidy refers to cells having the same number of chromosomes as the classic diploid cell but, in addition, it features slight numerical and/or structural alterations that may remain undetected in less favorable karyotypes. The initial description on this subject was provided by Yerganian *et al.* (1960); more recently, Hauschka (1961) has further extended the hypothetical implications to additional systems of tumor oncogenesis.

Until now, quasidiploid cells in human peripheral leucocytes had not been considered (Fig. 1). The male studied in this illustration had a surprisingly high frequency (60 percent) of quasidiploids and tendency for trisomy of chromosome 3. Note that to compensate for trisomaty, other members of the complement are reduced randomly to a monosomic state. The male donor's wife (lower half of Fig. 1) was normal, as seen in the third idiogram. However, she too had an occasional trisomy for chromosome 3. The sex chromosomes are designated according to the *Triheterosomic* scheme, i.e., $X_1X_2{:}X_1Y$ (the X_1 of the uppermost male idiogram was, unfortunately, lost while photographing the composite plate). This couple now has two normal children and the quasidiploid condition in their peripheral leucocytes was due to random nondisjunctions. Other workers, notably Hauschka and associates, prefer to substitute the term pseudodiploid, in place of quasidiploid. However, I cannot see how one may find anything "false" about such numerical relationships.

Dr. Conger: Were all of the male leucocytes that you examined like that?

Dr. Yerganian: The husband had an incidence of 60 percent quasidiploidy. The wife was pregnant at the time of these studies and

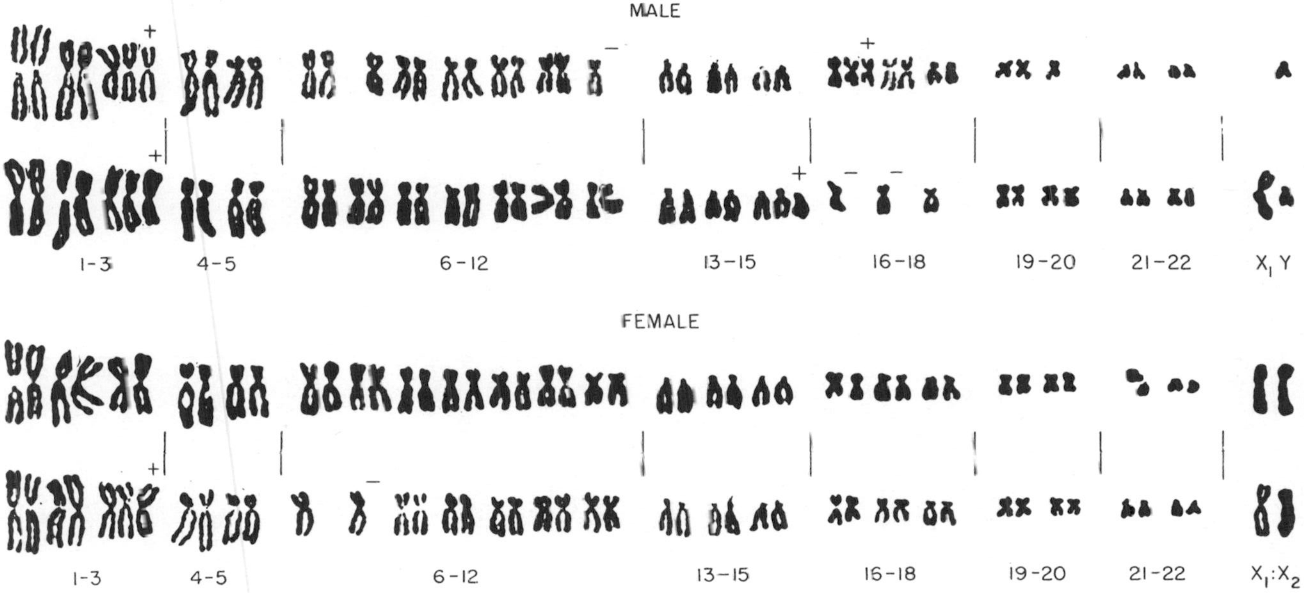

Fig. 1. Normal human peripheral blood leucocyte cultures

Top: normal male showing quasidiploid relationship with consistent trisomaty for chromosome 3. *Bottom*: normal female also showing sporadic quasidiploidy and trisomaty for chromosome 3 (husband and wife with two normal offspring). Note designations of X_1Y and X_1X_2 for sex chromosomes following the *Triheterosomic* scheme for sex determination.

was conducting the chromosome analyses as a donor-assistant. She tried hard to arrange the idiogram to be as normal as possible as she approached term.

Dr. Conger: But he did have normal cells, too?

Dr. Yerganian: Yes.

Dr. Chu: This also could be explained by a reciprocal translocation rather than by a monosomic-trisomic combination.

Dr. Yerganian: We have taken the simplest and most probable event, i.e., nondisjunction, to account for random quasidiploidy, even though trisomy for chromosome 3 was unusually high.

Dr. Atwood: This 60 percent or so of the pseudoquasidiploids— are they all the same kind?

Dr. Yerganian: No, they varied and involved other autosomes in monosomic and trisomic relationships. This was the main reason why we hesitated in suggesting a translocation as having given rise to the chromosome designated as an extra 3. Quasidiploidy noted in the Chinese hamster ranges from 5 to 10 percent (regenerating liver and normal bone marrow).

Dr. Atwood: How much is it in most people?

Dr. Yerganian: It is quite rare. We were anxious to follow the male in Fig. 1 because of his wife's pregnancy. We wished to record this striking example of quasidiploidy to illustrate trisomy in an otherwise normal fertile male with high intelligence. It should be stated that trisomy of a large metacentric autosome in a 47-chromosome female has been reported by Sandberg *et al.* to be associated with mental retardation (1960).

Dr. Pavan: What would you expect to find in the scheme, for instance, in other tissues?

Dr. Yerganian: We did not study other tissues.

Dr. Pavan: But are there indications where you have this type of thing in the blood and examined the autotissue and have something else, or not?

Dr. Moses: Is the number of trisomics equal to the number of monosomics?

Dr. Yerganian: Yes, and the total was always 46. If we failed to make idiograms from representative squashes or air-dried preparations, we would have concluded that he was normal, when only scanning the slide and making routine counts.

Dr. Pavan: How can we be sure it is not a question of method rather than that type of variability?

Dr. Yerganian: One tries to adhere to the general rule of employing only those cells which have an intact membrane and, later, aligning the individual chromosomes in an idiogram.

Dr. Pavan: I am surprised that you have the same amount of chromatin and that the only viability would be for one chromosome to go to one side and the other to go to the other side.

Dr. Yerganian: I brought this up now as another area that requires further exploration, and not to give explanation at this time.

Dr. Swanson: May I ask whether, in this same population, you find aneuploids (e.g., $2n-1$)? The chromosomes are really within a continual size pattern and any variation in terms of structure is going to throw it one way or the other. Having looked at enough of these, I would be awfully suspicious of what you are saying simply because it is so difficult to tell sizes.

Dr. Yerganian: As I tried to point out, this individual was examined on several occasions and showed the persistent high frequency of quasidiploidy over a period of some three weeks. He is certainly exceptional in relation to what we know thus far and I discuss it now to stress the point that individuals with disturbed karyotypes in peripheral leucocytes may function normally, and that certain kinds of peripheral alterations may be limited in expression. Aneuploidy, of which quasidiploidy may be regarded as the slightest of the aneuploid alterations, is always present in normal tissue and, in some instances, aged persons have increased frequencies.

Dr. Swanson: I agree, but along with this you should also have the $2n-1$'s, rather than coordinated loss of one and gain of another.

Dr. Yerganian: That is true, and I have taken the liberty of restricting the illustrations to the classic diploid versus an example of quasidiploid having the trisomic 3.

Dr. Moses: How many replications did these go through?

Dr. Yerganian: These are the first *in vitro* divisions fixed 72 hours after initiating the culture.

Dr. Conger: Of the various tissues that are used for these chromosome analyses, which one has the highest frequency of aberrancies, in your experience or belief? Does one show much more than the others?

Dr. Yerganian: I don't believe that I can judge this on an individual basis. There might be differences in the population as a whole, but I would say that skin has more spontaneous breakages than peripheral leucocytes, and bone marrow has the least.

Dr. Conger: Do you feel that it is appreciably different?

Dr. Yerganian: I am not prepared to answer, since I have not reviewed the literature.

May I continue the discussion with respect to the localization of satellited regions on specific chromosome types? The satellited chromosome is unique for the human and primate karyotypes. Present laboratory species of rodents fail to exhibit protruded satellites or constricted secondary regions to indicate sites for the formation of nucleoli. To illustrate satellited chromosomes, an idiogram of a female having Down's syndrome is provided in Fig. 2. Note the now classical trisomy for chromosome 21. The satellited chromosomes are 13–15, 21, and 22 (Ohno *et al.*, 1961; Ferguson-Smith and Handmaker, 1961; Lehmann and Forssman, 1962).

Dr. Ris: Satellited or short arm?

Dr. Yerganian: The short arms of chromosomes 13–15, 21, and 22 have satellited ends, as seen in better preparations published by other investigators. Until recently, the short arm of chromosome 22 remained unclear, but it is now generally accepted as being satellited, thus making a minimum of five pairs of autosomes involved in the formation of nucleoli. These particular chromosomes are also important because of their participation in a number of syndromes (Sohval, 1961; Hirschhorn and Cooper, 1961) and in the formation of marker chromosomes in malignancies of children (Yerganian and Kato, unpublished). The persistence or association of satellited ends well into metaphase, with or without nucleolar remnants, is clearly seen (Ohno *et al.*, 1961; Ferguson-Smith and Handmaker, 1961; Lehmann and Forssman, 1962). In addition to leading to nondisjunction, failure of prometaphase nucleolar chromosomes to align properly along the spindle equator due to delayed breakdown of

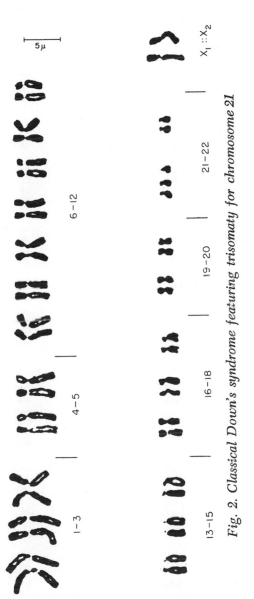

Fig. 2. Classical Down's syndrome featuring trisomaty for chromosome 21

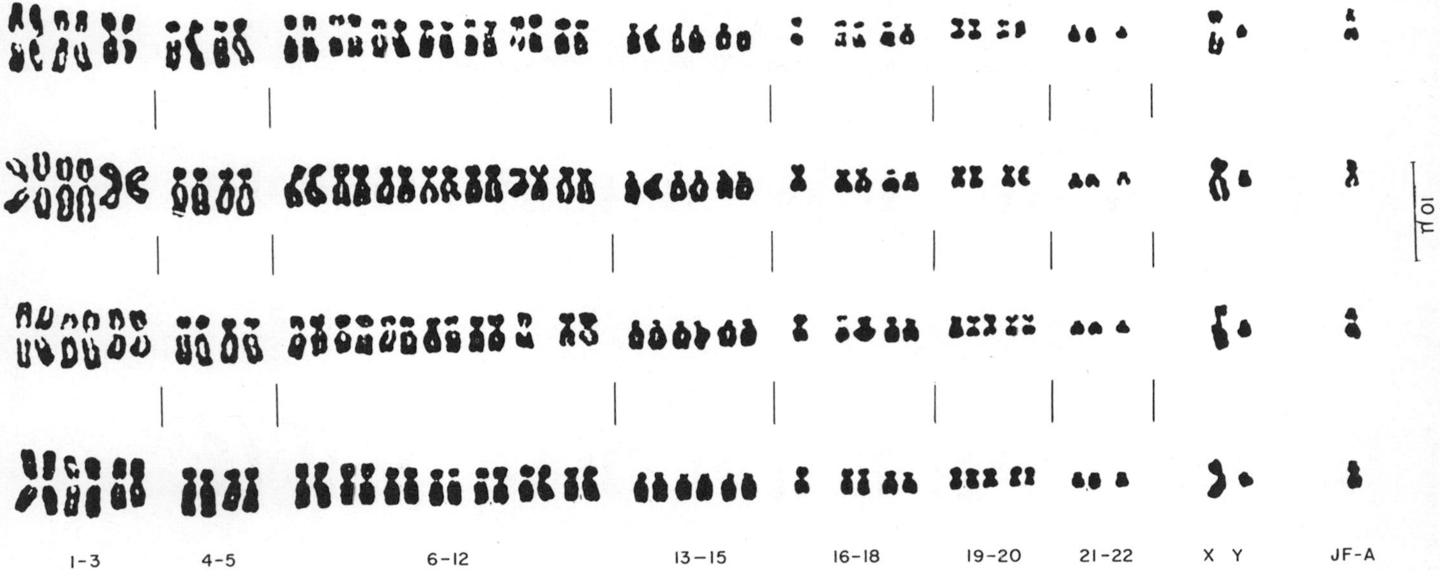

Fig. 3. Idiograms of human ependymoma (9-year-old male)

Forty-five chromosome modal frequency with marker chromosome, JF-A, placed to the right. Note monosomic relationship for intact members of 16 and 22. JF-A marker chromosome is the result of a translocation involving altered members of 16 and 22 chromosome types.

1–3   4–5   6–12   13–15   16–18   19–20   21–22   X Y   JF-A

10 μ

nucleolar substance may encourage the formation of select rearrangements following spontaneous breakage at closely associated centromeric regions. Examples of this theoretical consideration are now recorded in families having structural translocations involving chromosomes 15 and 21 (references in Lehmann and Forssman, 1962).

An example of a satellited chromosome taking part in the formation of a marker chromosome in a tumor found in children is provided in Fig. 3 (Yerganian and Kato, unpublished). The tissue cultures were derived from a malignant ependymoma, which occurred at the base of the brain in a nine-year-old white male. A striking modality of 45 chromosomes involving 90 percent or more of the metaphases continued for many transplant generations. The persistent monosomic nature of chromosome types 16 and 22 suggests that, in the absence of additional rearrangements, the new marker chromosome JF-A (nomenclature using the Denver System) is a translocation arising from the missing members of the 16 and 22 groups. Judging from the appearance of JF-A, the initial breaks must have taken place at the centromere of a chromosome 16, and distally on the long arm of a chromosome 22. The upper telomere appears as an intact, satellited short arm of chromosome 22. The possibility that JF-A is a "dicentric" with only one functioning primary constriction may be deduced from the general outline of the structure. The lost acentric portions resulting from the translocation could readily have been the short arm of 16 and a very small distal portion of the long arm of 22, which were lost soon after formation of the mutant stem line. Although all the centromeres may be accounted for, there has been a loss of some chromatin, thereby leading to partial monosomy for 16 and 22.

Another example of a near-diploid human tumor is given in Fig. 4 (Yerganian and Kato, unpublished). It is a Wilms' tumor from a young female, which has a 47-chromosome modality. In addition to having the "normal" and "quasidiploid" chromosome relationship, a marker of unknown derivation was also present in all the cells (right hand). Judging from the size of arms of the marker chromosome, it could be the product of a reciprocal translocation between members of the 6–12 and 16–18 groups in an early cancerous cell that was trisomic from one of the types mentioned.

The dual nature of the two X chromosomes (X_1X_2) was readily noted in the Wilms' tumor, providing some support for our earlier belief that rapidly proliferating tissues facilitate the identification of two forms of the X chromosomes in normal and malignant derivatives (Yerganian *et al.*, 1960).

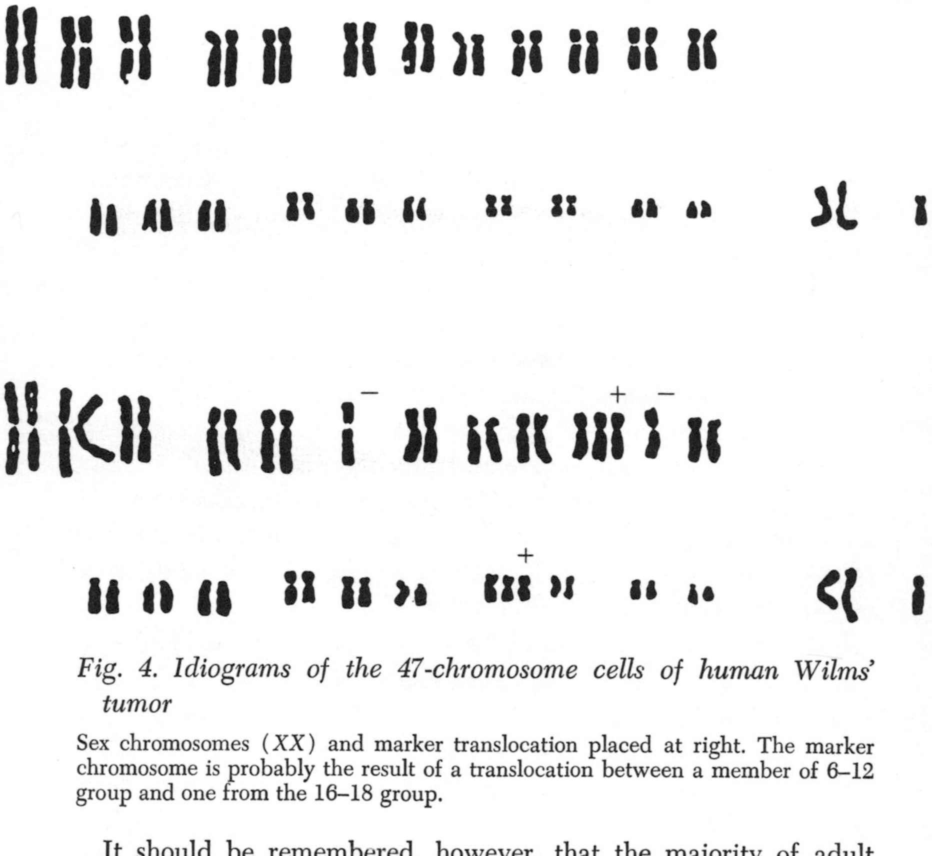

Fig. 4. Idiograms of the 47-chromosome cells of human Wilms' tumor

Sex chromosomes (XX) and marker translocation placed at right. The marker chromosome is probably the result of a translocation between a member of 6–12 group and one from the 16–18 group.

It should be remembered, however, that the majority of adult malignancies have a wider range in the distribution of chromosomes and are in the high-aneuploid (near-tetraploid) range (Makino *et al.*, 1959).

Dr. Sparrow: Are these two different cells?

Dr. Yerganian: Yes, the upper idiogram shows the presence of the 46 "normal" complement, in addition to the marker chromosome. The lower idiogram provides an example of a quasidiploid relationship among the 46 "normal" members, plus the persisting marker. No two cells were alike in the "quasidiploid" condition of the "normal" elements, but every cell had the marker.

An example of recent findings on human chronic granulocytic leukemia by Nowell and Hungerford (1961) is given in Fig. 5, which they so graciously provided for this occasion. This is a marker quasi-

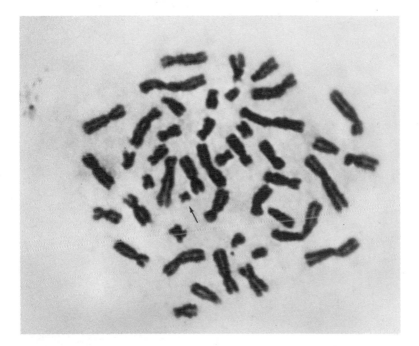

Fig. 5. Karyotype of human chronic granulocytic leukemia
Unpublished photograph provided by Drs. D. A. Hungerford and P. C. Nowell.

diploid state, in which one of the type-21 chromosomes experiences a medial deletion along the long arm. This marker chromosome, now termed the Philadelphia (*Ph'*) chromosome, has been recorded in the great majority of cases reported independently (Jacobs *et al.*, 1959; Sandberg *et al.*, 1960). It should be recalled that trisomy for chromosome 21 leads to Down's syndrome (previously termed mongolism). Reports of increased incidence of leukemia among individuals having Down's syndrome require further and more widespread

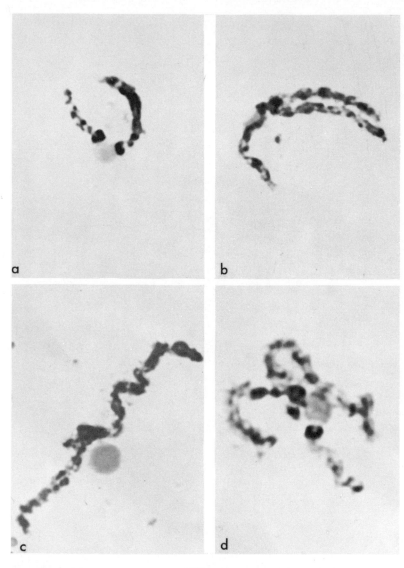

Fig. 6

(a) Nucleolar-associated chromosomes, pachytene chromosomes of Schultz and St. Lawrence. Considered here as actually being a satellite association of bivalents of 21 and a member of 13, 14, or 15. (b) Satellite association of bivalent 13, 14, and 15. (c) An anomalous association of nucleolus and chromocentral masses of unidentifiable isolated human pachytene chromosomes. (d) Satellite association of chromosome 21 bivalent (short arm of Schultz and St. Lawrence nucleolar chromosome) with two bivalents of 13–15 group. Note pale appearance of long "arm" of chromosome 21 (6 o'clock).

analyses. If we may recall Fig. 2 for the moment, we again note the satellited ends of chromosome 21, which are suspected as being one of the sites upon which nucleoli form.

A most timely approach to provide a better understanding of human cytogenetics is the matching of pachytene bivalents with their mitotic counterparts. Examples of pachytene bivalents are given in Fig. 6, initially recorded by myself in 1951. Previously, Schultz and St. Lawrence (1949) described the chromomeric pattern of the human nucleolar chromosome which was later confirmed by my work (1957), as seen in Fig. 6a. At that time, very little was known about mammalian nucleolar bivalents and since 50 percent of the nucleolar chromosome "arms" were observed to have separated from the nucleolus, it was assumed, in both of the above reports, that the secondary constriction was oriented medially. In reassessing my earlier findings, I wish to now submit a revision on the origin of the nucleolar chromosome in man, first reported by Schultz and St. Lawrence.

To assist in this matter, I have included in Fig. 6 pachytene bivalent associations involving several bivalents in the formation of a nucleolus. Figure 6 shows the affinity of dense "chromomeres" of three bivalents in the absence of a common nucleolus. If one considers the allocyclic nature of heterochromatin, the juxtaposed "chromomeres" may readily be the hyperactive phase (allocycly) of the otherwise slender and pale satellite regions of chromosome types 13, 14, and 15, as seen in mitotic metaphases. Returning to Fig. 6a, the Schultz and St. Lawrence nucleolar chromosome, I now consider it a product of an association to form a common nucleolus involving bivalents 15 and 21. In so doing, the Schultz and St. Lawrence nucleolar chromosome must, hereafter, be considered as an artifact representing two of the five autosomal types that may associate during the formation of nucleoli. The dense medial knobs on either side of the nucleolus are the condensed or hyperactive (allocyclic) state of the satellited short arms. Supporting evidence for considering the "nucleolar" bivalent as actually being composed of intact and paired members of types 21 and 14 is provided by Lehmann and Forssman (1962) in their description of satellite associations in familial mongolism having a chromosome translocation between

15/21 types. It has taken virtually 13 years to attempt further clarification of this, the first bivalent described in man.

An anomalous association of two bivalents is seen in Fig. 6c. Although lacking in some detail, Fig. 6d is comprised of several bivalents sharing in the formation of a nucleolus. Bivalent 21 can be recognized as the lowermost portion extending downward. At least two other bivalents are present.

Dr. Lindsley: Can you count pachytene chromosomes?

Dr. Yerganian: I published nine pachytene bivalents in 1957, and there are still eight more to prepare. I do wish to make a plea, along with this presentation, that we return to pachytene analyses wherever possible as a last resort to check some 30 odd syndromes currently regarded as *not* having karyotypical (mitotic) alterations. A number of clinically important syndromes may have minute detectable deletions or additions when viewed in pachytene.

Dr. Wolff: If these are isolated, you cannot count them in a cell.

Dr. Yerganian: With renewed efforts one can do a little better today. I am certain that if one takes the time for such an endeavor, by reducing efforts to chase each suspected patient having a syndrome that has already been described, we may get somewhere. The time has come to stop the recording of the same cases in different individuals having identical (now classic) anomalies and concentrate on the more subtle possibilities of chromosome defects. It is virtually impossible for an anomalous individual to pass through a hospital today without having his blood, skin, or bone marrow studied. This is not meant to be facetious since a great majority of the participants are doing a fine job. Nevertheless, many syndromes remain unanswered and will still require explanation. Pachytene analyses and the use of classical cytological terminology will add greatly to human cytogenetics.

Dr. Giles: In reference to the nucleolus situation, do you see more than one chromosome pair associated with a nucleolus in cells that have two nucleoli?

Dr. Yerganian: In the 1957 paper, I was unable to justify the possibility of two nucleolar-forming bivalents, since the pachytenes were prepared as isolated elements. The situation was confused by Sachs when he sharply criticized Schultz and St. Lawrence (1949) and, in turn, considered the nucleolus as being the plasmasome which had detached from the sex bivalent or amphinuclear complex. Therefore, the individual pachytenes which I described in 1957 as having small nuclei were considered as detached long "arms" of the "nucleolar" chromosome. Today, I consider them as intact members of the 13–15 group.

Dr. Chu: Kodani observed two nucleoli, one large and one small, in human spermatocytes at pachytene. This agrees with our observation on human somatic cells that basically there are two pairs of nucleoli, one large and one small.

Dr. Yerganian: There is a plasmasome associated with the totally heteropyknotic sex bivalent to which the term, "amphinuclear complex," has been assigned in the past.

The varied sizes and densities of the "chromomeres" of human pachytenes may be the result of the specific activities so prominently noted in Dipteran salivary gland and Malpighian chromosomes by Drs. C. Pavan and G. Rudkin. Thus, the "chromomere" pattern in less descriptive material may partially reflect their views on gene action.

Dr. Wolff: Are these male cells?

Dr. Yerganian: Yes, and you can observe similar features in gonadal tissues of rodents.

The over-all clarity of human pachytene bivalents is quite surprising when compared to rodents. They have no lampbrushing, assume characteristic and replicable shapes when isolated from the intact nucleus, and feature chromatic knobs and chromomeric patterns down to very delicate satellited telomeres, which should not be confused with the nucleolar-forming satellites seen in mitotic metaphase.

Dr. Moses: Before you get away from this, I would like to qualify your statement and say that there are no lampbrushes in acetic-acid squashes.

Dr. Yerganian: I was alerted to this condition in your presentation. However, there is lampbrushing present in male and female rodent pachytenes fixed with alcohol-acetic.

Dr. Conger: Is that characteristic of rodents?

Dr. Yerganian: Yes, and quite striking when the human complement is compared with that of rodents. One can work quite freely
with human pachytenes.

The prospects for inducing sex anomalies in experimental animals
as a means of checking environmental factors as causative factors
are gradually being considered by a number of laboratories. Figure
7 is an early photograph of a "female" suspected of having a chromosomal anomaly. Unfortunately, this animal did not fare well during

*Fig. 7. Possible chromosome anomaly due to high temperatures dur-
ing embryonal development*

transport to another laboratory, and a cytological study was not conducted. It never matured and may readily have been the Chinese
hamster counterpart of the *XO* mice reported by Drs. Russell and
Chu (1961). There were environmental factors suspected in another
example.

In referring back to the records, both instances occurred during
a period when uncontrolled high temperatures of the summer increased the temperature of the animal room above 85°F. The litters
in question were considered to have been at some vital stage in
embryonic development at the time.

Previously, the availability of suitable experimental tissues in various forms of laboratory specimens aided in estimating the effects of radiation on man. This approach is rapidly becoming a thing of the past as excellent human cell types grown *in vitro* are now available. Continuity of trials with cultures of human derivatives of adult origin is limited, since cultures are difficult to retain with high mitotic activity, for periods greater than a few months. Repeated cultures would necessitate biopsying the donor, in order to retain

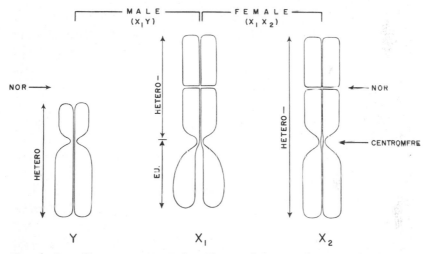

Fig. 8. Sex chromosomes of the Chinese hamster (X_1X_2:X_1Y *or* Triheterosomic *scheme*)

genetic constancy. Continuous or long-term cultures of human epithelioid cell types still have to be developed. The mongoloid derivative (Fig. 2) was epithelioid and retained typical features for only 6 passages.

Triheterosomic scheme for sex determination in man? During the course of viewing rapidly proliferating cell types of the Chinese hamster, it became quite evident that the two X's in normal female derivatives were different in morphology (Fig. 8). Additional trials with malignant derivatives and alkylating agents further emphasized duality of the X chromosome pair (Yerganian *et al.*, 1960). Subsequently, it became necessary to consider some other sex pattern—the *Triheterosomic* scheme—for this species, in contrast to the previously assigned $XX:XY$ mechanism. The present system states that normal animals have an X_1X_2 or X_1Y sex chromosome relationship. In order for other combinations, such as X_1X_1 and X_2Y, to survive after fertilization, the X's would have to undergo differentiation to the appropriate phase, i.e., $X_1X_1 \rightarrow X_1X_2$ and $X_2Y \rightarrow X_1Y$, if random fertilization were taking place. Otherwise, selective fertilization favoring the production of only X_1X_2 and X_1Y zygotes would be naturally favored; the static X_1X_1 and X_2Y being eliminated. More recent observations indicate that X chromosome differentiation may take place, specifically during meiosis and early embryogenesis in the Chinese hamster.

On a morphological basis, we postulated that one of the X's, the X_1, was prevalent in both sexes and, therefore, was termed the "predominant X." Its short arm is euchromatic and heavily spiraled; the slender long arm is entirely heterochromatic and possesses a medially placed secondary (nucleolar?) constriction. The Y chromosome, of course, is restricted to the male. It is totally heterochromatic and similar to the long arm of the X_1. In the female, the alternate form or X_2 is totally heterochromatic, in sharp contrast to the half euchromatic-half heterochromatic X_1. Its development (spiralization) is delayed and, therefore, termed "the retarded X_2." In a later report, Taylor (1960) substantiated the use of this terminology, while studying the sex patterns of tritiated thymidine uptake. The heterochromatic portions are the last to replicate in the synthesis period, thereby emphasizing the delayed features of the heterochromatic arms of the three sex elements. On these premises, the X_2 is considered, physiologically, to be the feminine counterpart to the masculinizing Y chromosome. For example, placing the X_2 with the neuter X_1 imparts femininity to the individual, whereas replacing the X_2 with a Y chromosome, in association with the X_1, imparts masculinity.

The *Triheterosomic* scheme is now being considered by others as well, in postulating duality of the X chromosome in man (Grumbach and Morishima, 1962; Ishihara *et al.*, in press; Miles, 1962).

Dr. Lindsley: Do you think of these two chromosomes as maintaining their identity from generation to generation, or are they genetically identical and does their morphology differ simply as a consequence of the physiology of the cell in which they lie?

Dr. Yerganian: I do not wish to treat this aspect now because it is a topic in itself and involves many opinions. I can speak to you later, since I have no slides with me to help illustrate this point.

To prove duality of the X chromosome pair, we are attempting to tritiate sperm and prepare squashes of the dividing two- and four-cell-stage embryos. By means of autoradiography, we may be able to determine whether or not female embryos have a "hot" X_2 in the presence of a "cold" X_1. If labeled X_2's are noted in 50 percent of the samples, then differentiation from the X_1-X_2 phase had to occur some time during meiosis. This would be ample evidence in favor of chromosome differentiation.

The X_1 chromosome is not static in its role. Dicentrics involving X_1 chromosomes persist and nondisjunction can lead to as many as four in a single diploid cell. Contrast this with expected lethal events to follow when similar aberrations involve autosomes. Persistence of the X's may be the result of passive selection or their failure to evoke an immediate antigenic response or lethal expression. By means of single-cell cloning, new lines containing multiples of aberrant forms of X_1 chromosomes have been isolated. These are excellent materials with which to delve into the problem of heterochromatin.

What is heterochromatin? This is an area to which many *Drosophila* geneticists have been contributing for some time. In an effort to conduct somatic trials in mammalian systems, we have only mutant X's of the Chinese hamster and multiple-X syndromes of man.

The X_y and Y chromosomes of the Chinese hamster, mouse, and man can be deleted *in toto*, without accompanying lethality. In the Chinese hamster, loss of the distal half of the short euchromatic arm of the X_1 leads to an extensive despiralization of heterochromatin on sex elements and autosomes. The euchromatic portions remain normally spiralized. The euchromatic short arm of the X_1 is actually present in the monosomic state, since the short arm of the X_2 is totally heterochromatic due to differentiation. Therefore, any deletion occurring in the short arm of the X_1 is expected to be expressed immediately as a dominant mutation. After a period of some 10 years of observation, we have concluded that all portions of sex chromosomes, with the exception of the short proximal portion of the X_1 chromosome, can be deleted without affecting cell survival.

Are there counterparts of similar events in other rodents and man? The closest situations are the XO conditions in both mouse and man. Rodent experimentation may help to disclose additional factors leading to viable aberrations now witnessed in the human population. Classical approaches in cytology, based upon previous findings in *Drosophila, Tradescantia,* and some rodents, are expected hereafter to assist more strongly in understanding human cytogenetics.

Dr. Taylor: I would like to very briefly summarize what we found with respect to the human complement and late-replicating X chromosomes. We have looked at three normal females and each has one X that is late-replicating. We have looked at three normal males, and they have no late-replicating X chromosomes. One XO female which has been examined also has no late-replicating X.

We looked at one Turner's syndrome mosaic, which was XO, XX, and XXX. It had several combinations of late-replicating X chromosomes, one or none in XO cells, one and perhaps none in XX cells, and one or two in XXX cells.

Dr. Atwood: Ferguson-Smith mentioned finding an isochromosome. Have you noticed that?

Dr. Yerganian: I have not studied them personally, but I have reviewed several cases studied by Engel and Forbes in Boston.

Dr. Lindsley: Are they truly isochromosomes?

Dr. Yerganian: As long as there is a loss of one arm of the X, the classic isochromosome can be formed as in plant material. This is still a bit presumptive, however, since we really do not know whether the chromosome is actually the X.

Dr. Atwood: His argument is very convincing.

Dr. Yerganian: I believe that he has also noted changes in the sex chromatin pattern which can be helpfully interpreted as reflecting a loss of a portion of one of the X's. Variation in the sex chromatin pattern, I would judge, is the prime motivator now in stating whether or not the marker chromosome is an isochromosome involving either arm of the X chromosome.

Dr. Lindsley: I would question the use of the term isochromosome, because isochromosomes generally arise through misdivision of the centromere. For instance, I wouldn't consider an attached X in *Drosophila* an isochromosome, even though its two arms may be identical for the majority of their length.

Dr. Yerganian: At least one of the human X's can behave in a very passive manner, as seen in *XO, XXX,* and other examples of multi-X conditions. Since additional X's may be incorporated, there is equal opportunity for misdivisions to persist.

Dr. Lindsley: You don't see the misdivision process?

Dr. Yerganian: One sees the derived product that survives.

Dr. Swanson: I think that what they are talking about is the taking over of classical terms with a considerable lack of discrimination by the mammalian cytologists. Everyone here excepted, of course.

There seems to be a good deal of confusion. It is very easy to pick up these terms and to use them; the term isochromosome is an example of this, but I think that having a definition associated with particular phenomena that are found in other materials, and then using it indiscriminately in mammalian cytology, is only going to compound the confusion.

Dr. Yerganian: One factor that has led to the indiscriminate use of cytological terms has been the indiscriminate appropriation of funds to sponsor such work in laboratories or hospitals which have yet to teach a course in classical cytology, or which fail to have classically trained cytologists on the team.

Dr. Swanson: Don't blame it on the money.

Dr. Yerganian: It has encouraged it. However, I must state that many of the contributors have done quite well in utilizing classical terms to describe the similarities and dissimilarities in patients having the same syndrome.

Dr. Auerbach: I am terribly puzzled by this X_1-X_2 situation. Do you mean that the X_1 or X_2 character is imposed on the X chromosome in the zygote? In the mouse a heterozygote for a sex-linked gene gives a perfectly normal one-to-one segregation, so that both X chromosomes are transmitted equally well.

Dr. Yerganian: I cannot venture into this feature of the Chinese hamster now because it is a separate topic.

Dr. Auerbach: It would be nice to get heterozygotes for sex-linked genes and to observe segregation.

Dr. Yerganian: Because we lack a clear sex-linked marker, your suggestion would require much more lengthy experiments in our present situation.

Dr. Lindsley: The one-to-one ratio of males to females is pretty good circumstantial evidence that both maternal X's are being transmitted.

Dr. Yerganian: This is why the sex elements are so unique. It is a comparatively new area for mammalian cytology, and one which requires classical approaches in a manner similar to that leading to the work presented at this conference.

Dr. Auerbach: But if you have regions of heterochromatin which are not of equal length in the two X chromosomes, you should have genes which behave in the female as though the female were hemizygous. That is, some recessive genes should show up in the female and that, again, is not known from the mouse, or man. If cytological information is to be reconciled with the segregation ratio in mouse and man, then the difference between the two X's must be imposed on them after fertilization.

Dr. Yerganian: This is the premise which we are now attempting to clarify. By means of tritiated sperm, we may be able to follow the proposed X chromosome differentiation, i.e., the labeled X_1 from the male parent differentiating to the X_2 phase after fertilizing an egg bearing an X_1 chromosome. I think that Dr. H. Crouse's observations on sex determination in *Sciara* are most impressive (1960).

Dr. Taylor: I think that an example of transition from one type of behavior to another with respect to condensation and genetic expression is well illustrated by the dipteron, *Sciara*.

Dr. Auerbach: This is true, but in *Sciara* the genetics is crazy, too, whereas in the mouse and man it is quite orthodox.

Dr. Taylor: I was referring to the fact that a chromosome inherited from a male can be changed by passage through the female germ line so that it will not behave in the next generation as it would have in a previous one.

Dr. Yerganian: Another point we must remember is that there has always been a mouse associated with man throughout the evolution of both species. They might have been under the pressure of both systems.

Dr. Wolff: Do you think that the eggs preferentially get your X_2 chromosome?

Dr. Yerganian: This is being checked presently with tritiated thymidine-labeled sperm. Until we know the outcome, we have postulated reciprocal differentiation of the X chromosomes to be patterned during meiosis and early embryogenesis. Evidence suggesting meiosis as the time and place is provided by the allocyclic behavior of sex bivalents in spermatocytes and oocytes. At these stages of *cellular differentiation*, the male bivalent indicates an X_2Y relationship because of its wholly heteropyknotic appearance (a feature that never occurs somatically) and newborn females show a striking uniformity of the pachytene X-bivalent which can be interpreted as being X_1X_1.

References

Awa, A., M. Sasaki, and S. Takayama. 1959. Japan. J. Zoöl. 12: 257.

Barr, M. L., and D. H. Carr. 1960. Can. Med. Assoc. J. 83: 979.

Crouse, H. V. 1960. Genetics 45: 1429.

Ferguson-Smith, M. A., and S. D. Handmaker. 1961. Lancet 1: 638.

Grumbach, M. M., and A. Morishima. 1962. Acta Cytol. 6: 46.

Hauschka, T. S. 1961. Cancer Research 21: 957.

Hirschhorn, K., and H. L. Cooper. 1961. Am. J. Med. 31: 442.

Ishihara, T., G. E. Moore, and A. A. Sandberg. J. Natl. Cancer Inst. In press.

Jacobs, P. A., A. G. Baikie, W. M. Court-Brown, H. Forrest, J. R. Roy, J. S. S. Stewart, and B. Lennox. 1959. Lancet 1: 591.

Jacobs, P. A., D. G. Hamden, W. M. Court-Brown, J. Goldstein, H. G. Close, T. N. MacGregor, N. Maclean, and J. A. Strong. 1960. Lancet 1: 1213.

Koisin, I. L., and H. Ishizaki. 1959. Science 130: 43.

Lehmann, O., and H. A. Forssman. 1962. Acta Paediat. 51: 6.

Longwell, A. C. 1961. Hereditas 47: 641.

Makino, S., T. Ishihara, and A. Tonomura. 1959. Z. Krebsforsch. 63: 184.

Matthay, R. 1958. Experientia 14: 240.

Miles, C. P. 1962. Calif. Med. 96: 21.

Morishima, A., M. M. Grumbach, and H. J. Taylor. Proc. Natl. Acad. Sci. U.S. In press.

Newcomer, E. H., and G. M. Donnelly. 1960. J. Heredity 51: 208.

Newcomer, E. H., G. M. Donnelly, and W. C. Forbes. 1959. Poultry Sci. 39: 1030.

Nowell, P. C., and D. A. Hungerford. 1961. J. Natl. Cancer Inst. 27: 1013.

Ohno, S., and S. Makino. 1961. Lancet 1: 78.

Ohno, S., J. M. Trujillo, W. D. Kaplan, and R. Kinosita. 1961. Lancet 1: 123.

Ohno, S., and C. Weiler. 1961. Chromosoma 12: 362.

Patau, K., E. Therman, S. L. Inhorn, D. W. Smith, and A. L. Ruess. 1961. Chromosoma 12: 573.

Russell, L. B. 1961. Science 133: 1795.

Sandberg, A. A., L. H. Crosswhite, and E. Gordy. 1960. J. Am. Med. Assoc. 174: 221.

Sandberg, A. A., G. F. Koepf, L. H. Crosswhite, and T. S. Hauschka. 1960. Am. J. Human Genet. 12: 231.

Schultz, J., and P. St. Lawrence. 1949. J. Heredity 40: 31.

Sohval, A. R. 1961. Am. J. Med. 31: 397.

Sohval, A. R., and W. G. B. Casselman. Manuscript in preparation.

Taylor, J. H. 1960. J. Biophys. Biochem. Cytol. 7: 455.

Wilkins, L. 1960. Pediatrics 26: 864.

Yerganian, G. 1957. Am. J. Human Genet. 9: 42.

—— 1961. Nature 95: 252.

Yerganian, G., and R. Kato. Unpublished.

Yerganian, G., R. Kato, M. J. Leonard, H. J. Gagnon, and L. A. Grodzins. 1960. In Cell Physiology of Neoplasia, 49. Austin, Texas: University of Texas Press.

Part 5

Genetic Consequences of

Aberration Induction

General Survey of Genetic Effects
of Chromosomal Aberrations

Dr. D. L. Lindsley: I do not know whether "the genetic effects of aberrations" quite fits into a symposium on the biochemical and biophysical nature of chromosome aberration, but since that is my assignment and my field, it is what I will discuss.

It seems to me that the genetic behavior of chromosome aberrations is of interest from two general points of view: the first is that it provides us with insight into chromosome behavior, and into chromosome structure and function The second point is that the genetic effects of aberrations are what geneticists use in place of the metaphase cell to score induced aberrations; unfortunately, some of these same genetic effects also seriously bias our scores of these aberrations. It is mostly this latter area that I want to discuss this morning.

It occurs to me that practically the whole discussion up until now has concerned itself with cells observed in the first metaphase after treatment and that, furthermore, the chromosomal aberrations that cytologists score are the ones that will almost certainly kill cells that carry them or their immediate cellular descendants. Geneticists score the surviving residue and, generally, never see the aberrations which have been discussed up until now.

The genetic effects of aberrations can manifest themselves in a hierarchy of different stages. They can have their effect in the cell in which the aberration arises, or in the cellular progeny of that cell. When we are talking about aberrations in gametes, the aberration may affect the individual that is produced by the affected gamete or the progeny of that individual or the population in which the aberration exists. Depending on the number of these stages that intervene between the time of origin of the aberration and the time of sampling, we get a more or less distorted picture of the incidence with which the aberration actually was produced in the treated cellular population.

The material which I want to discuss this morning concerns the mature *Drosophila* sperm. It is the cell type on which the genetic effects of radiation have been most thoroughly studied, and it is the cell that I know most about.

The spatial considerations that were discussed earlier by Atwood seem to be in force also in the *Drosophila* sperm as evidenced by the fact, first, that neutrons give a linear increase in the aberrations that we measure with dose and, second, that there seems to be a preference for intrabrachial over interbrachial aberrations. That is, we tend to get more inversions and fewer translocations than expected on the basis of random arm involvement. This leads to the belief that the site concept can very profitably be applied to the *Drosophila* sperm.

Dr. Steffensen: Excuse me, does this refer to the reunion at fertilization in the egg versus the sperm? Do you mean that the site will remain constant throughout this whole process?

Dr. Lindsley: Yes, I don't see any alternative interpretation of the facts that I mentioned; that is, if breaks in the sperm head rejoin at random, then when the number of breaks is doubled by doubling the dose of neutrons, more than double the number of aberrations should result. The observation, however, is a doubling of aberration yield; this is good evidence that breaks do not interact at random, i.e., that there are spatial considerations. Even though the chromosomes in the sperm are broken at the time of radiation, and there may be a great interval of time during which this sperm with its broken chromosomes is first swimming around in the seminal vesicle in the male and then in the seminal receptacle of the female and finally fertilizing the egg, the breaks remain open, and it is not until after fertilization that we think the reunion occurs.

Dr. Auerbach: The male pronucleus remains separate from the female even on the first cleavage spindle.

Dr. Lindsley: We do not know when after fertilization rejoining takes place; it may be before pronucleus formation or after. Breaks could conceivably remain open until the second cleavage division.

First, I want to consider what happens when we have a single break. I might say that I don't think we know, but at least I have some ideas on the subject. In the first place, the break can reunite (Fig. 1a). The question is, does this restitution leave us with any-

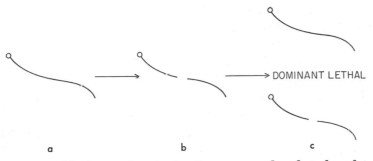

Fig. 1. *Possible fates of a single chromosome break induced in a* Drosophila *sperm*

thing that we can score? It may leave a mutational scar, but when we pick up a mutation in an unaberrated chromosome, we cannot say that that mutation is the result of a previous break. So, this event at the moment is unscorable.

Skipping now to Fig. 1c, we see that the break could remain patent. The terminal acentric piece would be lost, and the centric piece could be recovered in the zygote; we should detect this as a terminal deletion. The fact is, terminal deletions are not recovered; this is not because of inviability of terminal deletions as such, because we can create terminal losses by aneuploid segregations from translocation heterozygotes and show that such segregants may be viable. It appears that terminal deletions are not formed in *Drosophila;* why they are not formed, we just do not know.

Dr. Revell: I am not quite sure that I know what the evidence for breakage is here.

Dr. Lindsley: I have a little note, as a matter of fact, which says that single breaks don't exist on exchange hypothesis.

Dr. Revell: Could you expand on that?

Dr. Lindsley: It was my understanding from the exchange hypothesis that you do not expect a single-break type of site; that is, you don't expect breakage in a site where there aren't two strands that can undergo exchange. I would say that there is no evidence that such single breaks occur, although it is my intuitive feeling that they do.

Dr. Wolff: Wouldn't you expect, on the basis of the exchange hypothesis, to get terminal deficiencies?

Dr. Gray: Not until the exchange is formed, it only takes place in the egg.

Dr. Lindsley: I would say that there is no such thing as an incomplete in *Drosophila*.

Dr. Auerbach: I think that this has been accepted for a very long time and has led to Muller's telomere concept. This assumes that you get a breakage-fusion cycle unless there is a specified chromomere at the end of the chromosome.

The evidence that terminal deletions do not persist in *Drosophila* comes from the fact that what looks like teminal deletions or detached X's usually turns out to have the truncated chromosome capped by one or two genes from another chromosome.

Dr. Lindsley: This is what I meant when I said that terminal deletions are not found.

Dr. Auerbach: I thought you said that you do not know what the evidence is.

Dr. Lindsley: I know what the evidence is that terminal deletions are not found, but I don't know what the evidence is that single breaks which should lead to terminal deletion are produced. If one can recover only products of two or more breaks, it is hard to say categorically that single breaks occur.

Dr. Steffensen: Similar evidence is available in fairly good detail in corn, where we can show that a number of the breaks in somatic cells are undoubtedly due either to dicentrics or rings which form bridges. The fragments arise as a result of "two-hit" aberrations. Most of the breakage ends formed from breaking dicentric bridges will heal as McClintock has shown long ago.

Dr. Lindsley: It is interesting that a terminal produced, let us say, in an interphase cell by irradiation does not seem to give you loss.

Dr. Steffensen: You can show that these genetic factors are being lost on both arms to form a centric ring or that the long arm of nine is involved in an interchange. The loss of the acentric fragments seldom arises as simple deletions.

Dr. Lindsley: I know that a terminal deficiency can survive in the sporophyte of maize.

Another point of view has been that a single break can give rise to dominant lethality (Fig. 1b). It has been assumed that either a single chromosome is broken and replication of the two fragments produces two broken chromatids, or that an isolocus break is produced in chromatids. The two broken chromatids may then undergo sister fusion to produce a dicentric, which produces a dominant lethal when the sperm carrying it fertilizes an egg.

What is the evidence for this? One bit of evidence that has been cited in favor of this hypothesis is that if dominant lethality, i.e., egg hatch, is plotted against the dose of irradiation delivered to the fertilizing sperm, there seems to be, at least in the low-dose range, a sizable linear component, and single chromosome breaks might have linear kinetics.

Let me say a few words about fertilization in the *Drosophila* egg. The oocyte nucleus produces by the two meiotic divisions a linear quartet of four nuclei that is normal to the surface of the egg. The inner nucleus sinks into the cytoplasm to become the female pronucleus. The maternal and paternal pronuclei undergo a separate first cleavage division. There is very little difference between the second meiotic division and the first cleavage division.

A dicentric chromatid that is brought in by the sperm should produce a bridge in the first cleavage division. By certain kinds of recombination events, we can produce similar bridges in the second meiotic division. It has been observed that an X chromosome bridge formed at anaphase 2 is excluded from the egg nucleus. Consequently, I would expect a similar bridge to hang up in the first cleavage division and to produce a zygote lacking a paternal X chromosome rather than dominant lethality. The incidence with which such patroclinous males are produced by high doses of radiation is extremely low (approximately 1 to 2 percent at 4 kr) and if we correct this figure upward to correct for bridges that could break, assuming that all the autosomal bridges break, we don't approach the incidence of dominant lethals produced by irradiation of sperm.

Another argument against the sister-union formation of dominant lethals in sperm is that the chromosomes in the sperm are probably in G1.

Dr. Ris: We know that they are in the rat.

Dr. Lindsley: That is good to know. Most of the aberrations which we recover from radiated sperm are chromosomal; however, the methods that are generally used are not likely to detect chromatid aberrations. Dr. Auerbach, you were talking about the data with the chemicals where you get mosaics for aberrations.

Dr. Auerbach: Even with x rays there are some chromatid aberrations after irradiation.

Dr. Lindsley: Some?

Dr. Auerbach: Yes, when one accepts the Watson-Crick model one should not be surprised. Mrs. Slizynska definitely got chromatid aberrations after x-ray treatment of *Drosophila* sperm, but much fewer after chemical treatment.

Dr. Lindsley: If the chromosomes of the sperm are mostly in G1, then I don't think that one would expect this sister fusion, because, judging from the plant material, chromatid rejoins are not produced following G1 radiation.

One final point that we can make about dominant lethality is that one can irradiate a sperm population and measure the amount of dominant lethality produced. Now one chromosome can be removed from half of the sperm, of a similar population, they may be radiated with the same dose, and the dominant lethality measured. It has been my experience that removal of a chromosome does not diminish sperm sensitivity to dominant lethality; consequently, I am not convinced that the chromosomal contribution to dominant lethality is important.

To summarize, then, single breaks that occur too far from another break to interact with it, if they occur, do not remain open (Fig. 1a), do not form dominant lethals (Fig. 1b), and thus by a process of elimination must restitute (Fig. 1c).

Dr. Sparrow: I object to drawing this as a general conclusion for all cells on the basis of sperm irradiation.

Dr. Lindsley: I do not mean to.

Dr. Sparrow: This is what I think you are implying. The somatic cell is quite a different beast.

Dr. Lindsley: That is certainly true.

Dr. Sparrow: You base most of your conclusions on the sperm irradiation. Is this your predominant observation?

Dr. Lindsley: Yes, and I think that it's remarkable that the plant root-tip cell and the insect sperm do agree in so many respects.

Dr. Sparrow: I don't think that it is safe to conclude that for somatic cells in general this conclusion that you derive from sperm cells should be applied as a general principle.

Dr. Lindsley: I think you are right.

Dr. Ris: Could lethality be an effect on the sperm centrioles?

Dr. Lindsley: It could. I have suspected the centriole, but do not have any way of manipulating it genetically. I can manipulate the genotype a lot and not get changes in dominant lethality, which makes me think that it might be something extrachromosomal.

Dr. Pavan: When you have not the chromosome—

Dr. Lindsley: I still have the other four or three or whatever it is.

Dr. Auerbach: Would you not say that single breaks that do not at once rejoin are required to explain the experiment done by Muller many years ago? Sperm was treated in the female for a month at a dose rate that gave one effective ionization only every five minutes or so, but at the end as many translocations were produced as when the whole dose of 2000 r was given at once. So during this month the single events, breaks, or latent breaks must have accumulated without rejoining.

Dr. Lindsley: My feeling is that this is the status of the chromosomes from the time of radiation until fertilization. Breaks are simply accumulated, irrespective of the rate at which they are produced.

Dr. Auerbach: You accumulate breaks?

Dr. Lindsley: Yes, but what I am saying is that the single ones which are not close enough to another break to undergo exchange restitute.

Dr. Auerbach: How do they know whether they are or not, when the next one occurs so much later?

Dr. Revell: This is the point that I was trying to raise.

Dr. Gray: I think the sperm shows that there is one particle involved in the initiation of the aberration, and that this one particle could have produced an effect in two threads. This is the usual concept, the fact that the effect of a given dose is independent of time makes it almost certain that one particle is involved, but does not tell us whether only one thread is broken at a time.

Dr. Auerbach: This contrasts then with the square law of translocations which is very well established for *Drosophila*.

Dr. Lindsley: I do not see the conflict. Chromosome breaks are simply accumulating in the sperm until fertilization of the egg; they then rejoin. Oster showed that he could irradiate pupae, then, after these pupae became adults, he could use the males to inseminate tester females, and then irradiate the sperm that had previously been treated in the pupae in the inseminated female. The breaks produced by these two doses widely separated by time did in fact interact.

Dr. Auerbach: Then I misunderstood you. I thought you said that breaks join at once. They remain open and available for a long time.

Dr. Lindsley: Yes, but when they are single breaks, when the time comes for rejoining, they restitute.

Dr. Revell: Did Oster irradiate sperm, and when do breaks rejoin?

Dr. Lindsley: He irradiated the same cells twice—when they were spermatids in male pupae and when they were mature sperm in inseminated females. He found that breaks rejoin after the sperm functions in fertilization.

But the instant that reunion occurs after fertilization is not established because we do not have very good experimental control of events following fertilization.

Dr. Gray: What I do find very surprising about this arises out of the point which Dr. Lindsley made right at the beginning, i.e., it is a condition of exchange formation that the two breaks must be produced in chromatids within 0.1 μ of one another. If this is so, it surprises me that after the movement of the sperm, and the entry of the sperm into the egg, those two breaks are still within 0.1 μ of one another.

Dr. Lindsley: This is indeed surprising; on the other hand, the sperm head is really a tightly packed ball of string and chromosomes may have no freedom to move around. I do not know the size of the site, but it seems that there are many chromosomes within a site, possibly because things are so tightly packed.

Dr. Gray: It does not require much movement to displace one of the breaks by 0.1 μ. The sperm has to penetrate the ovum and move about. It seems pretty remarkable.

Dr. Auerbach: It is packed in the sperm head even after it goes into the ovum. Only after the sperm head breaks open does rejoining

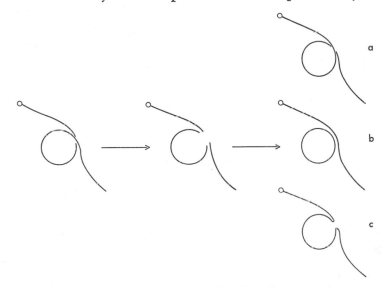

Fig. 2. Possible fates of two breaks induced in the same chromosome arm in Drosophila *sperm*

occur. Muller calculated the distance between rejoining sites, it came out very close to Wolff and Atwood's value.

Dr. Lindsley: The *Drosophila* data are not all that good.

Dr. Revell: All single breaks have to reunite without exception?

Dr. Lindsley: If they occur, they have to reunite without exception, at least that is my current prejudice.

We will now turn our attention to the case where there are two broken strands within a site, considering first the types of intra-brachial rearrangements shown in Fig. 2. In the first place, the two breaks can behave just as the single breaks did, that is, they may reunite to form a chromosome which is no different from the original

(Fig. 2a) except that it could have mutational scars as recollection of its former breakage experience.

Second, it can rejoin as shown in Fig. 2b to produce an acentric ring and a rod which is now deficient for the region included in the ring. The ring will be lost early in cleavage because it is acentric, but the rod will function in cleavage and development will proceed. If the ring is very small, then the deletion is very small and the rod chromosome should survive in the heterozygote, but will most likely behave as a recessive lethal. The deficiency may also lead to some dominant phenotype, e.g., Minute, Notch, or Plexate, which is known to be associated with small deletions.

Table 1. Cytological Classification of Lethals
(*percentages are percent of total lethals*)[a]

Dose (*in r*)	Number of lethals	Point mutation lethals		Lethals associated with translocations	
		No.	*Percent*	*No.*	*Percent*
700	81	69	85	7	8.6
2800	122	87	71	17	14.0

[a] From Valencia, *Cytologia Suppl.* VI: 895 (1954).

In Table 1 are some data of Dr. Valencia showing the results of his analyses of recessive lethals. Of a total of 122 lethals produced by approximately 3000 r, 86 were deficiencies. The size of deficiencies which behave as recessive lethals presumably varies from something that is invisible up to some moderately large regions; the size of this region must depend on where it is in the chromosome, but how many bands would you say is the upper limit for an X-chromosome deficiency that will survive in the heterozygote, Dr. Valencia?

Dr. Valencia: Thirty bands.

Dr. Lindsley: Out of how many in the X chromosome?

Dr. Pavan: Around a thousand.

Dr. Lindsley: In other words, about 3 percent of the X chromosome is the most that can be lost and still produce something that we can recover and score as a recessive lethal.

As the loop in Fig. 2 gets larger so that the acentric gets large, we fail to find the deficient chromosome. We don't think that this is because such acentrics are not produced. It is simply because the deficiency is so large that it won't survive in the heterozygous condition; it is dominant lethal. If we make the loop very large so that practically the whole chromosome is included in the acentric ring and the corresponding deficiency a very small chromosome, we may recover this centric fragment as a duplication. Thus the small deficiencies are recessive lethals, the larger ones are dominant lethals, and the very large ones, at least in the X chromosome, can be recovered as free duplications.

Dr. Evans: What is the relation between inversion size and the frequency of recessive lethals, because you would expect there to be a correlation between the two, wouldn't you?

Table 1. (*Continued*)

Lethals associated with inversions		Lethals associated with deficiencies		Total structural change lethals	
No.	*Percent*	*No.*	*Percent*	*No.*	*Percent*
4	4.9	1	1.2	12	14.7
10	8.2	8	6.6	35	28.8

Dr. Steffensen: They should be complementary.

Dr. Lindsley: Any inversion has a possibility of having a recessive lethal mutation or position effect associated with its break points, but only small deficiencies can be recovered as recessive lethals. The rest are eliminated from the sample as dominant lethals. However, there has been a study of very large deficiencies, i.e., the little duplications—and very large inversions, and they seem to be produced with roughly comparable frequencies; however, I think that this observation was based on a small number of observations, so you can't really say.

The third way that the two breaks shown in Fig. 2 may rejoin is to form an inversion as shown in Fig. 2c.

An inverted chromosome is an entire chromosome, i.e., it is not deficient, but it does contain two healed break points which may be associated with mutation or with position effect. Position effect is a phenomenon that was originally considered to be peculiar to *Drosophila*, but a number of years ago it was also found in *Oenothera* and more recently it has been found in the mouse and probably in maize. When a chromosome rearrangement transfers a gene to a new chromosomal environment, the expression of the gene may change; this change in expression is often characterized by variegation, either for phenotype that you can see or for lethality.

Therefore, it is possible to have a position effect associated with inversion. It could be a lethal position effect and if the inversion is recovered in an inefficient way it could be lost owing to mutation or position effect.

Inversions are generally recovered in combination with a normal chromosome. Synapsis in meiotic prophase of an inversion/normal heterozygote produces the configuration shown in Fig. 3. A single

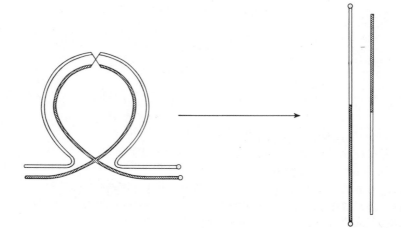

Fig. 3. The formation of a dicentric and an acentric as the consequence of exchange in an inversion heterozygote

exchange within the loop of this configuration yields a dicentric and an acentric recombinant.

First meiotic anaphase bridges which result from such dicentrics should be lethal. However, some organisms, *Drosophila* among them, happen to have a mechanism for reducing this lethality to practically zero by eliminating the dicentric chromatids from the primary oocyte nucleus so that the lethality is not a very serious factor, although in many organisms I think it would be.

Whether the dicentric is eliminated or lethal there is a preferential elimination of the cross-over chromatids, so there appears to be a great reduction in recombination. Therefore, an additional genetic effect of inversions is reduction of observed recombination.

Now I want to turn to consideration of interbrachial rearrangement and the situation where, within a site, there are two different arms (Fig. 4). Two such breaks may restitute (Fig. 4a), i.e., they

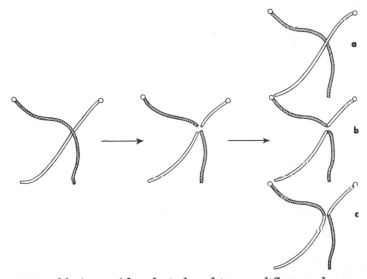

Fig. 4. Possible fates of breaks induced in two different chromosome arms in Drosophila *sperm*

may behave as if they were not in the same site, and give no detectable genetic effect except insofar as there is mutation associated with restituted breaks. They may rejoin as shown in Fig. 4b to produce a dicentric (or a ring chromosome in the case where the two arms are derived from a two-armed chromosome and the two centromeres figured are the same centromere) and an acentric. These aberrations are never recovered in *Drosophila*, but since reciprocal translocations are formed (Fig. 4c), we infer that the dicentric and the acentrics are formed and that they must be dominant lethals.

Finally, we have the formation of reciprocal translocations (Fig. 4c). Practically everything I have said about inversions applies to

translocations as far as position effects and break-associated mutations are concerned.

The two translocated elements of a reciprocal translocation are
generally recovered in combination with two normal elements, and
they form the type of configuration at meiosis shown in **Fig. 5**. The

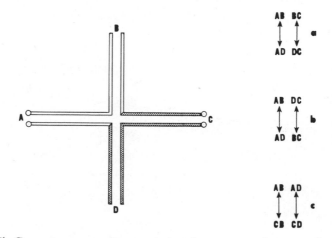

*Fig. 5. Consequences of segregation from a translocation heterozy-
gote*

chromosomes may separate from such a configuration in several
different ways. At first anaphase, elements AB and BC may proceed
to one pole and AD and CD to the other. It is evident that one resulting cell is deficient for D and duplicate for B, and that the other
is deficient for B and duplicated for D. In animals these cells proceed through meiosis but produce aneuploid gametes which give
rise to inviable zygotes; consequently, they are not recovered.

Separation may also occur so that AB and AD can go to one pole
producing gametes that are duplicated for A and deficient for C,
and CB and CD can go to the same pole producing gametes that are
duplicated for C, deficient for A. These gametes will also produce
inviable zygotes. Thus meiotic separations 5a and 5c will give rise to
dominant lethality. However, when the normal chromosomes AB
and CD go to the same pole, and the translocated chromosomes AD
and BC go to the same pole, each cell gets A, B, C, and D, so that

the whole genome is present in each secondary meiocyte and a balanced individual is produced.

Heterozygosis for a translocation has two consequences. In the first place, there is a lot of zygote mortality, and in the case where there is a gametophyte generation, gametophyte mortality manifests itself as semi-sterility.

Because in the only surviving segregants from a translocation heterozygote the translocated *A* and *D* are recovered together with the translocated *C* and *B* and the normal *AB* is always recovered together with the normal *CD*, in cases where recombination does not complicate matters, genes which are normally unlinked are always recovered together from translocation heterozygotes. This pseudo-linkage is the genetic effect generally used in the recovery of translocations.

Finally, I would like to discuss a particular class of translocations, those between the *X* chromosome and the autosomes to illustrate how the genetic effects of aberrations may affect the validity of our scoring procedures.

In 1934, Patterson and a group of collaborators did an experiment to recover translocations by means of pseudolinkage. They recovered an irradiated *X* and an irradiated set of autosomes from the male, and from the female they recovered a normal *Y* and a set of autosomes. Consequently, in the first generation, they selected sons that had an irradiated *X* and an irradiated set of autosomes in combination with nonirradiated *Y* and autosomes. Then they looked for linkage between markers on the nonirradiated chromosomes.

The expectation on the basis of arm length and random involvement in interchange is approximately equal numbers of 1;2 plus 1;3 translocations and 2;3 translocations; yet it may be seen in Table 2 that they found a great excess of 2;3's over 1;2's and 1;3's. If a

Table 2. Recovery of Translocations from Sons (Patterson et al., 1934) and Daughters (Warters and Lindsley) of Irradiated Males

	Genomes examined	Translocations recovered			
		1; 2	*1; 3*	*1; 2; 3*	*2; 3*
Sons	10,000	146	187	71	1,236
Daughters	2,838	76	65	33	142

translocation-bearing son of the irradiated male dies, it cannot be tested; consequently, X; autosome translocations with associated sex-linked recessive lethal mutations were preferentially eliminated from the samples of Patterson *et al.* We are in the process of completing an experiment in which we recover the irradiated sperm in combination with an X-bearing egg, and so the translocation is kept heterozygous in the female. Investigators do not usually do this because crossing over complicates the detection of translocations; since crossing over does not occur in the male, they usually try to recover translocations from males. When we recover translocations in the female, utilizing a special situation which reduces recombination, we find that the sum of 1;2 plus 1;3 is approximately equal to the 2;3's.

Table 3 illustrates the causes of differences between a population

Table 3. Preliminary Genetic Analysis of X-Autosome Translocations (Male)

	Fertile	Sterile	Lethal	Total
$T(1;2)$	16	46	14	76
$T(1;3)$	12	42	11	65
$T(1;2;3)$	5	16	12	33
Total	33	104	37	174

of translocations recovered from sons and one recovered from daughters of irradiated males. Females heterozygous for a translocation can produce sons that carry the translocation. Of a total sample of 174 X; autosome translocations, 37 were male lethal. These would have been missed by Patterson.

Dr. Auerbach: Lethal or sterile?

Dr. Lindsley: Lethal, I am starting at the right side of the table. An additional 104 which survived were male sterile, which left us with only 33 of the original 174 which were both viable and fertile; on further testing some of these may turn out to be nontranslocations. These are the counterparts of the ones that Patterson *et al.* actually picked up. This example should illustrate the extent to which the genetic effect of an aberration may bias scoring procedures.

Since it is getting late and we still have a summation, I will just quit on this point unless there are questions.

Dr. Evans: Does that ratio of 6 to 1 which you have there fit with Patterson's data?

Dr. Lindsley: Fairly well; he got 333 $T(X;A)$'s to 1,236 $T(2;3)$'s.

Dr. Revell: Have I understood correctly that the observations which one has on these structural changes could be reconciled perfectly well with a doctrine of what you might like to call latent breakage? According to this view, one would have a latent break which, if it encounters another latent break, may exchange with it.

Dr. Lindsley: I do not see any way of distinguishing this from actual breaks.

Summary

Dr. C. Auerbach: What I am going to say is the product of some midnight work because I did not know of the program before I came here and hence could not prepare anything. Also, since the space at my disposal is not large, I think that rather than summarize all of the very interesting facts and discussions I shall point out those special questions or findings which seem important to me. I want to warn you that it was perhaps not very wise to choose a geneticist as a summarizer, because we geneticists are somewhat isolated here among cytologists, and I shall probably bring in the genetic viewpoint rather strongly. In fact, I feel that one should not draw conclusions from cytological evidence which are not compatible with genetic evidence. Of course, the opposite is also true.

Unfortunately, I missed half of the first talk because I had forgotten to set my watch when I came from New York; so, when I came at ten, I thought it was nine. However, I heard from Dr. Evans what he had been talking about in general, which is a reappraisal of the target theory. When I talked with him about this privately, we fully agreed that, at the time when his book appeared, Lea gave a very beautiful and consistent picture of the target theory which in its essentials still stands, but which has to be modified in many respects. In fact, at the time when the book came out, I felt rather uncomfortable about the way some *Drosophila* data were used for drawing quantitative conclusions. I knew all too well how large the error, not the statistical error but the biological error, could have been in the collection of these data, because it was then already apparent that uncontrolled factors influence the quantitative results. Some of these factors are much better known by now. Thus I quite agree that it is necessary to reevaluate the quantitative conclusions of the target theory.

Also, one has to take account of complexities which keep on appearing. One, for instance, which was not mentioned at the meeting but in several private discussions, relates to x-ray fractionation experiments, which have played a great role in the formulation of the target theory. There were for instance, data by Lane some time ago, which however were queried by Sax, and more recent ones by Davies, which showed that a first dose of x rays may alter the sensitivity of the chromosomes to further x-ray breakage. All these facts and, in addition, the very great effect of the metabolic conditions in the cell will have to be taken into account. All the same, I do not feel that it is necessary to change the fundamental basis of the target theory, for the production of rearrangements visualizes a two-step process, breakage perhaps at first in the forms of some kind of metastable condition, followed by reunion as a separate event.

We have discussed the theory of Dr. Revell so fully that I do not think it would be profitable to spend much time in starting another argument about it. I just want to say two things which I personally would like to have clear and which probably everybody else wants to have clear. The first is this: What is the evidence that makes it necessary to throw overboard the old breakage-first theory? The second is: What is the evidence for or against the new theory?

I feel that before one accepts a new theory, one has to have good reasons for abandoning the old one, and, as far as I could make out, and I shall be glad to be corrected, there were only two reasons which led Dr. Revell to abandon the breakage-first theory. The one is that he interprets gaps not as breaks but as some other event, and this seems still to be a doubtful conclusion. Some cytologists accept it and others do not, so I do not think that it is a very strong reason for abandoning the old theory. Dr. Revell's second argument against the breakage-first theory is that what he accepts as true chromosome breakage increases not linearly with dose but according to a more than linear dose-effect curve. The nonlinear component was rather weak, and I cannot help feeling that on the basis of these two pieces of evidence alone one is not forced to abandon the breakage-first theory. I felt this even more when I saw in Dr. Chu's lecture that the clear terminal deletions in human chromosomes give a very good linear dose-effect curve.

If I have omitted any essential facts against the breakage-first theory, I should like to be corrected.

Dr. Revell: You have, but I do not think that there is any point in going into it now.

Dr. Pollard: Isn't it a question of the statistics of the things you do understand coming out correctly if you abandon the breakage idea? It is just a question of the total way they are grouped, and it seems to me that if you group them one way you do not make sense out of it as well as if you group them the other way. This is what I thought I understood Dr. Revell to say: In point of fact there are a number of things whose origin is not in question, and you can make good sense out of the total numbers if you put in a category of a whole lot of gaps.

Dr. Auerbach: That is what I said.

Dr. Pollard: I think that you have it inverted. You stated that you first ignored the gaps. I think Dr. Revell's argument was that he first made sense out of a whole catalog of things which were quite varied and which included much more than gaps, and then he found that he had left over a number of things. I think that his argument is much stronger; however, I am not a cytologist.

Dr. Auerbach: In Lea's interpretation, the whole pattern of chromosome aberrations made sense because he included the gaps as chromosome breaks. If this is not done, the calculations no longer make sense. This is, anyhow, what I understood Dr. Revell to say. However, since the interpretation of the gaps seems doubtful—

Dr. Revell: I don't think that there is any point in going into it now, but it is not true that the evidence which you have cited is the only evidence. There is, however, one point that I think you should be corrected on: Bender has not shown a real linear relation for chromatid breaks.

Dr. Auerbach: This is what I gave as your second piece of evidence. However, yesterday on Dr. Chu's lantern slide there were terminal deletions which followed a very beautiful linear curve.

Dr. Revell: The figures were 17, 44, and 79.

Dr. Chu: The slides I showed yesterday were my own. In our studies the terminal chromatid deletions followed a linear relationship with dose. On Dr. Bender's slide, in particular, he has assumed that terminal deletions are the result of single breaks, and exchanges of two breaks. When the breaks are plotted against dose you cannot say that the points deviate significantly one way or the other from a straight line. I showed my own slide and I did not discuss Bender's slide.

Dr. Steffensen: I really think that Revell's theory is divided into two ideas and that nobody really has discussed the facts of irradiation of an interphase nucleus, G1, in *Tradescantia*. The data are very clear in this regard. Most if not all of the aberrations that one observes are completely restituted exchanges where all the broken ends find each other. This has been known since the work of Sax and his students began, and there has been no reason to discard the breakage-first hypothesis. Much of the initial theory was established by following interphase irradiation, so that is it obvious to consider the completeness of exchange and the breakage-first hypothesis as separate items. I frankly cannot see the second part of Revell's argument; the completeness of the exchange is an acceptable and very likely idea. It is difficult to partition or even bear on the breakage and reunion theory from the data he has presented.

Dr. Auerbach: I am not quite clear what your point is. What I want to know is whether I am wrong in formulating the essential part of Dr. Revell's theory in this way: kinetically, it resembles the breakage-first theory in demanding two independent hits for one exchange. In its idea about the underlying mechanism, it resembles the contact theory, which however assumed one-hit events and therefore a linear dose-effect curve. Dr. Revell postulates that effective hits occur only at sites where the chromosomes lie close enough together for an exchange, and that at such sites two independent events are required for the exchange to take place. No events at all occur outside these sites.

Dr. Revell: I am very reluctant to be led into a discussion of this now, but it is not true that I postulate that primary events are confined to the sites of proximity.

Dr. Auerbach: Then I think that it becomes almost indistinguishable to me from the breakage-first theory. What seemed to me to be evidence against it, namely, that you can have breaks which at least for some time are variable without having formed reunion, is not really evidence against it, but there are quite a few pieces of evidence which show that at least in some cases there must be breakage available which is not the result of an exchange.

I mentioned the reverse repeats in *Drosophila* where it was necessary that one chromatid have an open break into which a piece of the other one is inserted. Then there have been two or three instances in *Drosophila* where a break in a paternal chromosome rejoined with a break in the maternal chromosome; thus, in these cases, too, breaks must have been available for reunion.

Dr. Parker: What is the evidence that a rearrangement has taken place in the zygote, between maternal and paternal chromosomes? The evidence shows only that the rearrangement is present in cells in the gonads, but not necessarily that it took place at that one particular stage.

Dr. Auerbach: No, but the breaks were not produced in the same cell. One occurred in the ovary and one in the sperm, so that they were certainly much more than one micron apart at the time they were produced.

Dr. Lindsley: It could have occurred as a spontaneous aberration later in development. It need not have been produced by the irradiation.

Dr. Auerbach: Either the male or the female or both were irradiated.

Dr. Lindsley: But one is not likely to be looking for chromosome aberrations in unirradiated material.

Dr. Revell: There is no reason in principle to suppose that primary events produced in two different cells could not develop an exchange if brought together later.

Dr. Auerbach: If this is so I find it even more difficult to distinguish between the breakage-first theory and your theory.

To leave this controversial theory, then, I feel on much safer ground when we come to the calculation of sites of exchange as presented by Dr. Atwood.

A similar estimate of the maximal distance between breaks has been obtained for *Drosophila* spermatozoa where reunion takes place in the zygote after fertilization. This seems to show that the tight packing of the chromosome in the spermatozoan remains preserved during entry into the ovum and for some time after. I am wondering if there are not possibilities of using the *Drosophila* system, where reunion is separated from breakage, to try to modify the number of sites. I don't know whether there are any conditions under which one could make the chromosomes of the male pronucleus change their position before reunion. Perhaps in plants it may be possible to create such conditions by desiccation or similar devices.

After this discussion of the targets of radiation, we had Dr. Swanson's talk on the nature of the bonds involved in chromosome cohesion. This was in itself a review, so I do not want to review it again. Dr. Swanson showed us the great complexity of the situation, at least in higher organisms, as it appears from studies of enzymic digestion of chromosomes, the action of chelating agents, metal ions, etc. So far as I saw, he supported Kauffman's conclusion that the chromosome in higher organisms is a highly complicated fabric in which DNA, RNA, and protein are very closely integrated.

I was particularly interested in his stressing of the role of protein, because it has become very fashionable to almost forget about it and to think only in terms of DNA. Dr. Swanson mentioned a number of points which implicate protein in chromosome breakage and reunion, such as Dr. Wolff's experiments on the necessity for protein synthesis for reunion and the finding by Dr. Kirby-Smith that the paramagnetic x-ray signals occur in the protein and not in the DNA. Members of the audience contributed to the discussion of this point. Dr. Moses showed that irradiation makes more binding sites available for methyl green, and this agreed with what Dr. Gray told about Peacock's experiments in which the first results of x rays were a stripping off of the protein.

I used to think that since protein is necessary for the formation of chromosome rearrangements one might not get any rearrangements in bacteria where the chromosome contains hardly any protein. So I was pleased when a few months ago Dr. Marcovitch described at the Gatlinburg meeting how he had been unable to obtain chromosome rearrangements in *E. coli*. However, just a week ago, a collaborator of mine came back from Paris with the news that Jacob has obtained bona fide inversions and transpositions in *E. coli.* So it seems the bacterial chromosome can make rearrangements without protein in its own fabric.

Dr. Kihlman gave us a review of the work with chemical substances. I think that the main interest which emerged from this is the evidence that chemicals are more discriminating than radiation, and differ from each other in their effects on the chromosomes. One very remarkable property which is not found for all of them is the high specificity of location of breaks, e.g., after treatment with hydrazide. At the time I asked whether this specificity could be related with the fact that chemicals also differ in regard to the stage at which they produce aberrations. I was wondering whether there was any evidence that chemicals which act at the same stage in the chromosome cycle tend to produce lesions in similar locations.

Dr. Kihlman: I do not think that there is any such evidence, no.

Dr. Auerbach: Another point which I think one should consider when one scores rearrangements is that there may be specificity of reunion as well as specificity of breakage. Dr. Kihlman himself has shown in some of his older experiments that 8-ethoxycaffeine produced a higher ratio of exchanges to breaks in *Vicia* than in *Allium*, and some German workers found that urethane produced a lower ratio of exchanges to breaks in *Vicia* than in oenothera. Also in Kihlman's experiments on *Vicia*, the ratio of exchanges to breaks was quite different after treatment with either EOC or x rays. Thus, I think one has to consider the possibility that chemicals may be specific in their effect on reunion as well as in their effect on breakage.

Another point which Dr. Kihlman discussed was the delayed effect of chemicals. The kind of delay with which he dealt is short. It is not the type of delay which has been found after chemical treatment of *Drosophila* or bacteriophage, where a latent lesion retains the ability to produce a mutation over a fairly large number of cell cycles. Dr. Kihlman's delayed effect corresponds to what would cause half-and-half mosaics in the F_1 of *Drosophila*. The evidence for delayed effect was that he found chromatid effects where chromosome effects would have been expected from the stage at which treatment had been applied. On the basis of the DNA model, this might simply mean that they are one-strand changes in chromosomes which later will appear as chromatid changes. But I noted that the whole question of timing of the treatment was involved there, and Dr. Wolff suggested that the time at which the chemical really had acted might be ascertained better by a method used by Davidson. He treated with x rays in addition to the chemical treatment and timed the presynthetic and postsynthetic stages by the presence of x-ray induced chromosome and chromatid breaks. He then looked for chemically induced chromatid breaks in cells which also had x-ray induced chromosome breaks, and in his particular case none were found.

The discussion of the chemical bonds in chromosomes has, I feel, not really clarified the issue. We just do not know yet. But there is one question which I should like to mention because of its broad significance. This is not so much concerned with the chemical nature of the bonds, but as to whether chromosome breakage is intragenic or intergenic or, to express it in terms of chromosome structure, whether the chromosome has nodes and internodes. There, I think, the evidence from *Drosophila* is fairly strong that at least in this organism breaks occur between genes and not within genes. This goes back to the old and classical experiments of Rattel and Muller where it was shown that breaks in a very small region of a complex locus occur only at definite sites. Similar results have been obtained later on other complex loci in *Drosophila*. In addition, there are many rearrangements in *Drosophila* which give no position effect, whereas one would expect position effects to be very frequent if breaks had a good chance of occurring within a gene.

Finally, there is a very curious observation which I made first with mustard gas and which Dr. Snyder from Minnesota has just been repeating in our laboratory with another chemical, TEM, with confirmatory results. When males are treated chemically and the spermatozoa are subsequently stored in the female, there is a very marked increase in breakage events such as deletions and translocations, but no increase in lethals, most of which are point mutations or small deficiencies.

Dr. Swanson: What is the chemical?

Dr. Auerbach: Triethylenemelamine.

Dr. Lindsley: How do you explain the fact that he doesn't get association of lethals?

Dr. Auerbach: Dr. Snyder is repeating the experiment now on a bigger scale to determine whether or not one gets a small increase in lethal frequency, as would be expected from the admixture of re-arrangements.

Dr. Lindsley: What about his translocations? Are they associated with lethals?

Dr. Auerbach: Not in heterozygotes; they are 2–3 translocations, or translocations between *Y* and an autosome. Dr. Slizynska is mak-ing them homozygous to test for their viability. The relevance of these experiments to our present discussion is that during storage something occurs that affects breaks but not mutations. This again seems to indicate an essential difference between intergenic and in-tragenic events in *Drosophila*. Even for the bacteria chromosome, there is evidence for internodes from Ozakis' data on transduction in *Salmonella*. There seem to be preformed breakage sites so that not any odd bit can be transduced, but only pieces with such breakage sites at the end. However, results obtained in Hayes' laboratory in London have thrown some doubt on the generality of this phenome-non.

All of this points to a chromosome model in which DNA portions are joined together by linkers, which may or may not be protein. I do not think I need go into Dr. Taylor's summary of his older beautiful thymidine labeling work. What was new to me and proba-bly to many of you was the work with the FUDR and the evidence for visible lesions produced by inhibition of DNA synthesis.

May I also remind you of the interesting finding that the lesions produced by FUDR could be prevented or cured by thymidine or uridine, and that the frequency of x-ray induced chromosome bridges could be very largely reduced by inhibition of DNA synthesis through this analog. I think that the interpretation of this latter ob-servation is still somewhat doubtful. I personally was not quite con-vinced that it was an inhibition of reunion. It might have occurred at an earlier stage, and Dr. Wolff pointed out that there might be possible effects also on RNA; but the finding in itself is certainly very interesting.

Dr. Taylor also expressed his conviction that the chromosome in higher organisms is one single DNA double helix. This seemed to agree well with Dr. Moses' electron micrograms, although there the strands were a bit too thick for single DNA molecules. Perhaps this extra material might be protein. The main difficulty is apparently that cytologists are convinced that the anaphase chromosome is visibly double, and this is a difficulty which I certainly do not know how to resolve.

I did not like Dr. Taylor's speculations on chromosome reunions within genes, because I think we would get more genetic evidence of scrambling up of sites within a gene if this were the usual mechanism of rearrangements formation.

Neither did I like Dr. Kirby-Smith's idea that uv breaks DNA, and x rays break protein. One reason against it is that uv breaks as a class would then be very different in nature from both chemically induced and x-ray breaks. Now these latter appear to be similar in nature, since Oster showed that in *Drosophila* breaks induced by either mustard gas or urethane rejoin indiscriminately with each other or with x-ray breaks. It is true that, as mentioned, this is not so for x-ray breaks and breaks induced by maleic hydrazide, but this is probably due to maleic hydrazide producing highly localized breaks.

Dr. Wolff: Kolmark working on mutagenesis in *Neurospora* found that chemicals and x rays affected one the adenine loci similarly with a high mutation rate; uv gave a lower rate. Another locus, the inositol locus, was affected by uv so as to give a high rate of mutation, but this was not so with chemical or x ray. It looked as though chemicals and x rays were doing one thing, and uv was doing something else.

Dr. Auerbach: But this was not chromosome breakage. When you deal with gene mutation, I don't think anyone doubts that it is DNA.

Dr. Lindsley: If the chromosome is DNA intercalated with chromosome sections of protein, that is, some of these linkages that Taylor postulated are linkages, then DNA breaks and protein breaks might still interact, because on this model they are linked linearly.

Dr. Auerbach: Then you would get half a gene linking up. Well, I don't say it is quite impossible, but it does not appeal to me.

Dr. Swanson: The data that I presented were really for time of reaction. They interact all right, but I was concerned about differential time of interaction rather than saying that they cannot interact.

Dr. Auerbach: I did not want to go into too much detail. I understood that breaks produced by maleic hydrazide occur at definite loci and also have a shorter time before reunion than x-ray breaks. Those which have a longer time before reunion are mainly x-ray-induced ones; they, therefore, rejoin mainly with each other.

Dr. Swanson: There are so many parameters here that one really cannot begin to define them.

Dr. Conger: I think that this demonstration and other ones like it, such as uv causing radical signal in DNA and x rays in protein, are interesting. They may bear some relation to breaks, but we don't have any proof that the radicals are the things that are making the breaks and it may well be that only a very small fraction of them are the ones involved.

Dr. Auerbach: I did not accept this as a proof.

Dr. Kirby-Smith: I would be the first one to recommend that this be viewed with some skepticism; nevertheless, it is an interesting possibility.

Dr. Auerbach: I think that it is time to finish up and I must apologize to the rest of the speakers for not referring to their work. I only wish to mention two more points which are of special interest to me. One is the very interesting discussion which Dr. Hart gave us and from which I learned quite a bit about radicals. I was especially interested in his hot spots, with a diameter of 40 Å; this should quite easily accommodate the whole DNA diameter. If the hot spot is so big, the chance that two radicals would attack two nucleotides more or less opposite each other should then be quite high, and this might explain why so many x-ray mutations and breaks affect the whole chromosome and not only one strand.

The other point I wanted to make refers to Dr. Chu's paper. It was very interesting and reassuring to hear that the sensitivity of human chromosomes to x-ray breakage is not higher than that of *Tradescantia* chromosomes. But there is a certain discrepancy here with the genetic data on mouse chromosomes. Whether one uses dominant lethals or translocations as evidence for chromosome break-

Table 1. Relationship between Nuclear Volume and Frequency of Micronuclei Produced per r of Daily Exposure in Five Species [a,b]

Species	Chromosome number	Calculated nuclear volume	Daily dose (in r)	Number of cells scored	Mean number of micronuclei per cell	Micronuclei per r per day per μ^3 of nucleus ($\times 10^{-6}$)
Lilium longiflorum (4x)	48	2,525	40	6,441	0.129 ± 0.008	1.28
Lilium longiflorum, var. Croft (2x)	24	1,660	40	6,000	0.055 ± 0.006	0.83
Vicia faba	12	510	40	51,500	0.035 ± 0.002	1.70
Ornithogalum virens	6	225	180	3,539	0.050 ± 0.009	1.23
Crepis capillaris	6	105	300	7,000	0.058 ± 0.004	1.82

[a] These experiments were performed in the radiation greenhouse between January and May, 1961, without artificial light and with day-night thermostat set at 22° and 20°C.

[b] From A. H. Sparrow and H. E. Evans, Brookhaven Symposia in Biol. 14:76 (1961).

age, the mouse genome certainly is very much more sensitive to chromosome breakage than the *Drosophila*.

Dr. Lindsley: There are many more centromeres. Could that not be the reason?

Dr. Auerbach: Yes, this would give you more translocations.

Dr. Steffensen: On a DNA value for diploid cells, *Drosophila* has 2×10^{-12} g, humans have about 6.5×10^{-12} g, and *Tradescantia* about 50×10^{-12} g of DNA.

Dr. Auerbach: This raises another problem which came out in the meeting: How should we account for the very great difference in DNA between the chromosomes in different species, and for the fact that, as Dr. Sparrow mentioned, in spite of this great difference in DNA, the breakage sensitivity is more or less the same?

Dr. Sparrow: The breakage sensitivity per unit volume or per unit of DNA is the same, but is proportional to the volume (Table 1).

Dr. Auerbach: That might account for the higher sensitivity of the mouse genome. Then the question is what is all this excess DNA? The mouse cannot have so many more genes than *Drosophila*.

Dr. Ris: The variation in the amount of DNA per chromosome set among animals is tremendous. In mammals it is 3×10^{-12} g, while in certain salamanders it amounts to 168×10^{-12} g. It is unlikely that salamanders have 56 times as many genes as man. We must look for some other explanation and the most likely one appears to be that the number of strands per chromosome is different.

Dr. Sparrow: There is another very interesting situation in the algae where apparently closely related lines differ greatly in chromosome size.

Dr. Ris: Some recent studies of the Schraders are relevant here. Certain species within the same genus have twice as many autosomes as others. The total DNA per nucleus is the same, but the chromosomes are about one-half the size. They also found related species with identical chromosome number and morphology, but where one has twice as much DNA per chromosome set. They suggest as explanation a doubling in the basic number of strands per chromosome and separation and autonomization of chromatids.

Experimentally induced chromosome autonomy in sea urchin eggs has been reported by Biebring and Mazia, and Dr. Nebel has mentioned a similar case in mammalian cells.

Dr. Nebel: Stroud and Brues obtained in tissue culture of pig kidney sometime after irradiation a chromosome out of a complement that went along very nicely with half the thickness of the rest of the complement, appearing observationally to have only one chromatid instead of two.

Dr. Ris: There are thus many different kinds of observations which indicate multistrandedness of chromosomes, as well as different degrees of multistrandedness in different species. Natural or experimental autonomization of chromatids indicates that such subunits or chromosome halves are functionally complete.

Dr. Lindsley: There is an interesting case in *Drosophila virilis*. I do not know whether it bears on this. There were two strains, one of which had a lightly staining sixth chromosome and one which had a heavily staining sixth chromosome. Recombination between these two sixth chromosomes produces chromosomes where the proximal half is heavily staining and the distal half is lightly staining or the converse. I don't know whether this is a reflection of DNA content.

Dr. Yerganian: Wasn't it reported that *D. persimilis* has three kinds of Y chromosomes, as measured by length?

Dr. Lindsley: The Y chromosome is heterochromatic. This difference in chromosome 6 of *virilis* is one of euchromatic stainability.

Dr. Gray: When nucleoprotein is irradiated, the protein is the first thing to be affected under all of the circumstances examined by Peacock. I referred to Peacock's work which I think is very interesting. He studied calf thymus in dilute solution, but the whole subject is very complex and under other conditions and with other materials, e.g., herring sperm DNA protein, Alexander finds direct effects on the DNA hardly influenced by the protein. I think that this is probably as complex as all of the other things to which you refer. I would like to make a clear distinction.

There is one thing more that I want to say at this time, first, and perhaps most important, on behalf of all of us to express our thanks to Dr. Wolff and the organizers, the National Research Council, for organizing this conference. At the bar last night I was having a conversation, near to one o'clock, and the person I was talking to said, "You know, I don't like that man's theory, but I think I have a jolly good system to test it with in so and so, and when I get back home I am just going to prove he is wrong."

I think that is exactly what we hoped would come out of this conference, and I hope that the organizers, including Dr. Nickson, will feel that we did the sort of things that he wanted us to do. A word of thanks, therefore, and a very sincere one, to everyone who has been involved. On behalf of those abroad, I particularly want to express our thanks to the organizers for bringing us over here to participate.